Frank M. Chapman
in
Florida

Made by Mr. Chapman from the feathers of the Ivory-bill that March 24 and sent to me as a Christmas present Dec. 25, 1890.

Frank M. Chapman

in

Florida

HIS JOURNALS & LETTERS

Compiled
&
Edited
by

ELIZABETH S. AUSTIN

University of Florida Press
Gainesville - 1967

A University of Florida Press Book

COPYRIGHT © 1967 BY THE BOARD OF COMMISSIONERS
OF STATE INSTITUTIONS OF FLORIDA

Library of Congress Catalog Card No. 66-30436

MANUFACTURED BY ST. PETERSBURG PRINTING CO.
ST. PETERSBURG, FLORIDA

Introduction & Acknowledgments

SOME YEARS AGO Dr. Dean Amadon, Chairman of the Department of Birds at the American Museum of Natural History in New York, sent to the Florida State Museum at Gainesville a packet of letters and journals which Frank M. Chapman had written in Florida, most of them while he was living in Gainesville in the 1880's and 1890's. Dr. Amadon's letter accompanying the material stated, "Inasmuch as Gainesville has become a center of natural history studies, where long-term research projects may be carried out, it seems that some of this material might be of use."

My husband, Dr. Oliver L. Austin, Jr., Curator in Ornithology at the Florida State Museum, was sure the material would be of use, perhaps as a project for a graduate student, but no student ever indicated any interest. Except when shown to a possible compiler, the journals remained untouched in the Museum safe.

In the spring of 1963 I was preparing a paper on the explorations of nineteenth-century ornithologists in Florida for the meetings of the American Ornithologists' Union to be held in Gainesville that August. One day I complained loudly and bitterly at the paucity of documents on the activities of my subjects. At that point my husband produced the Chapman journals and letters and put them in my hands. They did not help my immediate project, but when I had read part way through them I could hardly wait for permission to go to work on them.

They were not just a history of, or a natural history of, the birds of Florida. They were the story of a career within a career, and a beautiful picture of the unspoiled countryside as it existed in many parts of Florida before 1900. With other available material, the story emerged of an enthusiastic young man coming to a sparsely settled Florida, observing its growth and development, and eventually becoming a world-famous ornithologist who still retained his youthful joy in Florida's fauna and flora.

Dr. Frank Chapman's one hundredth birthday was celebrated at the American Museum of Natural History in June, 1964. Appropriately the Hall of North American Birds, enlarged and restored, was reopened as the Frank M. Chapman Memorial Hall of North American Birds. Among the guests at the ceremony were many who had known Dr. Chapman. When a hundredth anniversary is celebrated for a man who lived a full eighty-one years, there are always people who can say "I knew him," "He was my friend," "I worked with him," or "I once met him." But the Chapman these people remembered was the mature, the middle-aged, and the older man. The young Chapman remains in no living memories today, but he lingers now and forever in his early journals and letters, and in those of the friends of his youth.

In the Chapman and the Brewster journals of the nineteenth century I have made only one change. I have replaced the scientific names of the birds they employed with the accepted common names as published in the "A.O.U. Check-list of North American Birds," 5th edition, 1957. The 1932-34 journals have received the same treatment, and are also slightly abridged, as indicated in the text.

The assistance I have had in the gathering of dates and data has involved a great many people who were generous with their time, energy, and information. I am grateful to every one of them, and most of all to the Frank M. Chapman Memorial Fund for a grant that made research in the archives of the American Museum possible and paid for clerical assistance, and to Dr. Dean Amadon, present-day successor to Frank Chapman, who made the grant available to me and encouraged and implemented my work.

The entire staff of the Bird Department of the American Museum included me in their esprit de corps and made work there a pleasure indeed. Mr. Charles E. O'Brien, Assistant Curator, apprised me of much Chapmaniana, and unearthed all but a few of the pictures used as illustrations in this book. Thank you Mr. O'Brien.

I am most deeply obligated to Dr. Robert Cushman Murphy, Lamont Curator Emeritus of Birds at the American Museum, for sitting up until the wee hours of the morning reading and checking what I had to say about his friend Frank Chapman. I am also obligated to Dr. Murphy and to his wife, Grace Barstow Murphy, for telling me many things that are not documented about FMC, his family, his home, his work, and his friends.

I thank Dr. Ernst Mayr, Director of the Museum of Comparative Zoology at Harvard College, for permission to use the Brewster material in the M.C.Z. files. I am deeply indebted to Mrs. Edwin A. MacDonald (nee Jessie Bell McKenzie) of the staff of the Widener Library and administrator of the M.C.Z. Library, for her interest and for her long hours of work extracting the Brewster material from voluminous files with discernment and understanding.

Mrs. Sarah W. Flannery, Coordinator of Humanities at the Boston Public Library, and Mrs. Kershner, of her department, made a tedious search through several years of the old Boston Transcript to answer my questions. Mr. Roland C. Clement, Staff Biologist of the National Audubon Society, and his assistants made an equally tedious search in the archives of the Society. Mr. F. C. Fraser, Keeper of Zoology at the British Museum (Natural History) in London; the late Dr. Alden H. Miller, Director of the Museum of Vertebrate Zoology, Berkeley, California, and editor of *Condor*; Dr. James N. Layne, Associate Professor of Zoology at Cornell University, Ithaca, New York; Dr. William B. Robertson, Jr., Park Biologist at Everglades National Park; and Professor Hayford O. Enwall, University of Florida College of Law, were all most generous with time and information, and I thank them.

The staff of the University of Florida Libraries has been so extremely helpful that in all truth they coresearched Mr. Chapman and his doings with me. Mrs. Madge P. Tams, in charge of the bibliography room, gave me expert and whole-hearted assistance, as did her staff. In the Science Room, Miss Louise Henley and Mrs. Antoinette J. Porter gave me aid far beyond the call of duty. In the P. K. Yonge Library of Florida History, Miss Elizabeth A. Alexander and Mrs. Linda B. Sasser furthered this book by their knowledgeable cooperation.

Dr. J. C. Dickinson, Jr., Director of the Florida State Museum, University of Florida, has helped me with suggestions and information, as have many members of his staff. Mrs. Helen Hunt, Museum Secretary, has been, and is, an outstanding amanuensis in taking care of most of the correspondence concerning Frank Chapman in Florida. Miss Elizabeth Baker, Museum Assistant, has answered a thousand queries about old Gainesville which she and her family know so well.

To Miss Barbara M. Wilmot of Gainesville who spent part of her summer holiday typing manuscript for me and to my elder son Anthony Austin I am grateful for work well done, as well as for their mastery of orthography.

Most thankworthy of all is my husband, Oliver L. Austin, Jr., who encouraged me to undertake this project, edited every word I wrote, and added so much of value by writing the final chapter on the "Birds of the Gainesville Area, Then and Now."

ELIZABETH S. AUSTIN
Associate, Florida State Museum

Contents

1

Frank Michler Chapman

*T*HE VALUE OF LETTERS AND JOURNALS to posterity depends very much upon their author's abilities as an observer and recorder. When a trained scientist who is also a gifted writer sets down his experiences, they become valuable source material to historians and to those in his own field who work in the areas he explored and try to follow literally and figuratively the paths he traveled.

Frank Michler Chapman, scientist, explorer, author, editor, photographer, lecturer, and museum curator, was one of the most influential naturalists and greatest ornithologists of his era. A versatile man of great achievement and widely traveled, his career was so broad that biographers passed lightly over his work in Florida which, if he had never done anything else, would have assured his place as an important ornithologist and mammalogist. His first major scientific paper, and his second appearance in print, "A List of Birds Observed at Gainesville, Florida," appeared in July, 1888, in *The Auk, A Quarterly Journal of Ornithology*, published by the American Ornithologists' Union. The studies and collecting upon which this paper was based are chronicled in his first field journal, which also contains the manuscript of the paper, written in Gainesville during the winter of 1886 and the spring of 1887, when he was twenty-two years old.

From that time until his death at the age of eighty-one in 1945, he spent some part of all but a very few winters in Florida. One of his last published papers, "Everglade Islet," which appeared in *Audubon Magazine* in January, 1943, tells of the flora and fauna of Royal Palm State Park, now a part of Everglades National Park. This paper, too, was written in Florida.

The year Frank Chapman first came to Florida, 1886, was a momentous one in his life, for that autumn he decided to make ornithology his profession. He resigned his position at the American Exchange National Bank of New York City where he had worked for six years, had risen to head of a department, and seemed to have a secure future before him. From his father's estate he had an income of about $2,000 a year ($500 more than the salary of a museum curator in those days) on which to live, and also had his mother's agreement to the step he was taking.

It was the second important decision he had made for himself. He made the first in 1880 when he graduated at sixteen from Englewood Academy and decided he would not go to college. Refusing to go to college and leaving gainful employment for uncertainty do not seem the right steps with which to begin a brilliant career in natural history. At that time ornithologists in this country gainfully employed in their own profession numbered about six and, even though biology was usually taught only to medical students, it was considered desirable for a young man who wanted an academic or scientific career to be armed with the classical bachelor's degree.

Frank Chapman was armed with an inordinate love of his subject, a thorough knowledge of all the literature then available, great intelligence, enthusiasm, and determination. After thoroughly studying his activities in Florida and reading much of his correspondence in the historic letter file of the American Museum of Natural History in New York, I seriously doubt that his mother selected Gainesville for a winter home fortuitously or that Frank Chapman left the American Exchange National Bank for the love of birds alone.

In his *Autobiography of a Bird Lover* he stresses his love of the out-of-doors and his interest in ornithology as the reasons for his decision, but he says on page 34: "As a matter of record, I feel that I should state that I have never had rugged health or great staying powers. Much of my work has been done under the spur of desire." There is definite evidence that as a young man he suffered from a susceptibility to pulmonary disorders, colds, coughs, grippe, and pneumonia. He did not necessarily have anything more serious, but in the late nineteenth and early twentieth centuries any disorder that involved the lungs hinted at tuberculosis, then the "great white plague," and was quite as unmentionable as it was dangerous.

In view of this, his choice of a profession that would keep him outdoors a good part of the time becomes highly significant, as does his mother's choice of Gainesville for a winter home. In those days Gainesville was advertised as a health resort[1] and its climate was claimed to be "Particularly beneficial to all pulmonary complaints, and to those of a nervous temperament; if not too far gone when they make the trial it is absolutely beneficial." Plans were actually drawn for a

1. See *The Eden of the South* by "Carl" Weber, 1883, p. 48.

sumptuous "Hygienic Hotel and Sanitary Cottages" with "skilled physicians in attendance" to be built just east of the town, but the project was abandoned after the yellow fever epidemic of 1888.

A number of friends expressed in letters their concern over Frank Chapman's health, and well they might. In 1887 he arrived in Gainesville on November 30, but was too ill to write in his journal until December 10. He was two months recovering from this illness. On November 7, 1889, Dr. Charles Slover Allen (a practicing physician whose hobby was ornithology) of 21 East Twenty-eighth Street, New York, wrote Frank Chapman at the American Museum of Natural History giving him a choice of appointments on the following Friday or Tuesday, when there would be ample time "to make a thorough chest examination" as Chapman had requested. No record remains of what Dr. Allen found or advised, but the events that followed in December are detailed in Chapter Four.

The cooperation of the American Museum of Natural History in making an annual pilgrimage to the South possible for him is also significant. Winters in the tropics or subtropics were not ordinarily arranged for young assistants, nor even for more important members of the staff, in those days of long hours and short holidays. Records of Chapman's illness crop up in letters and journals until well into the 1890's, usually during cold weather in the South or when he lingered too long in the northern winter. The respiratory difficulties of his twenties apparently vanished as he grew older.

If Frank Chapman had been survived by contemporaries of his youth, my suspicions might have been confirmed in one of the many memorials written about him. But they are not, and whatever brought him to Gainesville, his love affair with Florida and its wildlife started at the Great Sink on the edges of Alachua Lake, in the bogs of Bivins Arm, at Newnan's Lake, and on Sugarfoot Prairie. His interest helped to save the plume birds, the pelicans, the Everglades, and countless other bits and pieces of Florida for posterity.

Frank Michler Chapman's lifetime spanned the years between the War Between the States and the end of World War II. He was born on June 12, 1864, when Union forces were storming the strongholds of the South. He died on November 15, 1945, a few months after Japan's formal surrender. His years were passed in achievement. As the world moved into the machine age, Chapman moved with it, adopting each new development to further research, conservation, education, and exploration in the many fields in which he was a leader.

I have never met a dedicated ornithologist who did not pursue his interest in birds so early in life that he cannot remember exactly when it started. This was so with Audubon, and in reading the biographies of the founders of the American Ornithologists' Union, I find that each man evinced a love of the outdoors in general, and birds in particular, when he was himself unfledged.

William Brewster was eleven when he learned taxidermy and started the nucleus of a museum. J. A. Allen was thirteen when he started his collections. Alexander Wetmore, former Secretary of the Smithsonian and one of the country's greatest living ornithologists, contributed an article on the Red-headed Woodpecker to Frank Chapman's *Bird-Lore* magazine when he was thirteen. Roger Tory Peterson of the famous *Field Guides* was a Junior Audubon Society member at eleven. C. Russell Mason, Director of the Florida Audubon Society, published his first ornithological paper when he was ten. My husband's mother told me that Oliver L. Austin, Jr., chased and tried to catch his first bird when he was four.

Frank Chapman was aware of bird songs before he went to school. In the country town of Englewood, New Jersey, he learned the common names of dooryard birds almost as he learned to talk. He was fascinated by them. When he was eight, an uncle, recognizing his interest, gave him *Johnson's Natural History*, a work published in 1872, which devoted considerable space to birds. From that time on every leisure moment was spent in learning more about birds outdoors or from books made available to him.

By the time he was twenty he had learned enough about birds to make him a valuable volunteer observer to Dr. A. K. Fisher, then in charge of the Atlantic Division of the American Ornithologists' Union Committee on Bird Migration. Before and after banking hours FMC observed bird movements and reported them. From his correspondence and association with Dr. Fisher he learned still more about his subject and, under Dr. Fisher's tutelage, he was introduced to New York City's bird club, the Linnaean Society, and to the American Museum of Natural History.

He was elected an Associate Member of the American Ornithologists' Union in 1885, but his duties at the bank permitted him to attend only a part of the meetings held that year at the American Museum of Natural History. He was so intrigued by what he heard, and so thoroughly disappointed at missing the rest of the sessions, that I believe it was at this point that banking lost all chances of holding

FMC's attention. By the time the next meetings of the American Ornithologists' Union were held in November of 1886, he had made himself free to attend them and to proceed with his mother, Mary Augusta Parkhurst (Mrs. Lebbeus) Chapman, to Gainesville, Florida, and a winter of birding. As you read this journal please remember he had just turned twenty-two when he started it.

FRANK M. CHAPMAN
Journals, 1886—1887
Gainesville, Florida

Nov 27   ALTHOUGH I ARRIVED AT GAINESVILLE the night of the 22nd, I today for the first time went out with my gun. Many things incident to house furnishing were to be done and I decided that these must all be finished, and our home in order before starting in the business for which I came here. A fifteen-minute walk brought me to the pines and five minutes more to a dense hammock filled with moss-hung trees and bordered by cultivated fields from which the crops had been gathered. Crossing through the hammock and following its western edges I came to a small bush grown pond whose occupants, three Pied-billed Grebes[1] (*podiceps*) were greatly startled by my appearance—one of them I secured. This pond, about an acre in extent, was bordered on two sides by hammock land, the rest being cultivated fields—as cultivation goes, for they were filled with a growth of dry and leafless weeds taller than myself. At this point birds were more abundant than any place subsequently visited, the variety however was small, at least nine-tenths of those seen being myrtle warblers which were everywhere, the most abundant bird of the day. The remainder of the ground was similar to that first described—hammock, pines and old fields.

Birds as a rule were few and far between and so closely do they hug the bushes that it requires patience to shoot them.

I received a call on my return from "Johnson the Huntsman" as he is termed, a fine specimen of the full-blooded Negro. He has the

---

1. FMC often refers to birds in his journal by their scientific names and he occasionally uses vernacular names that have been superseded—"highhole" for "flicker" for instance. For clarity and readability these have been changed to their common names accepted by the A.O.U. Check List, 5th ed., 1957.

reputation of being the champion hunter of the vicinity and lives by the fruit of his gun. I have made arrangements to go out with him Monday—for ducks, etc.

Nov 28   I had this afternoon a glimpse of Florida bird life as it has been pictured.

Taking a road which I thought would lead me to Alachua Lake I followed through pine woods, hammock and fields until ascending a slight elevation the lake lay before me. I will not attempt to describe it now, but later when I have become more familiar with its characteristics.

As I approached the shore numbers of ducks arose and sought safety in the yellow pond lilies (*Nuphar advena*) growing some distance from it. Then there was a splashing and calling, a squeaking and squawking such as I never heard in my life before, odd noises of all sorts and descriptions all unknown to me, and I was without both gun and glass. The place seemed to be alive with birds, ducks were constantly flying from place to place, coots and herons were apparently common. On the shore near me birds were just as abundant; a pair of Pileated Woodpeckers with flaming crests were pounding away in a tree above my head and with them were hundreds of Flickers and one Red-bellied Woodpecker. Doves whistled through the woods at my approach, Bluejays screamed, Mockers chirped and hundreds of birds flew from tree to tree. Truly I was in an ornithologist's paradise.

Nov 29   There is ringing in my ears, a squawking and splashing of countless Coots. The lake swarms with them and their outcry is continuous. Reaching the lake at 7:30 I found birds so abundant that I was really puzzled to decide what to shoot, and as a result I did not fire a shot until I had been there an hour.

A wonderful scene, the water alive with water fowl, ducks constantly passing to and fro and occasional herons with long ungainly legs stretched out behind solemnly winging their way over the water. Ashore birds were equally abundant, and the calling of Jays, Flickers, and Mockingbirds was simply indescribable. I watched the play go on, content for the time to remain a spectator, but when at last my turn came, one shot spoiled the picture, the curtain dropped and the actors vanished. Securing a boat from a Negro fisherman I pushed out to procure some Blue Peters as they term Coots—but the tangle of bonnets was too much for me. Added to this the boat was evidently built for a long voyage somewhere, for safety rather than celerity, so I was unsuccessful.

"Johnson the Huntsman" called this afternoon. There was some misunderstanding about our trip this morning, but tomorrow we certainly go—(Deo volente).

He brought some ducks to show me—2 Black Ducks whose bills were entirely unalike, one being almost yellow with a black nail, the other dark olive green lightening anteriorly, the nail as before. There was no difference in coloration of plumage.

Nov 30   Gainesville is bordered by a fringe of darkeys' cabins, and each cabin will average I think two dogs. "Johnson the Huntsman" occupies one of these cabins, and at 4:30 this morning I endeavored to find it from his description of its location. I was unsuccessful but I found the dogs, such a howling and yelping was never heard before; it was perfectly dark and no one to inquire the way of, so taking a position on a high fence near where I supposed he lived I sat there and whistled. Finally he appeared. I had awakened him, so while he dressed and made his coffee, I sat before a fire he had hastily lighted. It was a picture that cabin—bare boards, scarcely anything else, a table, one or two chairs and a bench.

While he was grinding his coffee on a most dilapidated mill, whose life veritably hung by a string—another darkey attracted probably by the fire and the hopes of something to drink or eat, entered and the conversation which ensued between the two was as good as a play. At last he was ready, and we started for the lake, his "cur" dog in the rear.

Approaching the edge of the hammock cautiously, he laid his plans for a "shot." The hammock lies within one hundred yards of the water, the intervening space being open shore covered during the wet season. The ducks feed within about 50 yards from the edge of this, and there is not the slightest cover to enable one to get within shooting distance. I therefore watched Johnson with great curiosity to see what course he would pursue. Going back in the hammock to a safe distance he kindled a fire with dry hanging moss and after thoroughly warming himself took off everything below his waist, and holding up before him a bunch of fuzzy topped weeds, crawled crouching down the shore. It was a most ludicrous sight, the stooping unnatural posture, slow gait and general costume, with a bit of red shirt to add color to the scene. Ten minutes of this work and he was within shot. Dropping his weeds he raised and fired, one barrel missed, with the other he killed one Broad-bill.

At the sound of the gun hundreds of ducks rose from where they had been feeding, Coots croaked and splashed, on rising pattered over the water seeking safety in flight.

Returning, another fire was built, clothes resumed, and farther down the shore, a second "shot" was made, the result being one Coot and one Broad-bill. In a large hammock of live oak covered with hanging moss he killed two gray squirrels both of which I stuffed— returning him the bodies—and coming out of this we found a wild persimmon tree, most delicious things when they are ripe, but when they are not as Johnson expresses it "they make your mouth very rough."

Dec 1   The colored population are a never failing source of interest; they are extremely polite and always bow on passing. I meet numbers of them in the woods, they are ever ready to show me the way or give any desired information, rarely confessing ignorance on any subject. One I met today showed me a most interesting thing: lying side by side were the bones of a cow and the rattle snake that had caused her death. Striking so deep that he was unable to withdraw his fangs he had met the fate of his victim. Thus I explain it; my colored guide however had a slightly different theory. He said the blood of the cow was just as poisonous to the snake as the snake was to the cow, and being unable to loosen his hold, he had in consequence been killed. Some "black snake root" he dug for me, he explained, was the best medicine in the world, "I'se the fader of ten boys and eleben girls, I'se fifty yars ole, an I been taken dis all my life an neber been sick yet."

There is a lack of water birds excepting ducks and Coots; herons seem to be very rare and snipes, I have seen none beside a few Killdeer.

On the shore in certain places birds are very abundant, but away from the lake they are few and far between.

Johnson called tonight bringing a Meadowlark and Red-shoulder Hawk—the body of the hawk he desired me to return as he preferred eating it to a duck.

Dec 3   We walked today at least twelve or fifteen miles, equal to twenty miles at home.

I left home before four and again had to arouse Johnson, and wait for him to "cook" his coffee, this I object to.

We passed through beautiful hammocks, no undergrowth to obstruct the view, and there were long vistas offered by moss-hung trees beautiful beyond description. These heavy festoons of moss give the woods above a heavy dense appearance, the direct rays of the sun rarely enter here. Reaching an orange grove owned by some "northerners" we called out the man in charge, an aged colored man who lives the year around, alone in a board house of two rooms, near the center of the grove. He chatted a little and he walked out and knocked us down some oranges, using a long pole with a nail set at right angles near its end. In return for this he requested Johnson to be sure and bring him some whiskey the next time he came.

Farther on two more darkey cabins whose inhabitants were there to pick cotton, a few hundred more pounds to pick they said. The hammock beyond is immense, one could lose oneself here very easily; numerous "sinks" as they are called were seen. Some are an acre or more in extent and filled with water, others were dry holes in the ground 10 or 13 feet deep and as many in diameter. In the larger ones we saw some Hooded Mergansers which favor localities of this character.

On the lake a mile from me I saw a flock of about 30 Great White Herons and with them some of the same size but of a dark color. These birds, and Ibises, Spoonbills, etc., apparently remain on the other side of the lake where they can rest undisturbed; on the town side someone is constantly shooting which naturally alarms them. I had a long shot—a Louisiana Heron which I winged. It was some distance out in the water and Johnson's dog was sent out to secure it. He rushed bravely in and approached without hesitation, but no sooner had he come within striking distance than he received a sharp blow in the eye from the heron's bill which so alarmed him that he could not be induced to retrieve, but contented himself by remaining at a safe distance and barking, so Johnson waded in, made a quick grab, and secured it.

DEC 5   A cold windy day birds quiet and hard to find. With Jays and Flickers this was particularly noticeable; hardly a note was heard from either. A Cooper's Hawk dashing headway in pursuit of a screaming Killdeer created great consternation among a flock of Coots which were quietly feeding. They arose and with a great outcry and splashing sought safety among the lilies. At the edge of a hammock, within 50 feet of the lane on which I passed, a flock of buzzards and vultures were making merry over the remains of a hog. They arose as I approached them, and with hoarse grunts and flapping wings alit in the branches overhead, awaiting my disappearance ere they returned to their dainty repast.

On my way home near some pines I noticed a Loggerhead Shrike flying in their peculiar tanager-like flight, when suddenly he arose at right angles, going up twenty feet, then turning darted down at a Sparrow Hawk which was quietly sitting on a fence post, and had until now escaped my notice. If the Shrike's object was to call my attention to the Hawk he succeeded admirably for I secured it, and I should not have slighted the Shrike had he not wisely disappeared. I was watching one today (12/6) in a vacant lot in the town; he would sit motionless on the topmost branch of a small tree or brush-heap for minutes at a time, then with an evident object in view would fly to some part of the field and secure a grasshopper or beetle he had observed from his perch, after which feat he would alight on the nearest perch to the point of capture and devour his prey at leisure, sometimes holding it down with his foot and eating it piecemeal after the manner of a hawk.

Dec 6   At the edge of a weed-grown field bordered by a strip of pines and at present perfectly dry, I found great numbers of Savannah and Swamp Sparrows. Evidently this piece of ground was marshy when these birds took possession, but a long continued drouth has left them high and dry. The Jays here (*florincola*) have I think the power of mimicry more highly developed than the northern species (*cristata*); they give utterance to all kinds of odd and peculiar noises, one today amused himself by giving a perfect imitation of a Sparrow Hawk, the motive may have been to frighten a Killdeer, which calling, flew warily by, and the hoarse *ha-ha* that followed sounded like a derisive laugh at the success of his trick.

Seeing a flock of Jays alight in a group of live-oaks, I followed them and killed five before they left; after each shot there was a great outcry as if in protest.

Dec 11   A charming morning after a two-day light rain, and birds particularly active. Loggerhead Shrikes were remarkably common and as usual were frequently seen in pairs. Perched on the top of a tree or ridgepole of a house or weather vane, they gave vent to their song in notes whose peculiarities are worth noting. Unfortunately I had no notebook, and of the six different notes heard I can give but three.

The most common and call note of the species was a harsh call, a miniature of the Blue Jay's note but at the same time resembling a Mockingbird. Another was a guttural gurgle ending in a shrill pipe. A double toned whistle was also somewhat like the double whistle of the Jay but lacked its clearness. I dropped a number of bird bodies at the border of a small swamp, and in less than fifteen minutes a Buzzard was searching for them flying backward and forward, alighting, then continuing the search; I think he found them as a sudden swoop in his flight in their direction was made as I watched him.

Dec 13   In consequence of a gloomy rainy morning, thicket-loving birds were less shy and secretive than usual and seemed more disposed to seek the light of day.

At one place on the border of the lake the ground was perforated with the borings of Wilson's Snipe.

The spring-like song of a Quail was heard, two notes only not so loud and clear as those uttered by our [northern] bird.

Dec 15   Today and yesterday I found large flocks of Robins in full song, the air was filled with the chorus, and while I listened Bluebirds were warbling and a House Wren added his rippling melody to complete the illusion that I was at home [Englewood, N.J.] and spring had come.

Dec 16   The Brownheaded Nuthatch has at last come to me, two flocks were seen in both cases, Pine Warblers being associated with them. They proved to be noisy restless little mites. Their notes are peculiar and have no resemblance to those of either the Red-breasted or White-breasted Nuthatches. A single call note reminds me somewhat of the *chink* of a Purple Finch, while a *dee-dee-dee* note suggests a Chickadee trying to imitate a katydid.

I was greatly surprised to hear a Tufted-tit call *chickadee-dee-dee* with as much ease and precision as any Black-cap. The lower tones were slightly hoarser and louder.

Dec 18   I went Quail shooting with Wingate today. [William Wingate, frequent hunting companion, see Page 28.] Four bevies were found in one immense field and we had some excellent shooting. The birds are as hard to stop and as well worthy the sportsman's attention as the northern Bobwhite.

Dec 21   I have positively identified the call-note of Florida Towhee by taking a specimen in the act. When the Northern Towhee says *chewink* or *chewink chewee* in well-enunciated syllables, the Florida Towhee says only *chewee*, and the two notes are so fused that it sounds like one plain whistle, the two being somewhat higher than that of Northern Towhee. From a small flock of Palm Warblers I obtained a single typical example of the Yellow Palm Warbler.

DEC 23   A cloudy day has an evident effect on the feelings of the Loggerhead Shrikes, they are never so full of song as when the sky is overcast, the gloom seems to suit their disposition. Occasionally a Catbird may be seen in the depths of some briar boughs, and strange to say they are almost invariably silent; imagine if you can seeing a Catbird without hearing the customary *squak*.

DEC 27   A cloudy day again confirms my assertion that thicket-loving birds are, on such days, much less shy and retiring than when the sun is not obscured. I am positive I saw a Henslow's Sparrow in a tract of grassy pine but I was unable to obtain a shot. Grasshopper Sparrows are without doubt common, but so difficult to observe that one might easily pass them by. I have now found them in four widely separated localities. At one of these places, a grass grown bottom flooded during the wet season, I saw a wren which can be nothing else but a Short-billed Marsh Wren. I failed however to secure it.

Thicket-loving birds have here unlimited opportunities to display their fondness for the gloomy depths of impenetrable briar patches, palmetto clumps, etc. Thus it follows that such birds as Chewinks, Brown Thrashers, Catbirds, Wrens, etc. which in the North are easily obtainable are here procured with the greatest of difficulty. On the 20th I was struck with the distance at which the call of the Coot can be heard. Standing at the edge of a small pond at best a half a mile from the lake, their cries borne by a light wind sounded at my feet and I first supposed several birds had taken possession of the pond, so clear and distinct were the notes.

DEC 30   I cannot help being struck by the facility with which birds can here conceal themselves. Even such bright plumaged birds as Cardinals can disappear in a moment, and one may wait and watch without seeing them again. It may be safely said that every favorable thicket is filled with birds, and yet one may pass and repass and not see a feather or hear a note. But cautiously part the branches and enter, seat yourself, and chirp, and in a short time birds in abundance will appear from every quarter. Even then they are killed with difficulty, for if they are in sight the chances are they are too near, and vice versa. I had an excellent opportunity to test this today. It was a singular day, clear one moment, the sun pouring down, the sky a dazzling blue, and the next clouded, overcast, and raining pitchforks.

Birds were kept continually on the alert, and between the showers mounted trees, the second story as it were, to give the basement an opportunity to dry, and when the bushes had shed the drops sprinkled so liberally upon them, the birds returned, and the place was apparently deserted. One thicket I have passed almost every time I have been out and [have] never seen a Cardinal near it, but today five or six could be seen at once high up in the trees overhead, chasing each other from limb to limb. Then suddenly seeing me they would dive like a meteor southward, to disappear in a neighboring thicket.

JAN 5   On the 3rd a Savannah Sparrow with half-grown primaries was found and was easily captured.

A Bobolink was also found unable for some reason to fly and was caught by the dogs. The secondaries of one wing were missing, but whether this was the work of the dogs or not I cannot say.

JAN 8   I found one place today where birds were as abundant as I have ever seen them even in the height of the migration. The locality was a peculiar combination of hammock, pine, and swamp, bordering a small stagnant pond. While there in a very short space of time I heard or saw twenty-five species of land birds; of the Warbler family alone there were seven, viz—Orange-crowned Warbler, Pine Warbler, Myrtle Warbler, Yellow-throated Warbler, Palm Warbler, Ovenbird, and Yellowthroat.

I heard a low-voiced song, which was a familiar and yet out of place sound, and cautiously approaching I found a Hermit Thrush, apparently rehearsing for the season of song so rapidly drawing near. Later I saw several of these birds chasing each other from limb to limb with sharp outcries. Red-winged Blackbirds, ♂ & ♀ as I have observed them, go in separate places, the ♀ frequenting old fields and stubble in large bodies, while the ♂ feed among the pines in much smaller numbers.

JAN 10   Two Red-winged Blackbirds ♂ & ♀ were seen together. A strong wind somewhat interfered with my observations today.

JAN 11–12–13   Three days were passed in the pine barrens going to and returning from Jonesville, a settlement 16 miles west of Gaines-ville.

Four miles from G. is situated Sugarfoot Prairie, a large tract of swampy meadow with accompanying ponds, and surrounded by the best piece of hammock seen.

Beyond this the country is dreary and desolate beyond description, an unending forest of pines with nothing to disturb the monotony of the scene further than a clearing or a darkey's cabin.

Occasionally a few small Black Jack oaks were scattered through the woods, or near a "sink" a bunch of live oaks would appear, but the prevailing character of the country is the same unending pine-land stretching in every direction as far as the eye can reach, and the effect on our spirits is most depressing.

Sugarfoot Prairie does not differ materially from some of the ground near the Lake, its greater isolation however causes some birds to be more common there, certain of these I mention, but the notes following allude strictly to the pine barrens which lie beyond.

Pied-billed Grebes were apparently common, feeding in small pools, and way out on the prairie bunches of 7 or 8 Common Egrets could be seen grazing like white cattle on a distant meadow. Great Blue Herons and Snowy Egrets were both represented by a single specimen. Near the border of the prairie and in several wet places adjoining, Wilson's Snipes were very abundant, feeding in flocks of 7 or 8. In the same situations Palm Warblers were very common.

After leaving this excellent locality birds became very rare. One might ride for miles without seeing a feather or hearing a note, then perhaps a small flock of Pine Warblers and Brown-headed Nuthatches would appear or a company of Flickers would fly from the ground near some clearing. At intervals the hoarse, low notes of the Red-cockaded Woodpecker came to me through the woods, a sound to my ear greatly resembling the *yank* of the White-breasted Nuthatch, but started lower, and hoarser and not so distinctly articulated. I had never met with this bird before and regarded its actions with great interest. It apparently prefers the higher limbs of the pines, and may frequently be seen hanging nuthatch-like on a cone at the extremity of a branch. At one time three were seen together, but as a rule they were found in pairs. They were easily approached, and I rode under the tree they were in, without the slightest attempt at concealment, shooting them from the back of my mustang. Flickers were often seen in the "deadened" tracts of pines, but Red-cockaded Woodpeckers never leave the pines and apparently not only require pines, but vast forests of them distant from hammocks and swamps; for although I have explored many small prairies near the town bordered by hammocks, not an individual of this species has been observed.

Quail were extremely abundant in one large clearing, 5 bevies were found in less than three hours, in similar locations Mourning Doves were occasionally common.

The common sparrow was the Vesper Sparrow, Chippies were seen in immense flocks, and a few Savannah, Song, Grasshopper, and Swamp Sparrows were occasionally met with. The appended list gives only those birds met with in the pine region.

Florida Bob-white—Abundant, frequenting old fields and especially the ranker growth near the sinks, where they spend the night, seeking cover in the scrub palmetto or low brier patches which occur there. Often on being flushed, they take to the trees, and are then very difficult to find, the color harmonizing well with their surroundings.

Red-tailed Hawk—once met with.

American Sparrow Hawk—extremely abundant preferring clearings but sometimes met with in the pines.

Southern Hairy Woodpecker—two or three seen.

Red-cockaded Woodpecker—common.

Yellow-bellied Sapsucker—one or two.

Red-bellied Woodpecker—common.

Flicker—abundant.

Phoebe—common. This bird seems to be more generally distributed than any species I have met with. It seems to prefer the vicinity of some house but may be found in hammock, pine swamp or clearing, and can apparently adapt itself to its surroundings with great facility.

Florida Blue Jay—abundant.

Crow—3 or 4 Crows were seen—but whether they were Florida or Common Crows I know not.

Meadowlark—abundant in old fields, and also in the pines, many were in full song the notes entirely different from those of the northern bird.

Vesper Sparrow—abundant.

Savanna Sparrow—a few.

Grasshopper Sparrow—one or two.

Chipping Sparrow—abundant in large flocks.

Field Sparrow—probably occurs but none were identified.

Song Sparrow—two specimens.

Swamp Sparrow—one or two.

Purple Martin—breeds wherever gourds are placed for it to nest in. I saw two such places, the gourds hung in a line, two or three inches apart and about twenty feet from the ground.

Loggerhead Shrike—two or three in clearings.

Myrtle Warbler—tolerably common.

Pine Warbler—common in pines in large, widely separated flocks.

Palm Warbler—tolerably common.

Yellow Palm Warbler—one flock of five.

House Wren—two or three.

Brown-headed Nuthatch—generally found associated with Pine Warblers.

American Robin—a few.

JAN 15   Sugarfoot Prairie. Birds extremely abundant, but the ground is not suited for some birds which occur in abundance in suitable localities, Sparrows, Chewinks, etc., being missing.

Tree Swallows were very abundant flying over the ponds and marshes, and the shore was alive with Palm Warblers.

Several Little Blue and White Herons were seen, but they were very wild and although I hung on the side of my mustang keeping it between me and the birds, I was unable to secure one. English Snipe were quite common, we killed 12. Large numbers of ♂ Redwings with a few females in each flock were feeding along the shore, and with them were several Rusty Grackles both ♂ & ♀.

JAN 16   I today examined a number of birds mounted by Mr. Roth Reynolds, and obtained from him the following information. I add to my roll of winter birds, those which undoubtedly occur at that season, the Common Loon. Mr. Reynolds has the only specimen he has ever seen here. The bird was taken after a severe storm and was probably in poor condition for it was brought to him after it had died in confinement, it having been caught alive and caged for several days.

Anhinga, Water Turkey—He has several specimens.

Mallard Duck—Common.

Baldpate, American Widgeon—Not uncommon.

Green-winged Teal—Specimens seen.

Blue-winged Teal—Specimens seen.

Shoveller—Specimen seen.

Ruddy Duck—Common.

Roseate Spoonbill—Rare—two specimens.

Wood Ibis—Specimen seen.

American Bittern—.

Least Bittern—Common during summer.
Green Heron—Specimen seen.
Black-crowned Night Heron—.
Yellow-crowned Night Heron—Specimen seen.
King Rail—Not common. Two specimens.
Sora Rail—One specimen, rare.
Purple Gallinule—Not common in winter. Several specimens.
Florida Gallinule—Specimen.
American Barn Owl—Not common.
Screech Owl—Specimens.
Great Horned Owl—One specimen.

JAN 18   Coots were less common today than I have before found them, very few were seen, but one heard, a strong wind may have caused this. But on the other hand Orange-crowned Warblers were fairly abundant, a great increase in their number being noticeable. Several Black-and-white Warblers were also seen. To what extent southern birds are stationary, or the reverse, during the winter season I know not, but here on ground which I have before thoroughly explored I find the above sudden changes in local fauna.

A Loggerhead Shrike was observed feasting on a grasshopper which it had impaled on a thorn. The grasshopper was placed before it at a convenient distance and the bird was deliberately devouring it piece by piece. Here there was an evident object in impaling the insect, for having it pinned securely it could be eaten in portions with greater facility than if held hawklike under its claw as I before have seen them do.

Whether this is always the bird's object in impaling insects I cannot with certainty say, but I think this is the primary cause, and having no idea of quantity or in other words, not knowing when it has procured sufficient for its immediate wants, and like some other birds having at its command a method by which a supply of food could be stored for future use, he takes advantages of offering opportunities to capture his prey unable to resist the temptation which many grasshoppers etc. unknowingly and unmeaningly expose him to. Undoubtedly insects are left impaled only when the bird's appetite is satisfied, for he is much more frequently observed devouring his prey as soon as it is captured, than leaving it to be forgotten.

I cannot but admire the wonderful pluck and courage displayed by the Carolina Chickadee which I have before noticed in its northern cousin the Black-capped Chickadee. Today I held in my hand a wounded one, and the poor little fellow fought desperately, pecking my fingers, and again its wound evidently trying to remove the unknown thing which pained it so. It was a most pitiful sight.

JAN 20   Taking ponies we struck the lake at the sink and from there rode around the border of the lake to its head and some distance up the creek. The ground at the head of the lake is more favorable for waders than any I have seen. The water is now very low and there are vast tracts of boggy meadows with occasional swampy ponds and streams, bordered by or grown up with cypress, the whole being surrounded by hammocks.

Herons were exceedingly abundant and were frequently seen in flocks of 50 or more. They were chiefly Little Blue Herons, but many others were with them. The scene was beautiful beyond description; the frame itself of a moss-hung, cypress-dotted plain fringed with hammocks was all one could ask for, but add to this the picture of water fowls, blackbirds, swallows, etc., flying in every direction, or distant flocks of Common Egrets feeding in the meadow, and we have a glimpse of Florida birdlife as it has been painted.

JAN 23   Made a short excursion north of the town, where the country is almost entirely pine-land. One small cypress swamp was seen apparently bordered by pines on every side.

At the edge of this I saw a darkey capture a Bittern whose wing he had broken a moment before with a stone.

A pair of White-bellied Nuthatches were seen and one was heard to sing. They were in company with a large troop of the Brownheaded species whose animated conversation was most amusing. Some of the notes remind me of those produced by the twisting canary bird whistle.

With them also was a single Red-cockaded Woodpecker and also a single Carolina Chickadee. This last surprised me not a little for they are apparently rare everywhere, and all those I have seen were in thickets or hammocks.

JAN 24   A windy day but in sheltered places in the hammock birds were abundant enough.

A Carolina Chickadee was heard to sing for the first time. The song differs from the "elfin whistle" of a Black-capped Chickadee in being composed of 3 or 4 notes resembling those of the Black-capped in tone but not so loud. The gurgled notes, while sufficiently like those of the Black-capped to enable me to recognize them at once, are still entirely different. If they can be expressed on paper, I think they would say *my watcher key.* The chickadee call has the *dee* repeated five times thus *chick-a dee dee dee dee dee.*

A Tufted Tit found as usual in company with the above species was whistling persistently, frequently changing his tune.

JAN 25   A small unknown Flycatcher was seen but unfortunately not secured. The notes *prr-r-you* were strange to me.

JAN 26   The trilled notes so like a portion of the Field Sparrow's song prove to be uttered by a Pine Warbler. This bird therefore apparently sings occasionally during the winter, for I have heard the song on several previous occasions. A pair of Hairy Woodpeckers were seen in a long continued chase from tree to tree through the pines evidently mating.

Five minutes walk from the house is an empty wet field containing about an acre and surrounding a big house. I observed a Wilson's Snipe. On being flushed he flew a short distance and alit.

JAN 28   A second journey today to the head of the lake, the best place I have seen but unfortunately distant 8 miles.

Ducks are extremely abundant but so wild that I not only was unable to get within range but could not with certainty identify many. Several teal were seen.

One flock of alarmed ducks was so large that the splashing water as they arose resembled the wash of waves on a distant shore. At a point where on my previous visit I saw a pair of Red-shouldered Hawks, I again found a pair today, presumably the same ones and undoubtedly mated.

At a favorable spot we found a "bunch" of at least 50 Wilson's Snipe. In one hour and a half killed about 25. Mixed flocks of Red-wings, Rusty and Boat-tailed Grackles were met with at every swamp. Frequently these flocks would contain both ♂ and ♀ Red-wings and again the sexes would be separate. The call of those heard differs distinctly from the notes of the birds heard at the north. With the Boat-tails the case is very different, indeed from the disparity in numbers of the sexes one might suspect that Boat-tails were polygamous, for every ♂ was surrounded by at least 10 ♀ ♀.

My observation leads me to believe that the White-eyed Towhee prefers palmetto, overgrown with brush, etc., much more than the dense hammock where it is rarely found. The Red-eyed may be found in either, but is much more common in the last.

At sunset hundreds of Myrtle Warblers were seen dashing upwards into the air from the tops of weeds and tall trees, insect catching.

FEB 1   The woods are commencing to ring with song. The Cardinals lead the chorus.

The continued warm weather has driven field-loving sparrows into the moist bottoms where great numbers of them may be seen bathing. Under the head of field-loving sparrows I include Vesper, Savannah, Grasshopper, and Swamp, all until now inhabitants of weed-grown dry fields.

The Chipping Sparrow prefers the border of a hammock where on being disturbed it seeks refuge. The Song Sparrow and the White-throated Sparrow haunt dense briar thickets, the last only in the hammock, the first anywhere.

FEB 4   As I have before noticed, Red-winged Blackbirds found in the pines or clearing are in *sexed* flocks, while those flocks seen near the water invariably contain birds of both sexes.

A Baltimore Oriole was seen in the cypress bottom, the half whistle and scolding note reminded one of cherry trees.

White-eyed Vireos which during the winter have been so rare that I have secured but one specimen I find now they have commenced to sing to be quite common. Feb. 3—Mockingbirds could be heard singing in all parts of the town. Today the same is true, but in the woods they never are heard.

Robins have become much less common than they were a week ago, whether this variation is local or a true migration movement is a question.

FEB 5   I had the pleasure of listening to the full song of a White-eyed Vireo today, that rather rare performance wherein are introduced odd bits of stolen melody.

A number of Robins in possession of a sportsman were found to be in worn plumage, no signs of a moult as yet appearing.

FEB 8   The Creek [Hogtown]. Hiring a Negro I floated down the creek under the overhanging cypresses. On either side the savannas stretched far away, at every turn hundreds of ducks were seen, or dense groups of Coots scurried into the branches for concealment.

With a boat suited to the purpose one might kill an immense number of ducks here, but the heavy fishing craft are useless.

FEB 11   Robins are now seen singly or in twos or threes, no longer flocks. I flushed a pair of Quail, whether mates or not I cannot say. In a clump of low palmetto a bird was singing a song entirely new to me, it was I thought a warbler song, but imagine my surprise to find the performer a Maryland Yellowthroat. This song bore not the slightest resemblance to his ordinary notes. It was a rumbling kind of warble, reminding me somewhat of the Yellow Warbler.

FEB 12   While trying to induce a White-eyed Towhee to step outside of the thicket for a moment, my eye fell on a bird perched on a tree above. At a glance I knew what it was, there could be no mistaking the size and shape or the bright red and blue plumage of a Nonpareil. Fearing to trust to my "aux" I gave him a heavy load of 12 from my right, a cloud of feathers and falling bird, and already in imagination I held him in my hand and was stroking his richly colored feathers. The thicket was a dense one and for some time I was unable to gain an entrance, but I made up my mind to have that bird if it took me all day to get it.

After much pushing and twisting I succeeded in getting under the trees he fell from, and there at my feet lay a Myrtle Warbler. At first I was simply dazed, I could not believe my eyes. I felt of the bird again but it was perfectly warm, and there was no other in the tree where I fired, and I could explain it only as a clear case of optical delusion.

FEB 15   Quail without doubt have mated. I saw a second couple this morning and later heard one sing.

FEB 18   I am much puzzled by the crows here; the call of the most common bird is exactly similar to that of the Fish Crow which I at first supposed it to be, but find now that this bird is the Florida race of the Common Crow. Rarely I hear another call, the regular caw-caw of the northern bird. Now whether this is a simple variation in tone or whether my bird is the northern is the question. Maryland Yellowthroats were singing commonly, some of the songs were sufficiently like that of the northern bird to be recognizable, others have no resemblance to the typical song whatever but resembled more the song of the Hooded Warbler.

I have taken my first Florida Grackle; a Grackle not uncommon in the oaks in town I suppose to be this species.

FEB 22   Parula Warblers before unnoticed today become common in full song. A few may winter but undoubtedly the greater part of those noticed today were new arrivals.

FEB 25   I think both Mockingbirds and Ground Doves are mating.

FEB 28   The effect of the cold weather is being noticeable and is an excellent illustration of the relation of the song habit to meteorological conditions. Mockingbirds which were in full song on the 26th are today almost silent, their fiery passions quenched, and the same may be said of Carolina Wrens and Cardinals. I heard a Gnatcatcher singing an echo.

MAR 4   At the Creek ducks are much less abundant, many have gone northward. An Ibis was seen and missed at about 60 yards. Sp.?
    Five Lesser Yellow Legs were probably migrants.
    We floated through an immense flooded cypress swamp, the water a dense mass of the small green duck-weed.

MAR 5   At sunset two Purple Martins were seen flying over the town and the owner of some houses informed me that several had visited them.

MAR 7   It is remarkable how silent and retiring Woodpeckers have become, formerly the most abundant birds they are now met with in comparatively small numbers.
    Mockingbirds are now in full song everywhere. Each thicket has its songster who tries to surpass his neighbor.

MAR 8   Sugarfoot Prairie. Numbers of Herons are greatly increased, many new arrivals having appeared. The Red-bellied Woodpecker is evidently mating. The Loggerhead Shrike follows suit.
    Two Chickadees, probably a pair, were exploring some holes in a dead stump evidently house hunting.
    Red-bellied Woodpeckers, in bunches of 3 or 4, were making odd noises and chasing one another from tree to tree, in a swamp a ♂ Redwing was seen in full pursuit of a ♀.
    The most important factor in causing song is without doubt the surrounding meteorological influences. Birds sing out which will breed in a few weeks, and birds which will not breed until June in some

northern latitude may be heard singing at the same moment. Of the last I refer to Ruby-crowned Kinglet and Blue-headed Vireo.

MAR 11   Creek. Ducks have nearly all disappeared and but few Coots remain.

MAR 15   Although I have been prevented from going into the woods since the 11th on account of an unfortunate accident, I think little change has taken place in the local fauna since that date.

Comparatively cool weather is probably the cause of this stagnation and the migratory movement which opened so promisingly seems to have been suddenly nipped.

MAR 17   Continued cold weather prevents any movement by waiting migrants; since March 7th the avian status of this vicinity has not changed perceptibly, but with a rise in the temperature the migration should proceed from the point of its interruption.

A Quail was heard whistling the familiar three note song of the northern bird, *buckwheat ripe!*

MAR 24   No advance yet—A Pine Warbler ♀ was seen with some building material evidently looking for a house site.

MAR 25–26   On both days a single Bachman's Sparrow has been in localities which I have visited many times previously but where I have never before seen this species. On the 25th a single bird was taken at the edge of a palmetto pinery and on the 26th one was taken at the edge of a large field near the lake and at least a mile from the nearest pine-land. This last was flushed from the ground and flew first to a fence then to a holly about 10 ft. from the ground. These birds are probably true migrants.

MAR 28   During a pouring rain, a Mocker and numerous Blue Jays were heard singing.

MAR 31   A clear warm day after a still moonlight night shows that the migration has been resumed where it was interrupted on the 8th. Just two new arrivals were noted, Bachman's Sparrow and Prairie Warbler. The first were apparently common and I heard numbers singing in a palmetto pinery on my way to the Lake. The second puzzles me not a little. Prof. Allen records it as common at Jacksonville April 1, and also records many wood warblers not yet observed by me as appearing at Enterprise about the middle of March. Now

Enterprise is only 60 miles south of Gainesville, and the birds he records there (p. 269)[2] should arrive here before Prairie Warblers.

APR 2   Cold weather silences the Bachman's Sparrows singing so freely on the 30th.

APR 4   Little advance has been made, and the ranks of newcomers observed are very thin.

Evidently a vernal migration in midland Florida is a failure. In fact I think Florida may be likened to a funnel, into which Fall migrants on their southward journey are poured, but on their return few find the opening they left and the spout acts as a wedge dividing into two streams, which pass up either coast, the host of northbound migrants.

APR 5   A decided improvement on past inactivity is shown, two new arrivals appear and the ranks of several already noticed receive fresh additions.

The migration however is not yet a true Englewood [N.J.] migration, things in some manner are proceeding wrong end foremost, and whether the great army of transient visitants will adhere closely to the coasts, and pass me without a word, I cannot as yet say.

APR 6   No new arrivals today and a general dullness over everything. Cooler weather is undoubtedly the cause.

Above floating lazily along, beyond gunshot, a Sharpshinned Hawk, as I watch he suddenly grows larger, with a meteor-like rush drops to the surrounding trees, his distended claws, ready to clutch the prey below him.

APR 7   A ripple from the two waves flowing northward on either side of me was noticed today.

APR 9   Today and yesterday a cold NE storm completely checks the migration.

APR 11   If it ever was shown that the first and most important factor in the migration movement of birds is the weather, it certainly was today. After a hard NE storm of wind and rain, I naturally expected a decided change in the transient fauna, and the change had occurred, but in an entirely unexpected manner. Instead of a woods full of newly

2. *Mammals and Winter Birds of East Florida* by J. A. Allen, Bulletin of the Museum of Comparative Zoology, Vol. II, No. 3, 1871.

arrived migrants, a condition which other things being equal, I should be sure to find at Englewood, what do I find—why just the reverse; in other words, the wintering birds have been swept right out of the woods, thousands have started on their northward journey. Where on the 9th there were one hundred Myrtle Warblers today there is one, and comparatively speaking the same may be said of Prairie Warblers and Parula Warblers. And now with no abundant winter-resident bird life to clothe its nakedness, the bareness of the inward migration becomes doubly apparent, but one new arrival being noted, a single Worm-eating Warbler. Truly I am out of the swim.

Apr 12   From bad to worse, all the few remaining winter birds have departed, and still no others to replace. It is inexplicable, that in the height of the migrations, or what should be the height, the woods are almost deserted, at no time since my arrival have I seen so few birds.

Apr 14   Nothing has occurred to change my theories of the migration, on the contrary they are confirmed. Two single new arrivals were noted, one expected, the other, a riddle.

Apr 15   A few additional Yellow Warblers were the only migrative signs. A Carolina Wren was seen with building material in its bill.

Apr 20   A Mocker's nest found on the 18th containing one egg, now has three. March 15—Herons were more abundant at Sugarfoot than at any place I had found and new arrivals were constantly appearing. But poor things they had plumes and the plumes were wanted by men who camped there, and whose camp was found by one Butler with a heap of decaying carcasses near.

Apr. 18 to 20, two visits, I saw five Herons, all that are left apparently of the hundreds seen in March.

The migration if such it can be called, still drags, a single arrival every two or three days.

Apr 26   Mr. L. K. Rawlins informed me he saw a Pink Curlew [Roseate Spoonbill] at Bivins Arm today. He thinks he could have made no mistake as to the bird's identity. Hovey Bell also tells me he saw 3 flying on the morning of the 23rd, they were low enough he said for him to see the shape of their bills.

Apr 29   The ducks which I have been watching in the cove north of Bivins Arm are as I supposed Ringnecks, Johnson bringing me one he captured there today. This bird had been wing-broken and according to Johnson the ones remaining are also cripples, and it is not unusual for maimed ducks to stay in during the summer, but they have never been known to breed.

Bobolinks are present in great numbers, scattering flocks of 6-15 or immense bodies of several hundred, at least 90% are males and a flock of them in their gold and black costumes, and the confused medley of rollicking song which arises is a most inspiring sight.

As I neared the Lake there came floating over one of the most graceful beautiful birds I ever saw, a Swallow-tailed Kite, three times I fired without effect. It was like shooting at the moon.

2

Return to Gainesville

THE LAST WEEK IN May, 1887, Frank Chapman and his mother traveled north to their Englewood home. FMC had been corresponding with Mr. George B. Sennett, a wealthy manufacturer of of oil-well supplies, whose hobby was ornithology and who had brought to the American Museum of Natural History in New York a collection of birds he had made in the Rio Grande Valley. Mr. Sennett and FMC made an arrangement whereby the latter would spend half of each day assisting in the care of Mr. Sennett's birds for which he would receive his carfare back and forth to Englewood ($1.00 a day) and his luncheon at the museum. FMC gave the other half of his day to assisting Dr. Joel Asaph Allen, Curator of Birds and Mammals, who put him to work sorting and cataloging South American tropical birds. In his association with Dr. Allen he acquired a deep love and respect for the man and a great ambition to emulate his achievements in science. The friendship and partnership that were to continue until Dr. Allen's death began then and there.

Frank Chapman had deposited his own collection of birds at the Museum. These were put in order early in the summer and he also prepared his paper on "Birds Observed at Gainesville, Florida" for the *Auk*.

During September he watched migrating birds through a telescope on moonlit nights and then prepared a paper on "Nocturnal Migration of Birds" which he presented at the American Ornithologists' Union meeting in Boston October 11-13. Between the Boston trip and his arrival in Florida he was sick, but the only record of the illness is the first entry in the next journal.

The return to Gainesville must have been very pleasant, for this year he did not live in a rented house but moved into the one his mother had purchased for a permanent winter home. Also, this year Frank Chapman was welcomed back by friends and acquaintances he had made the winter before, Judge and Mrs. James Bell and their son, Hovey, a few years younger than Chapman. The Bells were northerners who had come to Florida from Poughkeepsie, New York, in the 1870's.

27

A lawyer and graduate of Columbia College in New York City, James Bell was appointed a judge in the Monticello Courts. Dissatisfied and unhappy in his work, he resigned and took a position in the land office in Gainesville where he and his family settled and became respected members of the community. In later years he was postmaster in Gainesville and later his son, and still later his granddaughter, served in Gainesville post offices. Mrs. Bell, a graduate of Vassar, wrote articles about Florida for the *Herald,* a New York City daily newspaper published from May 6, 1835, until March 18, 1924. Between Judge and Mrs. Bell and Mrs. Chapman a warm friendship existed for many years, for Mrs. Chapman eventually became a year-round resident of Gainesville, living there until her death on August 20, 1912, at the age of seventy-eight.

Another Gainesville friend of the Chapmans was Captain C. A. Curtis, U.S.A. (retired), commandant of the Gainesville Military Academy. In his youth Captain Curtis had served as supply officer in the same regiment in which Dr. Elliott Coues, a great ornithologist of the nineteenth century, served as medical officer. Dr. Coues, who was collecting for the Smithsonian between the Rio Grande and the Rio Colorado in conjunction with his army duties, introduced Captain Curtis to the cult of the naturalist. Inevitably Mrs. Chapman and FMC found him congenial.

William Wingate, a winter resident of Gainesville and one of its orange growers, was another friend. He was evidently a contemporary of Frank Chapman and became a hunting and traveling companion mentioned in letters and journals.

The Robertson family of Newnan's Lake was also friendly with the Chapmans, and their son, another contemporary of FMC, hunted and trapped with him, but this friendship did not develop until December, 1888, and is described in the Chapman letters to J. A. Allen.

CHAPMAN'S JOURNAL
December 1887 — February 1888

DEC 10   Gainesville, Florida. Although we arrived here Nov. 30, I have not until today felt well enough to venture out. When Wingate and I rode to Bivins Arm for Snipe, I soon found the bogs too much for me and after killing three birds retired to the shade of a neighboring hammock. Wingate in two hours and a half killed twenty-eight. They are very abundant, and many were left; we [were] hunting only a small portion of the ground.

The greatest change I notice in the appearance of the country since my departure in the spring has been caused by the drouth which lowering the lake has left thousands of acres uncovered where before the water was waist high; the extremely loose nature of the ground at this end of the lake being affected by a very slight rise or fall in the waters of the tributary creek, which now winds its way through a greatly extended savanna, which last year was "bonnet"-grown lake. The roots of these bonnets (*Nuphar adorna*) can now be seen, these are two or three inches in diameter and move over the ground like palmetto roots. A Cow-bird was taken from a flock of Redwings and Boat-tails.

DEC 12   The greater part of the morning was occupied in setting traps for gophers, *Geomys tuza,* which in small numbers were found in a cleared sandy field.

DEC 13   Seven traps were set for mice, none of which were successful, Cottontails in most cases overturning and springing them in order to procure the cheese contained.

With *Geomys* I had better fortune, my first trap securing a specimen, the only one I have ever seen alive; the second was sprung by the dirt shoved ahead of the advancing animal.

DEC 19   I have done little the first week but attend to my traps with rather poor success. Today a Turkey Buzzard was seen having most if not all the tertiaries missing from the right wing, which in no way diminished its sailing powers and it described graceful circles with the same ease at its fellows.

A loud hammering was heard in a bunch of palmetto which proved to be a Brown Thrasher pounding away at some unknown thing with as much force as would be used by a Flicker.

DEC 22   A Bachman's Sparrow was flushed in a scrub-oak pinery and flew directly down a gopher's hole distant about 10 feet, and no amount of pounding above would induce it to come out.

DEC 29   I rode to the Lake this afternoon to see the flight of Ducks from the Arm [Bivins] out into the Lake [Alachua] where they may pass the night in safety. It was a beautiful evening, clear and crisp with a touch of frost in the air, and a light breeze rippling the waters of the lake.

Along the shores flocks of Killdeers arise with wild frightened calls as I approach, and noisy troops of Blackbirds whirl downwind in small compact bodies as though moved by one impulse. Two Great Blue Herons calmly arise and flap lazily to some safer point, and up the Arm a single White Heron slowly wings its way against a background of dark forest trees making a striking picture.

As the sun falls the Ducks feeding at the edge of the lilies which border the shore take flight in small bodies and are lost to sight, flying low over the water.

Darker it grows, all is silent save the call of some restless Killdeer seeking a roosting place, but still the Ducks from the Arm do not come.

The wind sighs gently in the trees, the red glow of the western heavens grows fainter, the full moon appearing from the clouds shines with renewed light. Hundreds of Doves in one unending stream pass me on their way to bed. I can barely see them as they go whizzing by.

It is almost dark now, objects near the surface are dim and obscure, and as I ride along the border of the Arm, starting some sleeping Killdeer from its slumbers, I see high above the water the first flock of Ducks coming down the Arm at lightning speed. As they near the bridge they sheer to one side and pass safely, a second and third flock swiftly follow, and all escape by either following the course of the first or rising beyond gunshot until the danger is past, then descending.

The shooters on the bridge wait in vain, a harmless shot is fired as one flock less cautious than the rest passed near and I turn my pony homeward for a ride through a scene weird and beautiful beyond description.

DEC 31   What a change is seen in Sugarfoot. Last May when I was there the woods were alive with birds, Cardinals whistled, mockers sang, Tufted and Carolina Chickadees and Pine Warblers led their hungry broods from tree to tree, Yellow-throated Warblers sang gaily from the tree tops and there was a general bustle and activity in the bird world which was inspiriting. Now winter is on the land, the birds are either silent or absent, and the woods comparatively deserted.

JAN 1   A picnic on New Year's Day, strange but true. With Judge and Mrs. Bell and their family I went to Newnan's Lake. The packing house on its shore was our headquarters; at our feet the Lake, a beautiful body of water, its surface white with miniature billows; all around us were plume-like palmettos, their graceful heads held aloft by the curious swathed or sheathed body.

On the shore were Cypress growing so closely and so overhung with moss that the ground below was free of all growth but the strange cypress knees, which shoot up from the ground like roots excelling at their humble position.

Near us was a large orange grove and the golden balls were all the more welcome because they were few and far between, but careful searching brought us more than we could eat, and there were eight in our party. Here also we found a number of arrow heads and bits of Indian pottery, and a wild cat's track was plainly printed on the land.

JAN 4   Ducks are by no means as common this winter as they were last, the lack of water probably restricts the best feeding ground. Johnson had two Ringnecks, the species is evidently common. I have an idea that the Yellow-bellied Sapsucker can be at once identified by its rap, it lacks the force of even the Downy Woodpecker and is more rapid than any of them.

I learned a new (to me) note for the Boat-tailed Grackle today. Three birds were wading in shallow water, fishing for something on the bottom. There were no birds near them, and as I sat on my pony watching, I was suddenly startled by the flapping of wings as of a Coot tripping over the water, which proved to be one of the Grackles which had mounted a small bush and was indulging in sundry guttural musical efforts every few moments bringing in this odd queer run which sounded exactly like the flapping of wings. In effect the performance somewhat parallels the gurgling notes of a Cowbird in the breeding season. The sound was very familiar to me, but so excellent is the imitation that I have always ascribed it to some of the numerous Coots which abound in most places favored by Boat-tails.

A single Mockingbird was seen giving chase to a whole troop of Blue Jays which apparently had invaded its dominion. Later I saw two fighting together, a veritable war of the giants and no quarter. They would tumble over and over in the air and flight being forgotten would soon fall to the ground there to remain several seconds motionless locked in close and deadly embrace, then with rumpled dress hop to a fence and after a moment go at it again.

JAN 6   A perfect summer day; peas and strawberries are in blossom, roses and peach trees in bloom, and it is difficult to believe that at home they are having cold, blistering weather.

Several times I have fancied I heard the note of a Pine Siskin but not once have I been even able to see the bird to verify my ears, even with them, not to mention my eyes, but today when I was in a dense scrub, a Pine Siskin passed calling over my head and although the trees prevented my seeing I am as certain of the bird's presence as though I held it in my hand.

An Ovenbird was seen acting in a most excited manner and chirping as vigorously as though it was in some northern woods and had a nest on the ground below.

JAN 7   In the center of a dense hammock land I came across a covey of Quail feeding on acorns like a flock of Turkeys.

The Cardinal has a peculiar clucking note uttered when several of them are together. Some excitement then produced seems to be its cause.

Bluebirds were abundant, large flocks of a hundred or more were feeding on the berries of the mistletoe. They seem to be governed by one impulse and the noise as they all take wing together is like a sudden gust of wind in the trees.

JAN 9   In one shot Johnson killed nine Ringnecks two of which escaped, in a second shot secured two more, these birds I saw. It is rather singular that these birds should be so common here and not be recorded by observers from other localities.

Two Scaup Ducks were seen in the possession of a hunter.

Purple Gallinules were heard calling at the foot of Mr. Rawlins' place on Bivins Arm. This locality is just suited to them and they are apparently common there, but so impossible is this swamp that I fear I cannot enter it. Imagine a dense tangle of bushes and high grass growing in water so shallow that a boat will not float, and with mud so deep that one would probably disappear if one should attempt to wade in it.

JAN 10   Today with Wingate I went to Hogtown Lake, a locality before unvisited; there is now comparatively little water in what during wet weather is a pond about two miles long and the result is a large muddy savanna intersected with small streams, a most excellent resort for Ducks as is shown by the large number which frequent it.

In a small pond nearby numerous "gators" were seen and there also a single Water Turkey scaled around in the air.

So impressed were we with the amount of game to be seen that we decided to return the following day.

JAN 11   Reached the lake at 7:30. The morning flight was about over. The unmistakable note of an invisible Pine Siskin was heard. Someday I may get one of these birds.

Tree Swallows were abundant and apparently most in the bottom bushes which grow at the borders of the Lake.

Never before have I seen so many Robins; in a hammock near the shore they simply swarmed, attracted there by the berries of the holly on which they were feeding. The trees quivered with them, in fact favorite trees were just a mass of Robins and their calls, or the rush of wings as they swept from place to place, filled the air.

JAN 16   A very warm close quiet day, not a breath of air moving. Silences birds, and as a rule they are quiet and difficult to find.

FMC's autobiography reveals that the abrupt ending of this journal on January 16 took place when he left Gainesville with William Wingate to explore Pine Island and nearby Sanibel. They stayed at a newly opened hotel which may have been the San Carlos, a business venture of a friend of Wingate. This hotel, the first building erected on Pine Island, stood at what later became St. James City. Sanibel Island, too, had but one building on it in 1888, the lighthouse.

Frank Chapman found few birds on either island except a number of nesting Bald Eagles on Pine. Plume hunters had been there first. He was about to return home to Gainesville when the famous ornithologist, Charles Cory, appeared with his wife in their sloop. At Cory's invitation FMC collected with him in the nearby waters.

According to his *Autobiography of a Bird Lover*, while he was with the Corys, "One day there came a letter which, in a page opened a new life to me. It was from Dr. J. A. Allen offering me the position of his assistant in the American Museum. I read it at the lunch table and it was several moments before I could sufficiently compose myself to tell my companions of its contents."

He says he hastened northward, stopping in Gainesville only long enough to see his mother and pack his things before proceeding to New York to report to the museum on the first of March. Actually he was back in Gainesville on February 17 and 18 and made these two entries in his journal.

FEB 17   I have never before so thoroughly appreciated Gainesville as I did this morning; although the weather was cloudy and unpleasant, the change in surroundings of fauna and flora was so marked when contrasted with those of Pine Island, that it seemed to me as though I had suddenly passed from winter to spring. Instead of the dreary and desolate unending pine barrens, the dreary glaring sand-pits or stunted mangroves with bird life everywhere at a minimum, I am in a land of trees and flowers and cultivated fields at the height of the Florida spring, with the ringing whistle of the Cardinal or Wren echoing on every side, or the cries of Jays and Hawks and calls of numerous other birds coming from every direction.

FEB 18   The song of a Maryland Yellow-throat differed so greatly from the normal song of the bird at the North that I with difficulty recognized the singer. The call note also seems to vary. Instead of the short *chirp*, it is a more prolonged and harsh *char*. Mockers are singing abundantly in town and an occasional one is heard in the country.

Thus ends the journal for the spring of 1888. FMC had eleven and a half days to make his four-day trip north. In those days he had to go by train to Palatka, by boat to Jacksonville, and by train up the coast line as we do today, but much more slowly. He reported at the Museum March 1 and was probably at home in Englewood, New Jersey on Sunday, March 11, when the famous "Blizzard of '88"

started to blanket New York. He undoubtedly had at least a week's enforced vacation, storm bound, while the blizzard roared on, burying town and country in deep drifts, and stopping all traffic.

Through the summer and early fall of 1888 he continued his work and study at the Museum until he left to attend the meetings of the American Ornithologists' Union in Washington, D.C., November 13-15. There he was elected an active member of the Union, an honor conferred by his peers which greatly pleased him.

After the meetings he and his mother started to Florida, but word came of a yellow fever epidemic in Gainesville so they went only as far as their house in Aiken, South Carolina. There they waited for cold weather.

After the first heavy freeze in Aiken (18°) in early December, they proceeded to Gainesville. While the cause of yellow fever was then unknown, all were aware that it subsided as soon as winter temperatures set in, and after a frost all danger of infection was over.

The following account of the yellow fever epidemic in Gainesville was in Mrs. Chapman's scrap book.

Sunday Herald, Dec. 2nd, 1888

O H,   T H E   F E V E R!

A Characteristic Episode Connected with the Epidemic in Florida

REFUGEE LIFE IN THE WOODS
HOW THE "JUDGE" AND THE "MOTHER" FOUND RUDE SHELTER OUTSIDE
OF GAINESVILLE AND GUARDED THEIR LITTLE FLOCK

———

THIS THRILLING NARRATIVE is written by Mrs. M. C. Bell, wife of ex-Judge James Bell, of Gainesville, Fla., and it represents their own actual experience and that of their neighbors, in the yellow fever epidemic. Judge Bell in 1876 did good service for the *Herald*, in connection with its special correspondent, in the famous exploration of the great Pinhook Swamp, Jefferson County, Fla.

———

When Yellow Jack struck Jacksonville the whole state trembled. Eagerly the bulletin was sought each morning for the daily report of its victims, and anxious hearts scanned the papers, seeking familiar names among the lists of sick and dead.

Guards were stationed on all roads leading to the city and no strangers were allowed in town unless they could produce the most satisfactory proof as to where they came from and that they were free from infection.

After a little we had become somewhat familiarized with the danger, and as we had escaped so long fancied we were secure, but at last the blow fell. About the 10th of September our neighboring town of Fernandina was threatened with a labor riot, and the authorities called upon the Governor for aid in suppressing it. The local elections were just at hand and most of the local officers were candidates for re-election, and it was current rumor that they did not wish to antagonize the labor vote. Among other troops ordered from the interior were the Gainesville Guards, a finely officered and well disciplined corps of men, who for that reason bore the burden of duty while there. The weather was most inclement, heavy rains falling during most of their five days' stay. The Saturday night before their return they were detailed to guard the property of a Mr. Howell. The rain fell in torrents and they were without shelter, and at the same time within the house lay a body very ill with so-called dengue fever. Some apprehension was felt by the citizens of Gainesville about allowing the guards to return home, as there had been rumors of sickness and death in Fernandina from private sources, and we knew many citizens had left town, and the Mallory steamship line had been withdrawn. One of our physicians went on, and was most positively assured by the Board of Health and the local physicians that the city was perfectly healthy; no fever except a mild type of dengue, and no suspicious cases. Relying upon their word on Monday night the guards returned and were allowed to enter the city. Several of them were taken sick at once, but the exposure and fatigue they had been through was supposed to be a sufficient reason.

Fleeing Pell Mell from Church

A good deal of uneasiness was felt throughout the city as the cases became of a graver character, until the climax was reached on Sunday evening, when a public announcement was made at one of the churches at the close of service that there were five or six cases of yellow fever among the guards, and all were advised to leave town as soon as possible. No one waited for the benediction—down the gallery stairs they fled, out of the windows they jumped and poured from the doors, all intent upon one purpose, to reach home as quickly as possible. In our own home some were in bed and asleep, and others just preparing to follow their example, when the Judge came in with the news. It awakened us most effectually. Think of being waked up in the night and told to dress and pick up clothes, provisions and cooking utensils and flee for your life from pestilence!

The Judge went to seek some vehicle and the mother roused the children to dress and prepare for flight. On every side in the street were heard running and hurrying wheels rumbling by and the hum of voices, while nailing of boxes and loading of wagons sounded all about us. There was the more urgent need of our leaving as on one side by us, not twenty feet distant, a kind hearted neighbor had taken one of the sick ones into her house to care for, and so had brought the fever into her own home and perhaps ours, as the children from both families had been together all day.

A Lively Dilemma

The mother and daughter looked at each other and asked, "What shall we take and what shall we take it in?" Hardly time to stop to think. Hastily a packing trunk was brought down, and first there went into it some bedding, then a miscellaneous assortment of clothing for six persons. After this a large wash-tub was packed with crockery, cooking utensils and provisions. A pillow slip was put inside of a large tin and filled with flour from the barrel. Everybody flew around with a lamp in one hand looking for something convenient to carry—the two little ones getting in everybody's way. They had slept soundly and were hard to waken, but once up it was for all night. Before this the Judge had returned with a hack.

"It is all I could get," he said, "and I was mighty lucky to get that. The livery stables are crowded, and people are offering any sum for something to get away in. The back seats are out; pile your mattresses in there; your trunk you must leave, and we will try to send in tomorrow to get it."

We looked at each other in dismay. One hack to hold a driver and six persons and our belongings! But we must make the best of it. Two mattresses which had seen service were bundled in, a roll of bed clothing taken off the beds, some pillows tucked in, the tub and flour tin packed away, and after making a last tour of the house the mother locked the door, and with her pocket full of matches, a broom in one hand and a lamp in the other, seated herself on top of the promiscuous collection in the hack, with the daughter beside her, while the little ones fitted themselves into corners and proceeded to spread out arms and legs with a reckless disregard of space and neighbors.

An Ant Hill Put to Rout

We had decided to throw ourselves upon the mercy of a friend [Robertson] who had a packing house on the lake [Newnan's] about six miles distant and beg for a shelter there, and we started with stout hearts and a determination to make the best of things. On our way we drove through town, and such an indescribable scene the streets presented, just like an ant heap which has been freshly disturbed. The very air seemed filled with vague apprehension. Men were hurrying hither and thither, and every one carried a roll of bedding or a valise. It is said three thousand persons left town that night, many of them on foot. In every direction went a stream of people, and all the next day every road was filled with wagons and people, so that when on Tuesday Surgeon General Hamilton sent in a train of eleven coaches to take out the refugees only four persons were left to go!

For two weeks there had been a steady downpour of rain and the roads were in a fearful condition. As we proceeded on our way we found all the guards and outposts withdrawn, so quickly had the news spread, and the board shelters and tents used by them were all down and on the way to be put up for someone's benefit further on. No danger now of any one wanting to get into town. Everybody was anxious to get out. Very slowly we proceeded, so fearful were we of a breakdown, or of getting into some washout and breaking a leg of one of the horses. Finally, as the roads became worse, being submerged in water from one to two feet deep, the Boy [Hovey] put on his big hunting boots and tramped ahead to find out the pitfalls. Twelve o'clock sounded from the town clock and found us half way on our journey, no moon and only just starlight enough to show us the road, but fortunately no rain. Every once in a while the Boy would strike a washout and down would go one leg in a hole. This made slow travelling, but all things come to an end in time, and at last we reached our friend's house.

"Halloo! halloo!" shouted the Judge.

All was still, even the dogs, but no one ventures inside of closed gates in Florida, so there was more hallooing, which finally brought a response from inside, and before long our good friend Mr. R. appeared. Some of his relatives had preceded us from town in the afternoon, so that he was prepared for the news we brought. In answer to our query for shelter he kindly offered us one nearer by than the one we had hoped for, and himself conducted us to an old house about a quarter of a mile from his own. Most thankfully we accepted his offer, as it saved our crossing a stream that the mother had been dreading, fearing it would be over the wagon body, as the water was so high.

A PRIMITIVE LODGING

The door stood open and we entered a large room with a tumbledown cavern of a fireplace at one end and a perpendicular flight of steps at the other. An open door revealed a little cupboard under them, and the light of the lamp showed us a door opening out on the other side of the house. It did not look attractive just then, but bidding our host good night we took the broom and swept up the floor, closed the doors with the secure fastening of a button, spread the two mattresses side by side upon the floor and, making our beds, prepared to rest until daylight. But we had not reckoned on the mosquitoes. They came in companies, in divisions, in brigades, in armies. Slap! slap! slap! came from all sides. No sleep for us, and we regretted the lack of foresight which had left the mosquito nets behind. We might have got our heads under at least. The mother feared snakes and lizards might dispute possession of the old house with us, but fortunately none appeared. But the long night wore away at last and morning showed us such a lovely view outside as quite reconciled us to all our surroundings. A group of immense live oak trees, draped in soft, gray moss, formed a circle in front of the house, leaving a large open space carpeted with leaves and always shaded. Water had to be brought from "the branch," some little distance away, and looked like clear tea when you got it, but was sweet and cold and said to be wholesome. The first breakfast in our new quarters was not a success, and we began to discover that it was quite possible to overlook some essential articles when packing in such a hurry. There was no kettle and no frying pan, and the fireplace had not one level spot in it and was full of wet straw; but at last we found a dry rail and a fire was coaxed to blaze, and breakfast of some sort was got. Having vainly tried to borrow a fryingpan from a colored man in our vicinity he reported our need to our kind neighbor, who presently made his appearance with one in his hand and a pitcher of milk. Thank God for good friends! We improvised a table with a plank, extending from the tub to the flour bin, and doubled up the mattress for seats. The Judge and the Boy went to town after breakfast. They had to pull off shoes and stockings and wade most of the way. It was undignified, but vastly preferable to wet feet all day. Just before dark they appeared with a wagon load of things from the house—the stove, a table, chairs and provisions; also the mosquito nets. It was an easy matter now to cook pork and hominy, which formed the chief articles of our diet. No high living here. The staple articles it has been possible to procure from town generally, and occasionally fresh meat, but when the hunters come home with empty bags we have to fall back on pork. Several trips have been made to the house in town and now our little cabin is made comfortable with such things as were absolutely necessary. We even luxuriate in two rocking chairs. The upstairs is well ventilated, missing shingles afford an unobstructed view of the heavens and when a rain storm sets in, it takes some management to find a spot large enough for the bed to set in where it will not be rained upon. It has happened several times that we have been wakened at night by a drop of rain on our faces. Generally we spread a waterproof over the leaky place and lie down to sleep as if nothing had occurred. In the rear of our mansion the large tent is set up and appropriated by the boys. A creaking cot from the house was brought out for their use, but the Boy has discarded that and manufactured from some old boards his own bedstead. Split rails make the most delightful of bed springs; green moss from the trees, covered with palmetto leaves, over which is spread an oilcloth table cover, then a single mattress and a single feather bed, pieced out side by side— and little Jim says:

"It sleeps gooder than any bed in the house."

In addition the tent is occupied by a young 'possum and a six foot "gopher" snake as thick as man's wrist (this last is in a box), and also a huge terrapin. Consequently the tent is not a favorite sitting room.

LIKE A CITY OF THE DEAD

A few days after the flight the Mother declared her intention of visiting the house in town. It was useless to argue. "When a woman will she will, you may depend on't." If the Judge could go each day with impunity, so could she. So a mule cart took them in, leaving the Boy and the children to keep house and cook dinner.

The city presented a most desolate appearance. Every house where there was a case of fever had a yellow flag nailed at the gate and ropes stretched so as completely to shut off the infected place from all passers by. Outside, under the row of trees in the middle of the street, in a chair, sat a guard with a shotgun on his knees, to prevent any persons going into or leaving the fever stricken houses. Almost every house was deserted; not a sound to be heard or wagon seen and scarcely a person met off the business square. It seemed like a city of the dead.

The Mayor had fled; the president of the Board of Health and other officials—only a handful—left to attend to public affairs. Two groceries only were open and one dry goods store, besides two drugstores and the Judge's.

I cannot feel that any blame should be attached to those who left —self-preservation is the first law of nature—but all honor is due to those who stayed from a sense of duty. Without J. C. Carlisle at the head and Sheriff Winges to administer affairs, and Colonel Dutton, of the bank, whose generosity advanced the money needed to carry on the work of the Executive Committee, and the brave Major Gruelle, who attended personally to the fumigating and disinfecting of the premises and stores where the sick had been—what would be the history of Gainesville now? Major Gruelle paid the price of his work with his life. There were many others who remained and did good work also, and to the wisdom and foresight of those who stood at the helm and guided us through the storm the greatest praise is due. Colonel Dutton had just returned from Europe and was in New York when the news of the outbreak reached him. Though urged to remain his answer was:

"If Gainesville is to have an epidemic of fever my place is there, where I can do her some good."

A day or two after the exodus from town Lieutenant Evans, one of the guards, died. The others we heard were improving, and now the demand was heard on all sides, "How did they take the fever?" Fernandina reiterated her assertion of perfect health, and suggested and almost made us believe that the infection must have been taken from the coaches that conveyed them home. None of the other troops had taken the fever, but then none had been exposed as ours were, for upon them fell the brunt of the service, and while they were out in the rain guarding the fever stricken houses the others were sleeping in the armory. Whenever danger lurked from rioters or fever there were our guards—

Theirs not to question why,
Theirs but to do and die.

FERNANDINA'S RESPONSIBILITY

But see how our query is answered by facts. Before our dead soldiers are all buried or our sick ones well news comes of yellow fever in Fernandina; presently it is epidemic, yet the authorities persist in their denial of fever in their midst or any suspicion of it during the time the troops were in the city. Before me as I write lies a pamphlet, published in Washington, containing a report from a physician of Fernandina to the Surgeon General, bearing date September 10, in which he says:

"I feel positive we have the fever here and that it has been here since the first of August."

He then at some length gives an account of a post-mortem at which he was present, and says he reported to the Board of Health his belief that it was yellow fever and was asked to suppress his opinion, as the others were against him. He mentions other cases and speaks of infection spreading from that point and concludes by saying:

"Just recently from a labor riot, the State troops from Orlando, Gainesville, Ocala and Starke are here from those healthy interior towns and are now disbanding or soon will disband and go to their homes, and as I feel sure, will carry death and destruction with them."

Prophetic words! If we could have heard them what might we not have been saved! I have not yet seen one word of sorrow or regret from Fernandina, that she should have been the means, however unwittingly, of bringing death and desolation upon us—only angry self-exculpation.

While the Mother was engaged at the house in regulating and directing, a little stir outside brought her to the window, to see carried inside of the next house, where the yellow flag already floated, the last of the Guards to succumb to the fever. Poor Fitch Miller, the genial comrade and universally loved friend! The entire population of Gainesville at home and abroad mourned sincerely over the sad news of his death a few days later. The second victim of treachery! Fernandina may explain to her own satisfaction her duplicity when she asked and obtained protection for the lives and property of her citizens at our expense, but she never can remove from the minds of the general public the conviction that she was guilty of an inexcusable and deliberate outrage. When we remember our dead soldier boys it is poor satisfaction to know that they quelled her riot.

THE FEVER IN THE FAMILY

When the party from town reached the little cabin in the woods they found all safe, though dinner had suffered somewhat at the hands of the amateurs. Fortunately that was remedied, and the meal was soon over. Getting dinner was not so bad and eating was no trouble —but the dishwashing! The next morning the Mother rose with a fearful headache, which had come on in the night, and such a worn out, weary feeling, as if it was an impossibility to take a step or lift a hand; but breakfast must be prepared and cleared away, and she nerved herself to the task, and got through it, and then broke down utterly, too sick even to care whether anything was done or not. When the Judge came home in the afternoon he found her with fever and all the symptoms of the dreaded scourge. It was no time to take chances, so she was put through a regular course of treatment, orange leaf tea and sweats. For several days she was very sick. Isolation was not possible, and under the simple home treatment she recovered, although it was several days after she was up before she could walk without tottering; but as she refused to have a physician brought out we shall never be quite sure whether we have had a genuine case of yellow fever in the family.

The type of the disease which has prevailed at Gainesville seems to set all known rules at defiance. There have been only a few deaths and three or four times as many cases, but even in fatal cases there has been no spread of the disease among nurses or attendants.

Major Gruelle, who was the first to take the disease among the citizens, had opened a drain upon his place at the first appearance of the fever, and it is now believed that the newly disturbed ground became infected from the fatal case of fever at the house of Lieutenant Evans, about an hundred yards distant. The death of Major Gruelle, his nephew, Lute Hall, and the colored guard are directly attributable to that cause; also the one occurring on the 14th of October. Mr. Davis had not been away from his house in North Gainesville since the beginning of the fever except occasionally to look up a straying cow in a wood near the same drain. Since then there have been a number of light cases of fever in the vicinity of Mr. Davis' house. Mr. Collins, who is now convalescent, was Deputy Sheriff, and his duties have taken him in all portions of the town. A little son of Dr. Vidal, who is now recovering from a severe attack of the fever, was noticed by the guard playing on the fence between our house and the one next to it, where two cases of fever have been; one fatal. Since then the guard stationed there has also been attacked, so that in all of these cases the disease has been decidedly traceable to infected ground. But two cases occurring among the officers of the National Bank, who had not knowingly been exposed, and others breaking out in different portions of the city with little known opportunity for infection, caused the Board of Health to declare it epidemic, and refugees were not allowed to return to their homes in town.

[*A newspaper clipping found in FMC's mother's scrap book, probably 1901 and from a New York paper.*]

CARRY YELLOW FEVER GERMS

Dr. Reed, at Havana, Says Experiments Prove that Mosquitoes Alone Spread the Disease.

HAVANA, Jan. 9—The American Commission, under the superintendence of Dr. Reed, which has been making experiments at Quemados as to the propagation of the yellow fever germs by the mosquito, has obtained extremely satisfactory results.

Dr. Reed says the experiments show, beyond a doubt, that there is no contagion from an infected person or from infected clothing, but that the mosquitoes alone are responsible for the spread of the disease. In the course of the commission's investigations six non-immune persons were infected direct by the bite of mosquitoes which had previously bitten yellow fever patients, and five of these developed yellow fever.

The last experiment made proved conclusively, Dr. Reed contends, the theory of propagation by mosquitoes. A special building was constructed of disinfected material, and one of the rooms was divided into two sections by a wire mosquito screen. In one section were placed disinfected bedding and clothing, and in the other bedding and clothing from the yellow fever hospital, which had not been disinfected. Two non-immunes occupied the two sections. In the former were put several infected mosquitoes. The patient remained in this room only long enough to be bitten, and in four days a pronounced case of yellow fever developed. The patient is now convalescent.

The other subject slept in the infected bedding for many nights and has not contracted the fever.

Both patients have been sleeping for twenty nights in garments worn by yellow fever victims and in bedding from the yellow fever hospital. Dr. Reed says they are growing fat, and that in no instance in the course of the commission's investigation has a case of yellow fever developed from exposure to infected bedding or clothing.

3

Letters—Gainesville & Brevard County

*T*HE AMERICAN MUSEUM OF NATURAL HISTORY sent Frank Chapman on his first expedition in January, 1889. He was directed to collect mammals and birds in Florida. Though he had been in Florida only a month before when he escorted his mother to Gainesville in early December, 1888, he returned in January to take up the duty of supplying the Museum with a representative collection of small Florida mammals and to supplement the collections of Florida birds.

Instead of submitting a formal schedule or a journal, he wrote his report in a series of letters to his friend and mentor who was also his superior at the Museum, Joel Asaph Allen. The letters are more than a narrative of his activities, they are an interesting picture of places and people in Florida.

Gainesville, Florida
Jan. 17/89

My dear Mr. Allen:

It does not seem quite probable that the three days which have passed since I left you, are sufficient to cause so great a change as has occurred in my surroundings; but it is a great world, and given a little steam, some wheels, and consecutive rails, one may crawl over the map in a most astonishing manner. Nature had not donned a very wintry costume when I left, it is true, still when I look from the window at my right and see the glossy foliage of the orange trees, or cloud of pink blossoms and new green leaves which envelop a nearer peach, the contrast is indeed great and I feel it is "good to be here." From the opposite door this morning, in a vacant field across the way I saw a flock of about twenty Doves and several Meadowlarks; Ground Doves have also been mourning around the yard, Blue Jays, Shrikes and Palm Warblers, calling among the trees. It is a rainy day, just the kind these last four birds seem to enjoy.

I had a quiet, uneventful journey, and arrived feeling well rested. Of course I met a number of people who contributed no small amount of amusement to me on the way, for the percentage of characters was somewhat above the average, and some indeed were types.

I arrived too late last night to do more than unpack, and the morning has been passed in renewing last winter's acquaintances and making necessary preliminary arrangements. The town has not yet recovered from its attack of fever, but business is rapidly increasing and in a short time it will apparently be forgotten and everything go on as before.

Hovey Bell tells me he has some mammals for me, among them several gophers, and I learned of a new locality, one in which they (the Bells) camped during the fever, where mammals may be proven to be abundant. Two squirrels are also said to occur there; it is distant from town about five miles. My last year's pony has been stolen [probably by yellow fever refugees fleeing the town], but I have managed to find another, a colt under three years, and having a barn on the place, I have chartered her outright, and go out this afternoon to make necessary purchases of food, saddle, etc., incident to her reception, so I will be well equipped.

I see Bell coming up the street; remember me most kindly to Mrs. Allen and each one who inquires at the museum and do not work too hard.

Very sincerely yours,
/s/ Frank M. Chapman

Jan. 19/89
6 P.M.

Dear Mr. Allen:

The first day's work is over and while I hope the larger part of the results are still to be determined, I view with much satisfaction those already obtained. Leaving the house this morning with Hovey Bell as guide we rode four or five miles east of the town to the cabin in which they camped while shut out by the fever and where Mrs. Bell was ill. Imagine a family of six living in one room with no comforts or conveniences whatever, and the mother sick with fever.

It is a beautiful place, surrounded by ground of almost every character, pines, scrub-oak, low hummocks, and the old clearings, and is thus an excellent place in which to trap. There is probably no wilder region in the vicinity of Gainesville. Deer and Wild Turkeys occur in small numbers, Otters, and Wild Cats are not uncommon; at the right season Gray Squirrels are said to be abundant, but Fox Squirrels are rare. Coons, Possums and Skunks are of course also found there, and this list I hope to be able to add to considerably.

The entire locality is known as the Robertson Plantation, and here the family have their home, a magnificent large log house, and a mile further on, their orange grove, the finest in this region and from which they shipped four thousand boxes of fruit this year. There is a young man in this family about my age, he is very fond of hunting, has dogs, etc., and will probably be of great assistance to me.

Procuring a hoe at his home this morning we rode on another mile to gopher town, a scrub-oak pine woods, where I found these rodents for some reason did not burrow nearly as deep as they did in the locality I worked last year. Probably the soil is different, or, since this has been a very rainy season, and as last year it was very dry, they are not obliged to go down as far to find a stratum of soil damp enough to tunnel in. At any rate with Hovey's very efficient assistance, in fact he did almost all the work, we set eight traps, and then went to lunch in a beautiful place near a running stream with a good, clear, healthy looking spring, and after feasting, with a pipe for dessert, we put out a few traps for mice and then started back to examine those previously set, and you may imagine the yells I sent up when I found we had five gophers. Several traps were simply filled up with sand, but we rearranged them so in a few minutes his royal highness would appear to see who was letting daylight into his domain. One old fellow is very cunning. Three times in fifteen minutes he repaired his hole, every time avoiding the trap. Finally I put two traps in his runway and left them to return tomorrow. Leaving now we went to the hummocks, cabin, and old fields, and put out our mouse and rat traps. I have started a trapping book so that I can easily retrace my steps to keep notes on localities, bait, etc. Today's record reads in part as follows:

1. "Slayer"—(kind of trap, like the ones I procured Dr. Merriam, Richardson also has one). Bait, White-eyed Vireo (not *maynardi*). Locality, end of bridge across stream ten feet wide.

2. "Slayer"—Bait, walnut. Locality, hummock near dead stump.

3. "Cyclone"—Bait, peanut; foot of little hill in hummock.

4. "Cyclone"—Bait, pea, squash and melon seeds. Locality, at spring.

6. "Cyclone"—Spanish bayonet near cabin. Bait, cheese.

7. "Cyclone"—Another clump of same. Bait, peanut.

8–12. "Cyclones"—In old field, baited with cheese, peas and peanuts.

Bell has an equal number of traps and has his own record and we also have two in gopher holes, thus twenty-six in all; ought to get something hadn't we; I'm just like a child with a Christmas tree, in my desire to see them all tomorrow. I will write you about the results. Photographed a Shrike this morning as he sat singing on the extreme tip of the lightning rod which adorns our house, one of their favorite positions. Good night, I go out now to tackle the spoils.

JAN 20   A steady downpour all day, with frequent thunder and lightning; in the afternoon we started for Robertsons, and found the road under water fully one half the way, it was, in fact, one long ford and very slow riding.

This rain I hope accounts for our lack of success in trapping, as very few things were moving last night, and our total bag was two mice, one *gossypinus* [Cotton Mouse] and one similar to those I gave Merriam. The old gopher again evaded us but sprung both traps.

Several flowers are now appearing, and I noticed today elderberries, violets and yellow jessamine in bloom.

I have heard from Mr. Scott [W. E. D. Scott, ornithologist]. He thinks I could spend two months profitably at Tarpon Springs, probably I could, but probably I won't.

Remember me to Mrs. Allen and write only when you have time.

Sincerely yours,
/s/ Frank M. Chapman

Jan. 23/89

Dear Mr. Allen:

Rain, rain, nothing but rain, it pours all day and all night and is most unusual weather for this season. Naturally it is rather disagreeable out of doors, but I am well rubbered and do not mind it, but I *do* mind the flooded roads which stretch my ten mile ride into nearly twenty, and I *do* mind rusted traps which will *not* spring.

However, pleasant or not, I am making fair progress, thanks to my new friend Robertson, who, as I told you, proves invaluable. Born and raised in the woods he is familiar with the ways of all the larger mammals which occur here and also many of the smaller ones; he knows just how and where to place his traps and has the careful patient temperament so necessary for success in this kind of work. Above all he seems interested in my success, and having now more or less time at his command, gives me abundant assistance and information. Yesterday I dined at his home, the great log house I spoke of, and met his family. The parlor was without rug, carpet or ceiling, but there was a piano, a large well-worn writing desk, evidently in constant use, a well-filled book-case, and in an adjoining room, a rack with long rows of "Centurys" and "Harpers." The dinner was excellent and with the exception of the ever missing beef, might have been placed before our noble President (of the U. S.). After this meal we went down to the grove at the Lake, about two miles, and in a packing house set a number of traps for *Neotoma* [Wood Rats], and along the shore several more for cats, coons or others which I fear might take them, then after putting a basket of oranges in the carriage drove back to the house, for it was getting late and although we intended to try for Turkeys, with a dog, I decided to postpone this so that I should not have to ride home after dark, a rather perilous proceeding just now. After supper came the less pleasant part of the day's work in making skins until 11 P.M.

This morning everything up above was leaking badly, and on reaching the grove, after losing my way once in the hummock and traveling a mile or more just because I took the left instead of the right road, I found Robertson down there although it was settled I was to examine the traps, but fearing the rain would prevent my coming as it did his work, he had gone down to attend them himself. The rat traps were all sprung, but only one mouse caught (*gossypinus*), while the ones at the lakeside were untouched and we left them for better luck.

Going back now through the grove, they have in all one hundred and forty acres in orange trees, we came to a little, old, deserted log cabin in the hummock where several days before R. said he had killed a rat. I supposed *Sigmodon* [Cotton Rat], and was not particularly interested, but you should have seen me when he took from the rafters a magnificent female adult *Neotoma* [Wood Rat]. I guess he thought I was crazy. I just raved over it and would subside only to break out again whenever it reoccurred to me, for it is the first one I have ever seen in the flesh. In the corner of the cabin was a good cart load of sticks large and small, all heaped up together. These as I supposed, and as R. said, were brought there by the Rats and we have added one contribution in the shape of two handsome steel traps. This rat, I can't get over it yet, was larger than a rat of any species I ever saw and measured total length 395 mm., tail 178 mm. R. says they always build their nests under cover either in a deserted cabin or hollow tree and preferably near water. It ("it" being the rat for at least one day) had four mammae largely developed looking as though they had been suckled; perhaps there are some young in the pile of sticks.

R. is truly "Rough on Rats" for he has caught me some splendid specimens of *Mus* [=*Rattus*] *alexandrina* [Gray-bellied Rat] at his barn; is it not peculiar their occurrence so far out in the woods? Today I got an *M. musculus* [House Mouse] there also. Will you please give me the date of introduction of both these species and range of the former.

I enclose Ridgway's letter and acknowledgement which I will ask you to mail if O.K. As I suggested Ridgway had not looked at my Vireos and I suppose this subspecies (*atticora*) slips through. He proposes that I take it up and offers me all these specimens, but I have no desire to touch it, and told him so, saying also he might place it on the A.O.U. calendar for the coming fall, when the case may be tried in open court. Tell me of the Ecuador birds, are they what you supposed they would be from my description? Tell me also of your health and how you are feeling. My kind regards to Mrs. Allen and yourself.

> Sincerely yours,
> /s/ Frank M. Chapman

> Jan. 29/89

Dear Mr. Allen:

I am progressing, I suppose for mammals, fairly well, but naturally, after bird-work, my collection number seems to mount upwards very slowly.

The wood-rats are too many for me so far, bait as I will they rob without springing my traps, but I will fix them in time, and Robertson also will try for them.

He still continues of great assistance to me and his interest is unabated, but in his peculiar southern way he will barely let me thank him, and would consider it an insult if I should hint at pay. I desire to express my gratitude, however, in some way and think it would be an excellent plan to present him with a copy of Coues' Key,* for from my *own* experience I know this to be the most acceptable gift this world offers, and if I can create another ornithological student and pay a debt at the same time I shall kill both birds. May I ask you therefore to write Estes and Lauriat [a Boston book firm] and instruct them to forward me here the "Sportsman's" Edition of this work, and send the bill to you, securing the best discount they will give, then on your advice I will remit to you.

While I of course feel anxious to start on my future travels, I know that so far as the interior is concerned I can do no better work than I am doing here, and I think it best to stay at least ten days longer and then go eastward.

At last it has cleared off. I hope permanently. For seven days the sun did not shine and most of the time it rained.

May I further trouble you to mail me three copies of my "Birds of Gainesville"; you will find them in the *deep,* upper, corner drawers of my collection above the one marked *Cyanocitta cristata* [Blue Jay]. How are the invalids, express to them my sympathy and also kindly remember me to Mrs. Allen.

> Sincerely yours,
> /s/ Frank M. Chapman

*Key to North American Birds, Elliot Coues, 1872.

Feb. 3/89

Dear Mr. Allen:

Your letter of the 29th was most welcome and each item of Museum news appreciated; I fear with no one to interrupt you or ask questions you are working too hard and steadily. I should preach a little sermon on this question if I could do so consciencetiously but I reckon some of my remarks might fit my own case too closely.

Let us congratulate ourselves on the acquisition of a *bird* mounter; perhaps we may now be spared some of the unanswerable criticisms *several* of the groups elicited.

It is apparently just as well I did not decide to go to Nassau with Mr. Cory! Did you ever see such an uncertain man? He spends the greater part of his time in making plans, only to change and rechange them. Do you know whether he is coming further south.

Everything is sliding along very smoothly. Mr. Robertson's interest if possible increases and he devotes all his spare time in collecting for me. I am doing very little with large beasts, for they would consume too much time in every way to repay the trouble expended, and I count one *Hesperomys* [=*Peromyscus*, White-footed Mouse] of more value than a Coon. R., however, has determined I should have one, but my traps are too small, and they are caught only to break away after a struggle. If the water everywhere was not so high he could easily tree one with his dogs, and last night he decided to try it anyway and went to the lake to camp and hunt. The results I have not yet learned.

Friday last was a great day with me, the best by far I have had. In the first place it was *clear*, a condition of things our most exceptional weather caused me to appreciate, and I rode out in the morning feeling as serene and bright as the skies overhead. After reaching the pines the first event in the day's history served to illustrate very well my many sided occupation, and also that it is well to content ourself with a portion of the earth. Dismounting to examine some mammal traps, I stepped into a flock of quail, but with an empty gun I stared at them with an air of what must have greatly resembled typical "helpless stupidity." I marked them down, though, in a bunch of scrub palmetto, and immediately gave chase. You observe I have already gone down one step in the system. They flushed very nicely as I walked up and I got in four shots, and *downed* three birds, one of which was badly winged and as it led me a dance through the grass, I stumbled over a snake, a beautiful White-chinned Racer, and after the manner of his kind he tempted me, and I, of course fell, but by the time I had picked him up and twisted his neck a little, why my Quail had disappeared and I lost him. Now if I could only have found a "Micro" for Bentenmuller, and then a land-shell for Mr. Smith, resting on a piece of *nummulitic* limestone for Woodward, I might have styled myself "Collector in Biology."

Well, after the flurry was all over, and everything duly bagged, I remounted and rode on to the lake, where I had another "lay-out" of traps, which had yielded very little, five in particular had caught only one mouse in two nights and the others were not disturbed; so I made up my mind, as I approached, to move them to a more favorable locality. But arriving and finding two mice in the first (a "choke") I said I guess I'll leave *that* one, and when going to the second (a "cyclone") and seeing the upturned white belly of a large rat, a kind of thrill went through me, and I chuckled in a gratified but perhaps cold blooded way. I'll *surely* leave *that*, then turning to the third I saw a bedraggled-looking, wet (it had been raining) thing, like a young mouse. I paid not much attention to it for I had the joy of that rat still in my mind, as it is the only one I had obtained since I wrote you, but on stooping to release this little creature, and finding I had a *shrew*, my first, why the woods were too small for me, and if any one seeing me had been asked to guess my game, they probably would have said "grizzly" at least.

Of the other two traps one was sprung, and the other held a mouse, so I decided to leave them all, and the next day the fluctuations in the success of a mammal collector were well shown when I found not one of them touched. But to return to the *Rat*, which has continued to be a source of satisfaction ever since; if the young of *Neotoma* [Wood Rat] differ greatly from the adult, it may be *Neotoma*, but at the same time I don't think it is, for it measures 295 mm, tail 143 mm, certainly large enough to show adult characters though it is evidently not fully grown. In coloration it much resembles *Neotoma*, but is more tawny, and the fur seems different. The tail is bicolored for only two thirds its length, not entirely so as in my adult *Neotoma*, while instead of being hairy it is distinctly *scaled* and very tapering as in *alexandrina* [Grey-bellied Rat]. But the chief point of difference from any rat I have is the ears which are smaller even than in *Sigmodon* [Cotton Rat]. Were it not for this I would suggest its being a hybrid between *Neotoma* and *Mus alexandrina*, and perhaps it may be. I am of course making every effort to get additional specimens, and have all my traps in or near the locality where it was caught, and as Robertson slept near there last night he will look out for some.

I am doing actually nothing in birds for two reasons, first, because there is really nothing to do, and second, I find my time so fully occupied I could not squeeze in much more work. From start to finish mammals consume double the time birds do, but when I get in a region new to me I will not predict the result, still I think it will be safe to give odds on a few birds. It is too early for reptiles, the snake I mentioned was the first I have seen. Later when I return here it may be better, or Bell may get them in the summer at very little cost. Bats also are as yet very quiet and I have not taken any but with warmer weather they will be more active.

Thinking over your remark that I am not likely to get an increase in salary without applying for it I think with you I had better sail in and take my chances. As for the form, would it not be a proper way for me to make direct application to you as my superior, then if you see fit you can endorse it and hand it to the trustees for action. This I merely suggest, but will do as you say.

I greatly regret learning of Mrs. Allen's ill health and sincerely hope she may have a speedy and complete recovery; will you very kindly remember my mother and myself to her.

Remember me also to Mr. Sennett and tell me of Mr. Elliot's [Daniel Giraud Elliot, ornithologist] condition. I enclose a note from Mr. Sage [John Hall Sage, ornithologist] relating to Mr. Elliot's book. May I ask you to answer it at your leisure.

> Very truly yours,
> /s/ Frank M. Chapman

> Feb. 10/89

Dear Mr. Allen:

The week which has just closed ended my work here, for while further investigation might result in securing additional species, I refer of course to small mammals, the list would grow very slowly as I think I have skimmed the cream.

It is doubtful if any other three weeks of my trip yield as valuable results as the ones just past, and this I must attribute to the excellent assistance rendered by *Robertson*. Although I have made every effort to duplicate my unique? rat I have not succeeded; R., however, promises to look out for them and as I have given him a lesson in skinning we may yet catch some. Now concerning my future movements; I have written and just heard from Prof. Jenks* who advises me, on account of the unusually high water to delay my trip to his region as late as possible, say "March 1st" and this will give me time to arrange an excursion I greatly desire to make, i.e., to Cedar Key, in fact I had my plans all made to leave tomorrow, Monday, when who should turn up but one DuBoise, a most successful and celebrated hunter, in fact an ex-plumer, who has given up pluming because "there are no birds." I met this man two years ago and am thoroughly familiar with and know him to be reliable. Now he lives about thirty miles north of here

*John W. P. Jenks of Brown University, writing from Micco.

on the Santa Fe (pronounced "Santaffy"!) River [at High Springs]
which ten miles farther on flows into the Suwannee about sixty miles
from the Gulf and I have hired him to make this trip with me. He
furnishes boat, camp, outfit, etc., but above all his skill as a hunter
and he does not hesitate to take water and wade to his neck for a
desired specimen and is said to make good skins, his charge of two
dollars per day is certainly reasonable. About what I would pay a
Cedar Key man besides having at least an equal amount of board. As
to the probable results of such a trip:

We go through the best Ivory-bill region in the state, Limpkins and
Wood Ibis are also said to occur and these so far as the River is
concerned, are the only desirable *birds* we can hope to obtain. As to
mammals; the squirrels are reported common, and our traps must tell
the rest. Arriving at the mouth of the river, however, we should do
our best work, no one knows what *mammals* may inhabit the salt-
marshes, but Sea-side Sparrows, Marsh Wrens and Rail should be
abundant. In fact I know of no region on the west coast, which should
better repay a few days' work.

There is only one draw-back to the probable success of this "Expedition" and that is the weather, which still continues to be wet and
rainy with only an occasional fair day.

With the exception of a few *gossypinus* I have been unable to secure
any mice in the pines, but one would think that some species would be
found there which is peculiar to them. My series of *gossypinus*, by
the way, is a very beautiful puzzle and I can pick at least three good
species out of it, and these in addition to the "fuscan." *Hesperomys*
and *Mus musculus* are the only mice I have obtained and I think they
fairly represent the region as I have had an abundance of traps, from
thirty to forty, constantly set in ground of every character.

The man who secured the three examples of *Neofiber alleni* [Round-
tailed Muskrat] writes me that in seven years' collecting, these are all
he has been able to secure, but invites me to come and board with
him and look for more!

In photography I have not had time to do much, indeed I have
taken my camera out with me only once and had to work until 10
o'clock that night to pay for it. That day I photographed the wood-
rat's nest, (exposure ten *minutes*, a very dark place), then we pulled
it to pieces only to find a deserted nest of moss, but in a hollow
magnolia tree nearby R's dogs found where one of them had established itself in new quarters, though we did not at that time know
what it was. The tree had an inverted V-shaped opening at the base,
and a hole extending back under one of the roots. Into this place the
animals had brought a lot of magnolia "nuts," and in one corner was

placed a fresh spray of jessamine. R. pulled out the "nuts" and set a steel trap at the entrance, but on returning found the trap sprung, the nuts replaced, and a fresh twig of jessamine, and a hatful of mixed black and red berries piled up in a small pyramid. We now barred the opening leaving only a small space for the owner to enter, and set two traps one before the other, and this time I found the nuts returned but neither trap sprung. I left them, however, and the next morning success was ours, but I was almost as sorry for the beautiful creature as I was happy to secure it. *Alive* it resembled a rat only in name.

Tap-tap, a knock at the door, and in three minutes Judge Bell, who enters, changes all my plans. He has just heard from a party which went to the Suwannee to hunt but found the whole country flooded, the river over its banks, bridges swept away and the current so strong even the ferries are considered unsafe. Under these circumstances it is, of course, impossible for me to go and while I am much disappointed I congratulate myself in receiving this information in time, for the trip would have been an utter failure. I shall consider it postponed therefore until I return from the Indian River.

It is now after 10 P.M. and the train for Titusville leaves at 7:30 A.M. tomorrow, so I shall be obliged to lose a day in repacking for this more extended trip and start Tuesday A.M.

My kind regards to Mrs. Allen.

Sincerely yours,
/s/ Frank M. Chapman

[To reach Micco from Gainesville in 1889 one traveled as far as Titusville, the southern terminus of the East Coast Railway. Between Titusville and Jupiter Inlet a stern wheel steamship carried travelers on the Indian River. It was this steamer that marooned FMC at about 11 P.M. on what remained of a long, frail, wobbly pier after a steamship had gone through that part of it nearest the shore. The beginning of this letter was written on the lined pages of a shorthand-sized notebook, 8 by 4½ inches, in pencil. A note clipped to the 4 loose pages in FMC's handwriting says: "Micco, Fla., Feb. 14, 1889. Written on the bulkhead where I was landed by the steamer at 11 P.M. A break in pier prevented me from reaching shore. First page missing."]

. . . me ashore at once, in fact we could see a light. No attention, however, was paid to repeated whistles, calls, shots from my pistol, etc., and I had the choice of wading ashore or camping on the pier. As the water is above my waist and rather chilly I decided to remain where I was and I hope some day to show you the picture of my surroundings which I expect to take when the sun rises. This pier or platform is about

10 x 20 feet and on it are several bundles of shingles with which I have constructed a fairly snug house, placing over it my rubber coat, for my trunk, etc., were landed here with me and I have unpacked my shooting suit, extra vest and gray shirt for the night is rather cool and I awoke from my first nap feeling somewhat numb. My efforts at raft building were a signal failure, the lumber is all yellow pine and sinks almost from its own weight and even if I reached shore I might not be much better off, the outlook from here is beautiful but not very encouraging and consists so far as I can see of a long row of palms.

It *was* a magnificent moonlight night, but the moon is slightly obscured by clouds now. Still it gives me enough light to write by.

I am being saluted by the queerest collection of sounds; frogs ashore, ducks all around me, fish jumping and splashing and some animal is wading through the water in the shadow of the land. I keep a good outlook for *Neofiber* [Round-tailed Muskrat] but have seen no signs of one yet. I *will* go overboard for him. The moon is getting very dusky and I guess I had better give it up and turn in. I can see Prof. Jenks's shore opposite, a dim line in the distance.

Yours,
/s/ F

Micco, Fla.
Feb. 15/89

Dear Mr. Allen,

I thank fortune I have a camera with me, for my pen could never adequately describe this place or convey to you an idea of one half its charms.

It is by far the most tropical part of Florida I have visited, the west coast does not begin to compare with it.

Our home, for we all live here together with a gentleman named Latham, is placed right in the palms, the undergrowth has been cleared but the palms are so thick they give a good shade everywhere and you can readily imagine how they add to the beauty of the scene.

As we supposed I am on the outer bar *opposite* Micco, about quarter of a mile from the river and three quarters to the sea, the bar here therefore being one mile across. To the sea a trail has been cut, the undergrowth cleared away and as before the palms left standing. It is an ideal walk, but the bordering growth is very dense and difficult to penetrate. It consists chiefly of palms, palmettos and oak, and two hundred yards from the sea is simply scrub-palmettos very rank and dense with an occasional isolated pine. On the river side the growth is largely mangrove with inflowing creeks forming islands on which are ponds and open savannas, the ponds largely in excess just now. In these localities I hope to do my best work.

For the first time I am with workers; Everyone here is doing something, and the encouragement is immense. The Prof. [John W. P. Jenks of Brown University; see letter of Feb. 10] is forming a mounted collection of the birds of the locality and spends the entire day hard at work with as much enthusiasm as any of us. Mr. Baker is collecting birds for Southwick to help him pay his expenses. He says the locality is not a good one for shells, and down under the palms we have a small tent erected with every convenience in shape of desk, benches, etc., and here we do all our work. It would be hard to imagine a more pleasant place. It is grand to be right on the ground and not to have to spend the entire morning riding to and from my traps. Here I run out before breakfast and in half an hour can go the rounds and find an appetite in the bargain. Birds do not seem to be particularly abundant, they prefer the hammock growth to the palm forests, but there are some species here I am going to interview if possible, i.e., *Anas fulvigula* [Mottled Duck], I *saw* two today, and *Ardea occidentalis* [Great White Heron] of which I have seen one, thus in one day observing two birds I have never seen before. There is no reason in the world why both *Neofiber alleni* and *Ammodramus nigrescens* [Dusky Seaside Sparrow] should not be found here; I must not of course be too sanguine but the bare chance of finding either is enough to make one rejoice. I have heard some Rail in the mangroves, but they seem likely to stay there although I of course shall try for them. The species I do not know but a Barn Owl's stomach had the head of *Porzana carolina* [Sora].

I have never told you how I reached shore after being marooned on the pier. Well I simply sat out there and waited until the sun was high enough to make a picture, then when the Signal Service man came out I had him halt while I photographed him. On reaching the shore I found Micco consisted of two houses, one a post-office, the other the telegraph office and home of the Signal Service man. Both places were set in clearings *hewn* out of the surrounding hammock and reminded me very much of pictures I have seen of Brazilian homes. The nearest stores are distant twelve miles, but Mr. Latham owns a good sloop and is therefore independent and can bring in as many supplies as necessary.

So much for a rough sketch of my surroundings; if they were less beautiful I could give you a much better idea of them, but there are some scenes which practically paralyze my pen and I feel only too keenly my lack of descriptive power. I shall try now and keep a brief journal which I will ship in installments.

Remember me kindly to Mrs. Allen and Prof. Jenks joins me in best regards to you.

Very sincerely,
/s/ F. M. C.

Supplement

Mrs. Latham, our hostess here, is a woman in a thousand; a born naturalist with enough enthusiasm, energy, and perseverance to make a name for herself if she ever had been given the opportunity.

She has collected many things for the Smithsonian, and is unusually well posted, securing her information largely from the scientists who have been here, for it is her desire to make her house a resort for scientific people only and to offer them every facility for collecting. Well, last summer Mrs. Latham accomplished a feat of which any one might be proud; to appreciate it one only needs to be familiar with the climate here during the summer. As I have told you, the beach is three quarters of mile from the house, and every day for sixty days she made this trip to examine the nest and eggs of the Loggerhead Turtles which lay there, in order to secure the embryos from the earliest observable stage to the fully developed and hatched reptile, and her series shows the turtle from the egg three days old, to the end of the period of incubation which is *always*, sixty days. Of some days she has, of course, many specimens, and of others comparatively few—but there are *five* complete sets representing every day from the third to the sixtieth. Prof. Jenks is going to take one of these sets and she expects to dispose of others, and I have thought what a grand thing it would be for us properly displayed and labelled and how valuable and interesting it would be. She will give me an entire set for twenty-five dollars, certainly a reasonable price, and if you think we can afford! to buy them there will be plenty of time to remit the amount direct to me here and I can take them home with me. Just after finishing my letter to you this morning I put on my coat to come down stairs and in *very* few moments found I had put on a whip-tailed scorpion with it. I was quick but he was quicker and he stung me twice in the neck before I could get rid of him. A red hot needle would have been preferable. Fleas, ticks, red-bugs, mosquitoes, etc., abound in myriads, and scorpions and centipedes are common enough to satisfy the most ardent entomologist. I do wish Bentenmuller was here. Can't he come?

Sincerely,
/s/ F. M. C.

Micco, Fla.
Feb. 20/89

Dear Mr. Allen:

I have been rather unfortunate in catching a severe cold, probably the effects of my "marooning," it has rather interfered with my first week's work here, though I have managed to do a little and become acquainted with the ground. I do not see how I could be more favorably situated both as regards collecting and the people I am with. They take great interest in my work and render me every possible assistance in the way of showing me around, setting traps, etc., and at home in preparing specimens and all the many little accompanying details. And for this there is, strange to say, no extra charge and I have in addition row and sail boats at my free disposal whenever I choose to use them.

I have strong hopes of finding *A. nigrescens* [the Dusky Seaside Sparrow of Merritt Island] here, but I must now believe with Maynard that the bird does not winter so far north. The savannas are typical localities in which they should occur, indeed I have taken one *A. caudacutus* [Sharp-tailed Sparrow] there which looks very similar to those secured by Scott at Tarpon. This is further south than the species has ever been recorded (cf. Maynard). These savannas make about as tough collecting as one could wish; the grass is low but matted for at least a foot from the surface which now is covered with water and at each step the foot sinks in, making it very tiresome walking. It would be impossible to detect snakes here and I tramp along without thinking of them most of the time, for their protection is also mine I hope, and I do not think they could strike through this tangle of grass. One of the interesting formations here are the mangrove islands made by "cut-offs" or creeks flowing in from the river, sometimes they are several hundred acres in extent, dotted with numerous lakes and openings making grand places for birds if *not* for bird collectors. In localities of this nature Florida Ducks are found, but my cold has prevented me making extended excursions after them as the water is still unusually high and I want to be thoroughly well before I run any risks. Today is the second day of a severe norther, the wind blowing half a gale driving a fine mist before it. In the morning I walked to the beach with Mr. Latham; the surf was a grand, terrific sight, huge foamy breakers piling one after the other on the beach, a great long row of waves lost in a reddish haze up and down the beach.

Many birds driven in by the storm were coasting before it along the coast. I hoped some Shearwaters or Petrels might be driven in, but I saw none and secured only Herring Gull and Royal Tern. Brown Pelicans were abundant flying by in small flocks; shall I take some or use the room they would occupy for smaller and more valuable birds.

FEB 21   The morning was very stormy, the norther still holding on. With Mr. Latham I again went to the beach to watch for sea birds but had no success and we saw only *smithsonianus* [Herring Gull] *maxima* [Royal Tern], *Pelecanus fuscus* with several flocks of snipe (*Calidris arenaria* [Sanderling], etc.) all too wild to approach. Some traps set for skunks bore no result and although I enjoyed the morn-

ing and the sight of an even rougher sea than yesterday's my game
bag did not benefit by it.

Evidently the migration has just begun, for today on the trail I
observed Parulas and Prairie Warblers, birds I have not seen here
before though both winter in the state.

In the afternoon the men sailed the sloop to the mainland for grass
and I took passage with them. It was now cleared and the wind was
in the S.E. but still quite strong so we had a lively sail.

Leaving the men to cut the grass Mr. Latham, Baker and I went
inland. The river is bordered with Palms and dense undergrowth for
a few hundred yards, then a low scrub of palmettos and bushes, then
the pines half a mile back and behind these saw-grass flooded prairies; about as desolate a region after leaving the river bank as one
would care to see. The wind was too strong for birds, but I managed
to kill three Florida Jays, finding two, the first strange to say, I have
ever seen. They do not occur on the outer bar, and in a clearing I
got one ♀ Quail which is much darker than any Florida specimens I
have ever seen. Returning I killed a Royal Tern from the boat and
we put about to secure it. A north wind here blows all the water
"up" the river, that is from the Titusville end, and consequently all
the savannas and mangrove islands are flooded so we cannot work
them, but now the wind has shifted to the south the reverse occurs
and in a day we shall again be able to visit these more productive
localities.

There is a peculiar charm about being so far away from civilization and in such an isolated position; Beyond one or two small cabins
distant a mile or more ours is the only house I know of anywhere in
the vicinity and we are right in the middle of the wilderness where it
is possible to shoot Panthers, Bears, Deer, Wildcats, etc., from one's
windows. On the opposite shore it is almost as good only a few scattering houses.

FEB 22   I awoke this morning to find the wind again blowing a
gale from the north and driving a penetrating rain before it, in fact
it looked as though the storm of the past three days had received and
responded to an *encore,* while the outlook tonight shows no change
for the better.

In weather of this kind the beach is the only available place and
even there one needs protection from the spray. I am trying for striped
skunks here but had no luck in either birds or mammals. As I have
told you the hummock is several hundred yards back from the sea
and the ground here is covered with a dense and impenetrable growth
of scrub palmetto and in this I set twenty-one cyclones to see what
mice I catch here. Probably *Hesperomys gossypinus* [Cotton Mouse]

which is everywhere the most abundant mammal and I find it in ground of every nature except in large clearings where there are no trees. This evening while one of the men was chopping wood at the house he cut open a small hollow log and out from its nest jumped a ♀ *gossypinus* with five young attached to her nipples; in chasing her through a nursery of young orange trees one became detached and was soon caught by some chickens, then another lost his grip and we captured him but the parent still eluded us. Gaining a moment's rest she turned, grasped one of the remaining three in her mouth and again started when we pressed her too closely, and handicapped as she was we were unable to secure her, until finally losing all her young she easily escaped. It was a pitiful sight and I wanted to let her go but the others would not give up the chase and we compromised by returning the four young to the nest where I hope she may find them.

FEB 23   The rain has ceased but the wind is stronger than ever, blowing the water up over the wharf, a most unusual thing, so I am still confined to the higher land. My traps were successful but some beasts, cats probably had been there first and only two mammals were untouched. These of course were just the ones I did not want, i.e., *gossypinus* and *Sigmodon,* while two others, partially eaten were very desirable being the *merriam Hesperomys* [Deer Mice] which for the first time I find here and as usual in a treeless locality. I account for this by their nesting and living in the ground while *gossypinus* lives in hollow trees. At Gainesville in thoroughly cleared fields *gossypinus* never occurs while the other is found no place else. One of the men killed a deer yesterday and we feast on venison today which, with new potatoes and tomatoes from our garden, makes a fare fit for a king.

Oh if this wind would only go down and take the water with it; there is so much to do here and as yet I have only had a chance to look the ground over. From information the Lathams give me and also from a glance at the map I think this must be a grand place in the migration, birds should *swarm* here. It is just a typical spot in which to observe every coast wave and profit thereby.

FEB 24   I have just been awaked and asked if my mail was ready so this must go at once without revision.

Sincerely yours,
/s/ Frank M. Chapman

Oaklodge, Fla.
Feb. 24/89

Dear Mr. Allen:

I continue under date of Feb. 24. This morning fortune changed and I had great success with my traps, not one being disturbed by marauding beasts, and I secured *six* of the *merriam Hesperomys* which, if my memory serves me right, are here much paler than at Gainesville, In addition to these I caught my first striped skunk in the first growth west of the sea, where one of the guests in an early morning walk nearly stepped on it. His description of the scene was very laughable for in his words the skunk reared up on his front legs like a mule pointed his tail heavenward and prepared for war; he concluded he would not go any further that way this morning. When I went over, Mr. Richards the same gentleman, attracted the animal's attention while I went *up* the wind with a club. The first blow killed it and nearly paralyzed Mr. R. who *down* the wind received the full force of the perfume which escaped as I dealt the blow. As it was before breakfast we concluded to leave it until our appetites were appeased and to protect it from buzzards I covered it carefully with sand, trap and all, to the depth of several inches, but on returning there was a buzzard at the exact spot, and as the wind was very strong little if any odor remained. After this I am a firm believer in the power and use of the buzzard's nasal organs. Also Mr. Latham tells me that they buried the entrails of ducks killed here in a compost heap, but the scent attracted many buzzards to the locality.

Tonight many flocks of hundreds of Herring Gulls passed north, flying away beyond gun range.

As usual it is raining, what would I not give for *three* consecutive clear days. Without the least *exaggeration* it has rained for fully three-fourths of the time since my departure.

FEB 25–26–27   I might sum up these days in this way; wind and rain, rain and wind and wind; for our "norther" continues and the water is higher than ever. I tried to wade one of the savannas today, but was obliged to give it up, trying first one end and then taking a boat and going a mile farther up and starting at the other. At both places the ground which usually is dry was covered with water up to and over my knees and the dense, ever present sedge made it impossible to push a boat through. The mangrove islands are in an even worse condition and the duck ponds are filled to overflowing. Two days of south wind will remedy all this and I shall then be able to proceed with my many plans, for I see great opportunities for good work here, in fact I have never been in a more promising locality.

Notwithstanding the many drawbacks under which I am working I manage to employ my time profitably I hope though I am getting nothing very startling, but wait until the migration commences, then see! For it would be difficult to imagine a more favorable place in which to collect during that period.

I thank you most sincerely for your efforts in my behalf concerning the salary question; it is of course unnecessary for me to dilate as you understand the pros and cons of the question viewed from every point, personal and otherwise as well as I do, if not better, and while I might say a great deal, I will not. I do not know where Maynard's paper is, I tried to find it last summer but could not, though I know we used it in the spring.

I received both key and "extras" in due time, many thanks for your trouble. I think I have placed them where they will bring forth fruit.

FEB 28   A red letter day; it will be long I think before I surpass it in pleasure or profit. The water was a little lower this morning, the day clear though the high north wind continues, and I determined to try the mangrove islands for Florida Ducks, for the fact of its being here has made me ache for a chance to kill some. The first pond I tried was empty so I re-embarked, passed from the mouth of the creek out into the river, where the swell gave my boat a beautiful rocking, and made for another small lake.

The mangrove islands are dotted everywhere with these small ponds and lakes varying in size from half to fifteen or twenty acres, fascinating in their quiet, restful, loveliness, but abominable in their surroundings of mangroves with a dense undergrowth of "sedge," a small straight woody stalk which reaches to knee or waist. However all this answers the purpose of excellent cover. Well, on the second lake after a careful examination for *Fulvigulus* [Mottled Duck] I found only two Widgeon, but as I fired and secured these, two "Duskys" [Mottled] jumped from the mouth of a small creek just out of shot. Rowing now up a blind lead from the river, I rounded a point to see, several hundred yards ahead, a small bunch of my game quietly feeding. I marked the spot, immediately turned made a long detour, landed, crawled for a quarter of a mile through the sedge, and struck the desired point exactly making a long shot and securing my first *Anas fulvigulus*. Didn't I feel proud when I shook the water from his plumage and smoothed him tenderly. At another lake I secured one more, but my last shot I shall not soon forget. It was at a lake further on, I had dragged myself carefully up to the edge and *missed* a long shot much to my disgust, but I kept perfectly still and waited. Pretty soon a Blue-winged Teal flew in, and evidently desiring company, commenced to call, *quack quack, quack, quack quack* in rapidly accelerated notes. This was just what I wanted, if I had trained him he could not have done better. For a few minutes it had no effect, but looking up to an inflowing creek at the end of the pond, I saw two Duskys round the point swimming neck and neck, their confidence in the safety of the situation apparently completely restored; what a picture they made, for they were headed right towards me. I shrunk within myself, almost, as they glided on, not moving until through a small break in the sedge I saw them come abreast, then I blazed away killing one and dropping the other as he arose, and this made me the possessor of four times as many Florida Ducks as there is in the great Am. Mus. Nat. Hist. I made things fly this afternoon in skinning them for they are large, fat, and tender, but they're *done*.

MAR 1, 10 P.M.   I have just returned from an unsuccessful but thoroughly enjoyable fire hunt for deer, floating through the mangrove bordered creeks, the "jack" throwing a light into their impenetrable recesses, making fairy scenes of weird beauty. The water was very phosphorescent and alive with mullet which darting and splashing in every direction lit up the inky blackness with gleams of pale light, like a sea of fiery serpents.

3/2 A.M. The mail goes this A.M. and I close. My kind regards to Mrs. Allen.

Sincerely yours,
/s/ Frank M. Chapman

"Oak Lodge"
March 4/89

Dear Mr. Allen:

The weather has not yet assumed a normal condition, but we had one day of south wind which caused the water to fall a foot or more making the savannas and mangrove islands passable. I have secured another "Dusky" and also a fine male Gadwall the first ever taken here. If the water ever becomes low enough I should get some Rails, but now I am only tortured by hearing their cries way back in the high sedge where try as I will I cannot raise them. Scott shoots his birds by waiting for them to run out and feed along the water, but with the creeks extending beyond their limits into the bordering growth this is impossible.

After weighing the subject carefully in my mind, I have decided to place it before you and then leave you to judge whether, being now in one of the most favorable localities imaginable it would be advisable for me to stay here long enough to reap a harvest from the great waves of birds which pass through here during the month of April. From my own standpoint there is of course only one answer, but I feel that you have already been so kind in securing me the vacation I am enjoying, that I should be left out of the question entirely, and it should simply be; will my services here during this period be of more value to the museum than in New York. As for the second part I leave you entirely to state this side of the question, but for the first I look at it this way: there can be no doubt that after the last of March thousands of birds will pass through here on their way north, for not only is the position geographically excellent but the immediate surroundings are favorable for all these birds to pass the day in feeding. Now after traveling here from the north and undergoing all the expense incident to the journey, shall I leave just as the best collecting season approaches, or undergoing no further expense so far as the museum is concerned, shall I stay here and take advantage of offering opportunities; always being able to take my departure should the season not prove a good one. As for the specimens I might secure, you know of course as well as I; but there should be Kites, Nighthawks, Martins, Gray Kingbirds, Black Seaside Finches, Miami Wrens, etc., etc., and I can continue my search for *Neofiber* [Round-tailed Muskrat] which, so far, has been unsuccessful.

In accordance with your instructions and my own desires, I have paid strict attention to my traps doing little in birds, but with the exception of the last named animal and shrews (bless them) my twenty to forty traps a night have pretty well exhausted the fauna of this locality in species, I think, and this additional time would find me free to go in for bird work and also for bats which are not here yet, though they are said to come.

There, perhaps I have put a little too much *ego* in after all, but as it is I will leave it.

I can find no rabbit here other than *Sylvaticus* [Marsh Rabbit], should not *Palustris* [Cottontail] be here also?

I have yet to find a locality which will excel this entomologically, but here the bugs turn collectors and I have been collected by everything but a centipede of which I have seen only one. Each day I gather a fresh crop of fleas, ticks, lice, redbugs, etc., which immediately proceed to map out trails across my poor body, but I am getting used to them, all but whip-tails, which I imagine one can never be on very friendly terms with. I have not heard from you since my arrival and hope no letters have gone astray. The address is; c/o Prof. Jenks, Micco, Brevard Co.

Very sincerely yours,
/s/ Frank M. Chapman

Oak Lodge
March 6/89

Dear Mr. Allen:

We had a grand time today though failing in our main object. Starting early Baker and I took the Professor's little ducking skiff and started for a point on the river about three miles north. The wind was blowing a gale, and all went well until we left the creek and ran out into the river. Here the north wind had full sweep piling the water up into white-capped waves which tossed our small boat about in a very lively manner and made rowing almost impossible. However we pegged away. Baker would take a turn and pull until exhausted when I would follow and we finally managed to reach a small inflowing creek about half-way up. Into this we put for rest and council, when we decided that we had had enough and that the locality we were in was good enough for us. It was an immense savanna, with occasional ponds and swampy holes and we tramped to the end of it through a deep bed of soft yellowing grass I securing a Great Blue Heron (*Ardea-?*) and a number of dark ♀ Red-winged Blackbirds. Returning we shipped our mast and hoisted a well-reefed sail, and the little boat flew over the water like a bird skipping from wave to wave without shipping a drop of water. We made for the duck ponds but had no luck. I killed several Maryland Yellowthroats and had the pleasure of missing a fair shot at a Dusky Duck. At half past three we reached home and went to work at our specimens. My traps had yielded me two "pale" mice and at tea time I had prepared them and eleven birds, beating my best record by doing seven birds in little less than an hour. After tea the wind had fallen and we rowed about a mile out into the river to try for Cormorants roosting there on a "snag." The night was partly cloudy but a young moon gave just light enough for the birds to see us as we floated down to them and they flapped away just as we came within gun shot. Rowing back we had not been in the house five minutes when the dog was heard barking furiously in the hummock. Two of us took our guns and a jack-light and started at once for what we hoped was a "cat," but proved to be merely a "possum." A rifle shot struck its foot and started it earthward but meeting the dog it immediately worked its usual game and lay perfectly still, the image of death. Picking it up by the tail we carried it home, when I put a stick back of its neck, with a foot on either projecting end, grasped the beast's hind legs and pulled and jerked with all my might until I heard something snap. Then to make perfectly sure one of the men struck it heavily behind the head until it commenced to wriggle in its death agonies. Taking it down to the tent I wired one leg fastening the wire to the string we run along our ridge pole to hang specimens from, and left him there to do in the morning, but when the morning arrived behold! all that was left of our possum was the wire dangling empty and alone from the string above. This seems

incredible and I could hardly believe my own eyes when I looked
for him.

MAR 7   No hunting today, but passed the morning in setting traps
for *Neofiber*. I can say now that I have *positive* evidence of this animal's presence, and I am trying in every possible manner to secure
specimens. I also put out some traps for Rail as this is the only
way, I reckon, I can take them. Going into the deepest sedge I place
a trap in what looks like a favorable locality and then run strings
of sticks out in either direction.

This afternoon I indulged in a novel kind of trap shooting; Mr.
Richards had caught two striped skunks in box traps and brought
them to the house. So we took them down the wind in the clearing
and he opened the traps while I shot the beasts when they jumped
out and started on a run for the nearest thicket.

MAR 8   Hurrah, Ring the bells and sound the horn; today is a day
of general rejoicing at Oak Lodge, with myself as chief rejoicer, for
at last I have succeeded in securing the long sought for specimen of
Neofiber alleni ♂ ad.—the fourth known example, and now I feel at
liberty to tell you all I know about this interesting mammal for ever
since I have been here I have been studying its habits, but I determined to say nothing until I could speak positively, but this little
animal is evidently so shy and wary as to be exceedingly difficult to
trap and it has eluded my best efforts until today.

On arriving here I at once made inquiries of the Lathams if they
had ever seen anything resembling a muskrat. Of course they answered "No" but they told me of a nest found in the savannas which
corresponds well with those described to me at Fort Myers last year
as found in the Everglades and which I have always supposed were
the ones I desired.

At the first opportunity I made for the savannas and was not long
in finding the object of my search which at once confirmed my suspicions and from that day I have had no doubt their builders were
Neofiber. These nests are, in favorable localities, abundant, but probably only a small percentage of them are inhabited. All are practically
alike in construction and location, being composed of long dried grass
and placed in and about the bases of the yellow mangrove bushes,
whose roots and branches afford them a basal and lateral support. In
size and shape there is considerable variation, but they are generally
pyriform in appearance and averaging twenty inches in height with
the largest diameter about ten inches. The accompanying rough sketch
will give an idea of both external and internal structure.

[handwritten text, followed by a sketch]

Each nest, as I have attempted to show, has an entrance and an exit, one being always directly opposite the other and both these lead away in subterranean channels under the sedge, presumably to the feeding grounds, but of these later. Mr. Latham assisting me our first efforts were made directly at the nests by finding the underground passage and placing a trap in it covering the whole carefully over. This method however has proved a complete failure only one in many traps left out night after night being sprung and we were sure some at least of the nests were occupied as the fresh pieces of grass used in their construction proved. After some days we moved all our traps, now twelve in number, to a neighboring island, where in the vicinity of a small mangrove-bordered pond, nests were exceedingly plentiful. Here at first we used the same methods but as before unsuccessful, and we now endeavored to find the outlets to the runways which I felt sure must lead in the direction of water. This however is almost impossible, the thick matted grass under which they are made is filled with innumerable little openings any one of which might answer the purpose of a terminal exit for these passages which undermine the grass in every direction. Our search though resulted in a valuable discovery; Around the edges of the pond, growing in water which is now knee deep, is a species of tall succulent grass, and out in this we found little platforms made of grass stems and in one, fresh pieces of cut grass gnawed from some growing within reach. This with a piece of excrement showed me that here was the feeding ground of our prey. In two of these we placed traps carefully concealing them, also setting one near by baited with celery. This was six days ago and until today my only captures were a *Sigmodon* in one of the platforms and a Sora on the ground. In the meantime I had gone on experimenting, hunting underground runways in the grass and surface ones in the mangrove shoots and sedge at the edge of the pond, and these last I still hope will prove productive. Well, today, as usual I went the rounds with the same discouraging results, until I came to a platform trap set five days since and left undisturbed, as I approached I saw something black through the grass, I *feared Sigmodon*, but hoped *Neofiber* and when I found my hopes realized there was not a millionaire in the world who could have bought out my stock of joy.

Carrying him carefully home I exhibited my prize to the admiring household and received their congratulations, for everyone has been interested in my efforts and even Latham has three times been out to assist me. Then I took off the trap, after wiring his hind legs, and placed him in a tub of water to see how he would act and particularly to observe the tail was used in swimming, and I found it was in a peculiar, circular, gyratory manner, the tip describing circles, and even crippled as it was he swam and dived readily. Then I took him down to the tent and watched him for a while seeing him once sit up to dress his wounded fore foot, and then getting a good position I photographed him as I shall his nest and feeding stand. After which I slightly compressed his lungs and he expired, I proceeded to skin, stuff and skeletonize him and if there is anything more to do I shall be pleased to do it—but at present my chief object is to secure him a mate.

Very sincerely yours,
/s/ Frank M. Chapman

(Yours of 2nd received yesterday. Thanks for check and efforts in my behalf for larger ones.)

Oak Lodge
March 10/89

Dear Mr. Allen:

No more specimens of *Neofiber* yet, but one is due pretty soon. Today one of my traps, set in the water where a runway crossed a brook, captured a rabbit which I suppose to be *palustris* [Marsh Rabbit], though I have always understood this species was larger than *Sylvaticus* [Cottontails] while my specimen is larger than a *Sylvaticus* I have taken here. Other points of difference are, its much darker color, and coarser fur, shorter *gray* tail and lateral grooves in the upper incisors. Since my arrival I have argued that there must be a marsh rabbit on the savannas and mangrove islands, but was told there was only one kind, and as the two or three I have caught have left nothing but a foot in my traps I have been unable to prove my assertion until today, and now everyone gives in. Tomorrow morning I start on an expedition to the headwaters of the Sebastian River, a small stream flowing into the Indian River about five miles south on the opposite shore. My main object is Paroquets and I have positive knowledge of their occurrence there within a week, in fact I have seen three specimens shot from a small flock which frequents the river banks. Quail are said to be plentiful and I am very anxious to secure some males as the one female I have taken is very dark and I also have a chance for other things. My guide is the man who shot the three birds I mentioned and our craft is a small catboat on which we expect to live rigging the sail over the boom for a tent. Everything is packed and we make an early start so I'll turn in. In my absence Mr. Latham has volunteered to attend my *Neofiber* traps and keep probable captures alive until I return, so I lose no time at that. My regards to Mrs. Allen.

Sincerely yours,
/s/ Frank M. Chapman

Oak Lodge
3/18/89

Dear Mr. Allen:

We have just returned from our Paroquet hunt an account of which you will find in the leaves from my journal. [These pages are missing.] I find your letter of the 13th awaiting me and regret extremely to learn of yours and Mrs. Allen's ill health. Under the circumstances, I think with you it will be the better plan for me to return as soon after the first of April as possible, but unless you consider my presence very urgent, I will remain here about one week longer and try for *Neofiber* and *Ammodramus nigrescens* and then will proceed direct to Gainesville where it will take me several days to pack my specimens and my mother seems to think I should make her a short visit of one or two days also. However I will do the best I can and return as soon as I can break off and pack. I have received from you directed here, two letters, the first dated March 2nd and containing a check which I acknowledged, the second dated the 13th as before mentioned.

Remember me most kindly to Mrs. Allen.

Sincerely yours,
/s/ Frank M. Chapman

Oak Lodge
Mch. 20/89

My dear Mr. Allen:

In these last days here I am trying to make every moment count, and when night arrives I feel more inclined to retire or "sit around" than write. I am not trying now to secure a large number of specimens or "make a record" but am giving my entire time to a search for certain things, more particularly *Neofiber, Am. nigrescens* and *H. bachmani,* all of which are due. During my absence up the Sebastian Mr. Latham had little success with my traps securing only one *Lepus palustris* and on the day of my return after getting things straightened out and airing my specimens, in every sense of the word, I went over to my pet mangrove island to re-arrange them. The water at last is low enough for me to more closely study *Neofiber's* habits and I find runway exits with fresh mud thrown out where the animal comes to the surface; here I placed a trap and captured my second specimen, for the first time having a trap disturbed the night it was set. This was certainly joy enough for one morning but my good fortune did not end here for the same trap in which I had caught my first *Lepus palustris,* set in the water you remember, contained, when I approached it, a small mammal which I supposed to be a young *Neofiber* but on examination it proved to be a second example of the Gainesville rat concerning which I wrote you. You may imagine much more easily than I can describe the thrills which possessed me when I fully realized the importance of this discovery, for does it not prove beyond doubt that this animal is new to science and may require a genus framed to fit it? Even *Neofiber* was eclipsed and my general elation causes them to remark at the house that they will have to put a brick on my head to hold me down.

MAR 21   A busy day; starting at sunrise I went out on the trail in search of warblers and on returning rowed over to examine my traps then came back to eat a second breakfast. After this I skinned *two* birds; don't laugh, it took me a long time, why you will see. After this rest I made for the savannas to continue my *Ammodramus* search but found only mosquitoes, millions of them. They drive me nearly wild and I go out with my head wrapped up in a towel and even then I have to *switch* my handkerchief constantly backwards and forwards to prevent being devoured. This really is a serious subject, one which does not produce a calm and even line of thought so I'll drop it and pass to pleasanter things.

The first flight of warblers has arrived, all of the commoner kinds, Black-and-white, Parula, Myrtle, and Yellow-throated but in the hope of detecting a stray Bachman's among them, I passed them carefully in review before my glasses this morning. It was, perhaps, a forlorn hope, but while I was watching I fancied I saw a small yellow-breasted possibility flitting in the trees above me; in a second it was gone flying into the dense bushes where a chase was out of the question. I followed on, however, to the edge and taking a stand commenced to squeak determined to "aux" the first thing that showed itself and in a second bang! she went, a shot in the dark. I forced my way in but the imaginary image in my mind's eye was not greeted by its fellow on the ground, but two drops of blood on the leaves below caused me to look above and there hanging in a branch within reach of my hand was the lifeless body of a female Bachman's warbler. I tell you my pen cannot do justice to my feelings at the moment or to the scene which followed, for once clear of the scrub, I executed a war dance which would have done credit to a painted brave, and this having somewhat relieved me I immediately proceeded to look for a male and found him too, this time readily identifying my bird before I shot and between sight and sound there was sandwiched a few seconds of intense excitement caused by the fear that my game would escape me.

These captures have an important bearing, don't you think, on the question of Bachman's breeding ground, for once on the East coast it is not probable that this bird would cross Florida to further pursue its migration in the Mississippi Valley and we may yet find it breeding near the scene of its first capture by Dr. Bachman.

Chuck-will's-widow has arrived. Just one or two calls I have heard at dark, and in ten days the woods will swarm with birds, Prothonotarys, Swainson's, Kentuckys, everything, and on the savannas will be Kites, Ibises, etc. Maybe some time I can come here for the migration, now I am in a hurry to leave before I have to leave too much.

Kindly remember me to Mrs. Allen.

Sincerely yours,
/s/ Frank M. Chapman

Gainesville, Fla.
March 31/89
Sunday

Dear Mr. Allen:

Last Tuesday I tore myself away from Oak Lodge and sailed over to Micco, securing a few hours sleep in the post office while I awaited the steamer due from 2 to 4 A.M. Wednesday. After a restless nap I awoke just in time to find her trying to make a landing at the end of the long, frail, rickety old pier, which I expected to see her tear in pieces before she finally did come alongside, and I trembled for the safety of my collections, as they shoved them aboard on a long, narrow plank. Shortly after 11 A.M. we arrived at Titusville; the boat was crowded and unable to get a berth I considered myself fortunate to obtain a chair in the engine-room.

Taking the 12 N. train I reached Palatka at 4:30, and here I was obliged to pass the second night as there was no train to Gainesville.

For the first time since my departure I this day saw a *store* and although I am somewhat prejudiced against civilization as a leveller I appreciate and can avail myself of some of its advantages. Among the first, in the present case, was the Putnam House barber and I left his hands looking, no doubt, as he remarked, ten years younger for razors are tabooed at "Oak Lodge." Pretty well tired out I turned in early and was only once awakened by an alarm of fire and beating of an immense gong which in the confusion of a first awakening in a strange place I supposed was a signal at Oak Lodge calling us out to see what the dog had treed. I managed to arise and light my gas and ascertain that my room was a *jumpable* distance from the ground and then, too tired to inquire further into the cause of the still increasing disturbance I went back to my rest and slept soundly until morning. On going down to breakfast who should I meet but Mr. Hoyt of Stamford, here as they had planned with the Mr. Camp who called on us and a Mr. Eames also of Conn. Hoyt lives at the hotel, the others in a cottage in town which is also their laboratory. I reckon they have had a very jolly winter, they have taken about one thousand birds and forty mammals (mostly large ones) and expect to return this week. They mentioned important discoveries and when in reply to their inquiries I incidentally spoke of a series of Carolina Paroquets, a pair of Bachmans, several Florida Ducks, Round-tailed Muskrats, and one or two other little things they *cussed* themselves outright for not going further south. Next winter they all want to go to "Oak Lodge."

I also met a tourist at Palatka who had seen Scott at Tarpon. He told me of a hunter bringing in to Scott two hawks which S. declared settled the identity of a doubtful species—(*B. brachyurus* and *fuliginosus* ? [Short-tailed Hawk]).

Thursday afternoon I managed to reach Gainesville being thus longer in travelling from Oak Lodge than I would be in going from here to N.Y. One box of specimens I expressed from Titusville. There is nothing of great value or particular interest in it but *please* don't open it until I return. The balance and more valuable part of my collections I took with me in my trunk to G. here to repack in connection with any Gainesville material and this has consumed a portion of my time since my return.

I regret to say I find my mother who has been in unusually good health all winter, now quite unwell. I trust it is nothing serious and the Dr. does not so regard it, but with your permission I will delay my departure one or two days awaiting a favorable change in my mother's condition. This, I hope at the latest will bring me to N. Y. a week from tomorrow and if possible I shall arrive earlier, for while it is of course very pleasant to stay here my time is too limited to *re-start* collecting and I am very anxious now to get back and talk over with you the winter's experiences and have you examine the resulting specimens.

The orange trees surrounding our house are now in full bloom and the air is filled with a sweet fragrance. I wish Mrs. Allen was here to enjoy it. I beg you will kindly remember myself and mother to her.

Very sincerely yours,
/s/ Frank M. Chapman

On the same day FMC wrote the above letter, Joel Asaph Allen wrote him from New York, congratulating him on the success of the expedition as reported in the March 20 letter and adding: "Fifteen Paroquets, 2 Neofibers, 2 Bachman's Warblers, and 2 nondescript rats besides more common things is certainly a good record."

Though the Sebastian journal is missing, we know from other sources that FMC, guided by a nephew of Ma Latham, left for the head-waters of the Sebastian River on March 11. So rare had Carolina Parakeets become that a rumor of their presence was enough to send any ornithologist off immediately, and authentic news of them was not to be ignored. He found a population of about 50 in flocks of from 10 to 20 at the head of the Sebastian River, a few miles west of what is now Wabasco. In a paper delivered at a Linnean Society meeting and published in the proceedings of the Society he says:

Fifteen years ago, Paroquets were more or less generally distributed throughout Florida and in many places were extremely abundant, and even at a more recent date they were not uncommon in numerous localities, but to-day they have entirely disappeared from the more settled portions of the state, and we may look for them only beyond the bounds of civilization, indeed in regions which are practically uninhabitable. In just what numbers they still exist it is impossible for us to say.

The Sebastian is a beautiful river; no words of mine can adequately describe it. Half a mile wide at its mouth, it narrows rapidly, and three miles above appears as a mere stream which at our camp, eight miles up, was not more than fifty feet in width and about fifteen in depth. Its course is exceedingly irregular and winding; the banks as we found them are high and for some distance from the water densely grown with palms and cypresses which, arching, meet overhead, forming most enchanting vistas, and in many places there was a wild profusion of blooming convolvulus and moon-flower. Immediately back of this semi-tropical growth appeared the pines, which extended as far as the eye could reach, with occasional openings termed "prairies," varying in extent from two or three to as many hundred acres, where the trees were replaced by a species of tall grass growing scantily in the shallow water which flooded these meadows. Such localities were frequented by occasional Sand-hill Cranes, and perhaps here also herons once abounded; now the survivors have retreated to the more inaccessible prairies of the interior, and we heard rumors of rookeries to be attacked by parties organized expressly for the purpose. About these "prairies" and at the borders of small streams or low ground grew in abundance a species of thistle (*Cirsium Lecontei*, T. & G.) the seeds of which, so far as I could learn, constituted at this season the entire food of *Conurus* [the Parakeet]. Not a patch of thistles did we find which had not been visited by them, the headless stalks showing clearly where the thistles had been neatly severed by the sharp chisel-like bill, while the ground beneath favorite trees would be strewn with the scattered down.

From a favorite and productive patch, late on the night of our arrival, we started a flock of seven birds. Evidently their meal was finished and they were ready to retire, for they darted like startled doves through the pines, twisting and turning in every direction, and flying with such rapidity they were soon lost to view, the ring of their sharp rolling call alone furnishing proof it was not all a vision. Two days passed before I again met *Conurus*, and this time to better advantage. It was a wet and drizzling morning when we found a flock of six birds feeding on thistles at the edge of a "prairie." Perched on the leafless branches of the tree before us, their brilliant green plumage showed to the best advantage, as we approached through the pines without difficulty. Several were skillfully dissecting the thistles they held in their feet, biting out the milky seed while the released fluffy down floated away beneath them. There was a sound of suppressed conversation; half articulate calls. We were only partially concealed behind a neighboring tree, still they showed no great alarm at our presence; curiosity was apparently the dominant feeling. One of the three birds which fell at our fire was but slightly wounded, a single shot passing through the elbow, and his loud outcries soon recalled his companions—a habit which has cost thousands of them their lives, and in part at least accounts for the rapidity of their extermination—and one alone of this flock escaped.

There was an evident regularity in the habits of the birds we afterwards observed—in all about fifty, in flocks of from six to twenty. At an early hour they left their roost in the hummock bordering the river and passed out into the pines to feed, always, so far as I observed, selecting thistle patches, and eating the seeds only when in the milky stage. At about ten o'clock they returned to the hummock and apparently to some favorite tree, here to pass the rest of the morning and early afternoon, when they again started out to feed, returning to the roost just before sunset. A flock of these birds feeding among the thistles is a most beautiful and animated sight; one is almost persuaded not to disturb them. There is constant movement as they fly from plant to plant, or when securing thistles they fly with them in their bills to a neighboring tree, there to dissect them at their leisure. The loud rolling call was apparently uttered only when on the wing, but when at rest, or feeding, there was a loud conversational murmur of half articulate querulous notes and call.

Parakeets were very easy to shoot and Frank Chapman was a fine marksman. It speaks well for him that he collected only what he thought was needed at the Museum and not all the birds present.

When he learned later that a local hunter had captured the rest soon after his visit by putting a bag over the hole through which the birds entered their hollow tree roost and had sent them to a cage-bird dealer, he regretted not shooting the lot for the benefit of posterity.

The lack of laws protecting wildlife in the nineteenth century has deprived us of many beautiful creatures and some of those we have in Florida are here because such incidents as those he experienced on the upper Sebastian River pushed Frank Chapman into the forefront of the fight for State and National conservation laws.

Frank Chapman described five mammals from Florida new to science. Dr. James N. Layne, mammalogist at Cornell University, formerly of the University of Florida has very kindly supplied me with notes on the present day status of these forms.

A little creature Chapman called the "Big-eared Deer Mouse" was collected by Hovey Bell while he was a refugee from the yellow fever epidemic in October, 1888, and was living in a cabin near Newnan's Lake. According to Dr. Layne, "*Hesperomys floridanus* is now *Peromyscus floridanus*, the Florida mouse or Florida deer mouse, which is unique enough to be included in a separate subgenus of this large and varied genus. It occurs only in Florida, and there only in certain rather specific habitats."

FMC trapped the old field mouse, which he described as *Sitomys n. subgriseus,* on January 30, and he tells of this lucky Friday with full traps in his letter of February 3, 1889, to Mr. J. A. Allen. Dr. Layne says of it: "This is one of the beach or old field mice and is currently known as *Peromyscus polionotus subgriseus.* For some years this race was synonymized under the nominate race *Peromyscus p. polionotus* but in 1954 Schwartz (J. Mamm. 45:562) concluded that this race was worthy of recognition."

Frank Chapman collected the South Florida cotton rat while he was at Latham's Oak Lodge at Micco the same winter. Dr. Layne says in his notes on this mammal: "*Sigmodon hispidus littoralis*—this is the race of the cotton rat occupying the bulk of the Florida peninsula roughly south of a line drawn between Jacksonville and Cedar Key. It is still considered a valid race, but I should point out that this species is badly in need of revision, and the validity of various races has not been critically questioned. There is some confusion as to the exact limits of the range of *littoralis.* A subspecies, *S. h. floridanus* was proposed by Howell in 1943 in which the existence of the race *littoralis* was apparently not taken into consideration."

In 1893, Chapman described the Florida mole from a specimen collected on May 4, 1891. This indicates that he visited his mother after his Texas trip and did some collecting while in Gainesville, but apparently did not keep a journal. Dr. Layne says: "*Scalopus aquaticus australis* is a race of the eastern mole found in southern Georgia, north-central Florida, and much of the eastern part of the Florida peninsula. The race is still considered valid."

The ground mouse Chapman collected at Latham's opposite Micco in Brevard County on March 3, 1889, during his stay at Oak Lodge, was originally described by him as *Hesperomys niveiventris.* Of it Dr. Layne says: "This form is now known as *Peromyscus polionotus niveiventris* and is a race of the beach mouse occurring in the dune habitats along the lower east coast of Florida from about Cape Canaveral to Hillsboro Inlet." Dr. Layne ends his notes with this comment: "All of the above forms, then, still stand today, although there have been some nomenclatorial changes. It appears that Chapman's 'taxonomic eye' was pretty good."

In 1889 in the Bulletin of the American Museum of Natural History, Vol. II, Article XV, FMC published a paper entitled "On the Habits of the Round-tailed Muskrat (*Neofiber alleni true*)." The description of the habits of *Neofiber,* the first ever published, is taken from his letter started March 6 and dated March 8.

Before Frank Chapman collected mammals in Florida very little had been done here in this field. Mr. J. A. Allen collected on the St. John's River between Jacksonville and Enterprise in the winter of 1868-69. Intrepid ornithologists and botanists were much more widely traveled than other biologists in the Florida wilderness. Starting with Bartram, a botanist, and Audubon, an artist-ornithologist, they all collected those curiosities of nature they came upon in their travels. Frank Chapman did the same and brought back specimens for every department in the museum. It is interesting that a man who was primarily an ornithologist and who described many birds new to the world described only one in Florida, the Florida Yellow-throat, but has five Florida mammals to his credit.

The Florida Museum of Natural and

POLITICAL HISTORY.

J. H. HODGES, M. D., President.	ROBERT E. DAVIS, Corresponding Secretary.
J. H. U. BELL, Curator.	W. M. MYERS, Recording Secretary.

H. Z. SMITH, Librarian.

4

Young Men of the Gainesville Area

$\mathcal{I}$N 1933 FRANK CHAPMAN wrote in his *Autobiography of a Bird Lover,* "With Judge Bell's son Hovey and several other young men of Gainesville I tried to form a natural history society, but we never got beyond the adoption of a name and a constitution. One of the proposed members of this unborn organization was a boy named T. Gilbert Pearson who came up from his home at Archer, the other side of Alachua Lake, to see the bird man from New York."

Four years later in his autobiographical *Adventures in Bird Protection,* T. Gilbert Pearson says of this incident:

One day early in 1887 my father permitted me to take Snip and the buckboard and drive to Gainesville, fifteen miles away, where I attended to a few errands for my mother. At noon I went to the first public dining-room I had ever entered. It bore the name, GOOD SAMARITAN RESTAURANT. There was only one other diner. He sat across the table from me. He was perhaps ten years my senior, was carefully attired, and had the confident bearing of an experienced man of the world. I watched his nice way of eating and especially observed that he took his soup from the side of his spoon. I had not been much impressed with my teaching that this was the proper way to use a soup spoon, but after observing him for a time I became an ardent advocate of such a custom. It was usual in my neighborhood to speak to strangers and try to make them feel at home in our country. So at length I engaged him in conversation. He said very little but smiled as I described birds and nests that I had found. He left the table without expressing any special interest in what I had said. This did not particularly disturb me as people seldom responded to my enthusiasm about birds.

I went to see Hovey Bell, a boy of my acquaintance. While talking with him, the man whom I had seen at the restaurant came in smoking a cigarette. After delivering some messages, he departed. I told Hovey that I had seen him in the restaurant and said I supposed he was a city man from somewhere. Hovey then told me that his name was Frank M. Chapman, that he was from New York and knew a great deal about birds.

I was amazed. I had never heard of Mr. Chapman, but the fact that he was a man who knew the names of birds greatly excited me, and I rushed out trying to find him. Disappointed in my quest, I wrote him the next day hoping that I might get to see him again, but many years elapsed before I was to experience that pleasure.

Thomas Gilbert Pearson (1873-1943) traded the collection of mounted birds and bird eggs he made in Alachua County for two years of board and tuition at Guilford College in North Carolina. He later became one of the most articulate conservationists of the first third of the twentieth century and was instrumental in the passage of laws protecting birds throughout the civilized world. He was secretary of the National Audubon Society from its founding in 1905, and from 1920 until his retirement in November 1934, he served as president. T. Gilbert Pearson actually was first introduced to Frank Chapman in 1893 when he went to New York for that purpose and called on him at the American Museum of Natural History.

T. Gilbert Pearson very naturally worked closely with Frank Chapman, who was a founder of National Audubon and a member of its Board of Directors from the time it was founded.

Frank Chapman launched, owned, edited, and published *Bird-Lore*, the official magazine of the Audubon Societies. The first issue appeared in February, 1899, and he guided its path until in 1935 he presented it to the National Audubon Society, which changed its name in 1941 to *Audubon Magazine*. T. Gilbert Pearson's name first appears in *Bird-Lore* in 1902 as one of its advisory councilors. In 1904 he became editor of the department called "For Young Observers."

The letters written by eighteen-year-old T. Gilbert Pearson to twenty-eight-year-old Frank M. Chapman started a long trail of association that greatly benefited the Florida where they first talked as casual strangers. From their two published accounts and the dates on the letters one can see that memory played them false in the divergent stories of their passing contact in Gainesville.

I include two letters with headings that definitely establish the existence of one if not two early natural science organizations at the site of the University of Florida.

T. Gilbert Pearson came from a gently bred, educated, Quaker family, but money was anything but plentiful, even pennies for postage were hard to find. The answers to his letters from Frank Chapman were undoubtedly the greatest encouragement he received in his pursuit of information about birds, and the separate copy of F. M. Chapman's "A List of Birds Observed at Gainesville, Florida" (*Auk*, Vol. V, 1888) was his introduction to the *Auk* and the American Ornithologists' Union. There is considerable admiration to be read between the lines of T. Gilbert's letters. His warm respect and gratitude to Frank Chapman are confirmed by his choice of him to write the introduction to *Adventures in Bird Protection*.

A full month after his meeting with FMC, T. Gilbert Pearson wrote to him, probably unaware that he had left for Texas on March 10. Across the top of the letter is scrawled in Chapman's hand, "Received at Corpus Christi Apr. 14, 1891, ans. Apr. 14, 1891." It must have been difficult for FMC to tell the enthusiastic young Pearson that he himself had already published an annotated list of birds of the Gainesville area.

Archer, Fla.
April 8, 1891

Mr. F. M. Chapman
    Gainesville, Fla.
Dear Sir:

Although I had often seen you I never really knew you to be F. M. Chapman before.

I have often seen your name but had never thought of your being the man. I am very glad I got acquainted with you for I feel sure that you will help me in an undertaking of mine. It is this. I have for over a year now been trying to get a list of the birds of this County as I have never seen one published; I thought I might as well get out the first one as anyone else.

In fact I did not know of any one else in the County that would, or the State for that matter unless it was Mr. Stewert of Tampa.

I now have on my list nearly one hundred varieties that I have either seen or actually taken. And I thought that perhaps you would just as soon help me in my list as not, as you have traveled around over the County a good deal. I would like to ask a few questions. Have you ever found the "Limpkin" in this County, if so does it breed here? Do you know if the Caracara breeds in this Co.? Have you ever seen any Kites here but the Swallow-tailed and Everglade, and is the Everglade Kite very abundant in any part of the Co.? I have never seen but one pair of them.

Is the Nonpareil (Painted Bunting) found in any numbers anywhere around here? It is only migratory of course. I have never seen any Woodcocks here until this winter, are they commonly here?

Does the Wild Pigeon breed anywhere around here that you know of? And is the Ani (Savannah Blackbird) ever been found in Fla.? I could ask a hundred questions but I would not like to bore you to death first thing. Besides my collections of other eggs, I have in my collection eggs of about forty varieties of the birds of this Co. April 2, 1891 I took a set of Red-tailed Buzzard ½ and yesterday (Apr. 7) I took a clutch of Killdeer ¼.

I would be *very* glad if you could make it convenient to come down and see me. I would be *very* glad to have the pleasure of entertaining you.

Hoping that you will write me soon, I am sir,

Yours most respectfully,

T. Gilbert Pearson

Archer, Fla.

[The next Pearson letter lacks the usual Chapman notation of when it was answered. Perhaps it was not but the August 1 note was. Pearson wrote to Chapman again saying so and the second letter was answered three days after it was received on August 11, 1891. Unfortunately FMC's answers cannot be found in the Pearson files.]

Archer, Florida, July 17, 1891

Mr. Frank M. Chapman

New York City

Dear Sir:

I suppose e'er this you have again reached New York and are again in the museum.

We are having some very warm weather now. I have not been out in the field collecting much for some time, however I notice that the Wood and White Ibises are as plentiful as ever around the prairies, and the young of the White Ibis with its dull brown coat and its conspicuous white rump are very numerous. In the migration in May I noticed Redstarts, both ♂ & ♀ were very plentiful.

While over on the Suwannee River the fore part of May I observed several Swallow-tailed Kites and also had a splendid view of a Mississippi Kite, the first one I have ever seen. While collecting at Cedar Key on May 19 I was so fortunate as to find a nest containing a set of three eggs of the Fla. Sea-side Finch.

Yellow-legs and little sandpipers remained here until the last of April. Will you please tell me if the Barn Owl is found in many portions of the State, or is it as some claim only found in and around St. Augustine and Xnville [Jacksonville]? I do not believe this myself, however I have never been able to find one.

Have you any acquaintances with the Jacanas, did you ever meet with them in Florida? I have often met with Yellow-headed Blackbirds in the *swamps* as late as April, is it possible they breed here? The set of Yellow-headed Blk.-bird eggs in my collection were collected in Colorado. I have taken eggs of the Redsh'ld, and the Red-tail Buzzards and would like to ask you if there are any other Buzzards breed in the state to your knowledge, does the Swainsons Buzzard ever breed here or is it just migratory.

I had my left wrist badly torn not long ago by a four foot alligator I was capturing, having to lay down on him in the water to hold him. I now have him mounted and placed in my museum, and as I enter the room his glass eyes glare at me as though he would like to fasten on to me again. One more question and I am done. Is not the Musk-rat found here, and is the Manatee still to be met with in southern Fla. Hoping that you will see fit some time soon to spare a little time to answer this, I am Sir.

Yours most resp.,
T. G. Pearson

Archer, Florida, Aug. 8, 1891
Mr. Frank M. Chapman
New York City
My Dear Sir:

Yours of recent date rec'd. was very glad to hear from you. I have never rec'd. your list of the Fla. birds but would be *very* glad *to* do so. If I could aid you in any way in regard to the summer birds I would be *glad* to do so. In speaking of the White-bellied Swallow [Tree Swallow] did you not mean *"Iridoprocne bicolor,"* instead of *"Tachycineta bicolor?"* [He is questioning F. M. Chapman's use of scientific names.]

I have seen only one *"Iridoprocne"* so far that was on Aug. 7. (yesterday about 12 N.)

It seems impossible that the Yellow-headed Blackbird should be found this far east, but my note books show dates of flocks being seen in early spring. I do not have any specimens in my collection now although I have had. I wish I had one I would send it to you, if it is not the Yellow-headed Blk' bird then I am at a loss to know what it is.

There has been a Black Hawk reported to me several times by good persons. I suppose it must be *B. brachyurus* [Short-tailed Hawk] —have never seen one.

I asked about the Muskrat in my last letter. I asked because on three different occasions I had seen one (or what I had supposed was one). I have never succeeded in killing one yet. It was always a bad, muddy, swampy place where I saw them. Within the last two weeks I have collected and mounted the flg. birds, five herons, one Louisiana, one Little Blue and three Green Herons, one female Yellow-crowned Night Heron, a pair of *"Falco Sparverius"* (Sparrow Hawk), one Coot, and one Anhinga.

The season for nesting is very long here; and the birds take advantage of it. I have taken Quail eggs as early as April 10, and only yesterday Aug. 7 found a Quail nest containing eleven eggs. I have found young Cardinal Grosbeaks by April 15, and my note book shows a set of three fresh eggs Aug. 3, '91. But the little Ground Dove beats them all. I once took a set of two fresh eggs on March 3, and I have also taken fresh eggs as late as Sept. 25. While out collecting last week a Rail was killed, it answers the description of *"Rallus elegans"* with the exception of the rufous colored breast, there being only a slight tinge or streak of cinnamon-red down the throat and onto the breast. I concluded it was probably a young perhaps of the *"Rallus virginianus"* (Virginia Rail).

I would be very glad if you would propose my name as an associate member of the A.O.U. if you would be so kind. Will send on the dues ($3.00) after a little. Will you please tell me something about the Reddish Egret (*"Dichromanessa rufus"*), where is it found, and is it not marine?

Little Plovers have been here two or three weeks now, not very plentiful however yet. Is there any specimen of the Labrador Duck or their eggs in the Museum, if so what are they valued at?

Cahoon had a sad fate didn't he,—poor fellow, more than one of us will go that way if we do not watch sharp. Was up to Gainesville the other day. The boys are getting in quite a stock of specimens. My museum grows slowly as there is only one of me and I am not acquainted all over the country like Hovey and the rest of them. I have gotten in several minerals, arrow-points, and chards, lately, though I take mine out in collecting.

Hoping to hear from you soon I am Sir,

Yours most truly,

T. G. Pearson

John Cyrus Cahoon was a young field naturalist and professional collector who collected along the Gulf Coast of Florida in 1883. He was killed by a fall from an overhanging cliff 200 feet above a rock-strewn shore in Newfoundland on April 27, 1891. He let himself down on a rope to collect eggs from a raven's nest and could not regain the cliff.

J. G. Pearson.

Field Ornithologist and Oologist.

Birds Mounted in first class order. Nests & Eggs Collected and Exchanged.

ARCHER, FLORIDA. Aug. 1st ...1894

Mr. Frank M. Chapman
New York City :—
Dear Sir & Friend :—
Ridgeway of Washington once told me that with us that the Ardea Herodias was a rare bird, that the bird which I took for the Gt. Blue Heron was the Ward's Heron. You are acquainted with our birds and undoubtedly know. Will you kindly inform me which is really the bird we have here. I am desirous of knowing as soon as possible. Very truly Yours

T. Gilbert Pearson,

These two letters from Gainesville are of interest for their letter heads as well as for their content. I am sure Hovey Bell wrote Frank Chapman many times, but this letter of December 31, 1894 is the only one FMC kept. I have not been able to decide which bit of the amazing information in it he wanted to preserve but I'm glad something prompted him to keep it.

ORGANIZED 1890.

J. HARRISON HODGES, M. D.,
PRESIDENT

ROTH REYNOLDS,
COR. SEC'Y

ROOMS OF

Florida Society for Scientific Research.

Gainesville, Fla., DEC 31 _____ *1894*

Dear Mr. C.

Yesterday as I was walking to the Sink with Jim Bill Jr. I found on the rail R R a grease spot + on each side was the remains of a Putorius. I wraped up what was left of him and brought him to town I will send you the skull as the skin is no good His ear measurement is 23 Mil. m. Wide
"   "   "   " 19½ " long.

      Foot   36   "   "

      fore Arm   33   "   "

Chin White Throat Yellow Belly yellow feet on top white shaded to yellow + then brown on fore arm - head brown from tip of nose dark shades some what lighter a a it goes back with slight yellow.

Mrs. Smith (Howards) mother) discribes a little annual that has been catching her chickens and once it came in the house and fought the cat, that is when she saw it, the cat got the worst of it. I have no doubt but that it was a weasel too,

(from J C. H Bell.)

Gainesville, Fla., Dec. 31, 1894

Dear Mr. C.:

Yesterday as I was walking to the Sink with Jim Bell Jr. I found on the rail (RR) a grease spot and on each side was the remains of a Putorius [Weasel]. I wrapped up what was left of him and brought him to town. I will send you the skull as the skin is no good.

His ear measurement is 23 Mil M. Wide.

"   "   "   " 19½ " long.

" foot   "   " 36   "   "

" Fore arm "   " 33   "   "

Chin—White; Throat—Yellow; Belly—Yellow; feet: on top—white, shaded to yellow and then brown on fore arm; head: brown from tip of nose—dark shades, somewhat lighter as it goes back with slight yellow.

Mrs. Smith (Howard's mother) describes a little animal that has been catching his chickens and once it came in the house and fought the cat. That is where she saw it. The cat got the worst of it. I have no doubt but that it was a weasel too.

We have been having some very cold weather for Fla. lately. Friday night went to 9° at my house and max. only 28. Water works pipes all bursted all over town, i.e., all the small ones that go into the houses. All are mad (like fools generally are) because they were not told to let their water run.

As I passed the F. C. & P. water tank yesterday I saw ice cicles hanging as large as a man's body and 15 ft. long, that had been exposed to the sun all day.

Several days ago I wrote to the U. S. Coast and Geodetic Survey for Lat. and Longt. and Alt. of G'ville and received these figures. Thinking you may be interested if you have not heard before, I send you the following:

Memorandum referring to Gainesville, Fla.

Latitude of Court House   29° 39' 05.0"

Longitude " "   "   82° 19' 23.8" W. of Gr.

Approximate elevation of benchmark in Court House yard above half tide: 177½ feet. The benchmark is 10 ft. from the S. W. corner of Court House fence N. W. from corner.

I received from you several days ago Remarks on certain Land Mammals and etc. for which I am very thankful for and at any time I can be of any service to you, why let me know. Wishing you a Merry Xmas and a Very Happy N. Y. (And your mother too). I am your very respect. and obedient servant.

J. P. H. Bell

Excuse my bad writing as I can't see good.

5

The Suwannee River Trip

ONE OF FRANK CHAPMAN'S OUTSTANDING EXPERIENCES IN Florida was the Suwannee River trip he made in March, 1890, with William Brewster and Dr. Charles Slover Allen. None of Chapman's notes or journals of this trip are extant, but the story can be pieced together from letters written by Dr. C. S. Allen and Mr. Brewster, FMC's own few paragraphs in his autobiography, Mr. Brewster's journal, and the ornithological report of the voyage which Mr. Brewster and FMC co-authored and published in the *Auk* in April, 1891.

The three men made plans at the A.O.U. meetings in New York in November, 1889, for a spring trip in an ornithologically unexplored part of north central Florida's interior and coast. William Brewster's acquaintance with young Chapman, thirteen years his junior, warmed to friendship at this time and he entered into the plans with enthusiasm, as did FMC's friend and physician, Charles Slover Allen, the third member of the expedition.

The arrangements were for the junior member of the group to make all the preparations for the trip and eventually to use his Gainesville home as a base of operations. He started immediately to negotiate for transportation with Florida correspondents and kept his friends posted on his progress. Unfortunately none of these letters has been kept, but his intent to set up the entire expedition, except last minute odds and ends, by mail is obvious.

The first of Mr. Brewster's letters was written just three days after the New York meetings and addressed either to the American Museum in New York or to FMC's suburban home in Englewood, New Jersey. While this letter is not about the Florida trip it does show that he had it in mind.

Cambridge
18th Nov. 1889

Dear Mr. Chapman:

It was very kind of you to send me those references which I am glad to get. What think you of Everman's record of the Harlequin

Duck at Pensacola? It strikes me as even more *fishy* than the bird is reported to be. I think he must have been an Old Squaw. Kline has an interesting account of the breeding of the Bald Eagle and some suggestive notes regarding Herons but smaller birds do not seem to have attracted his attention. [Mr. Brewster is referring to articles written by the two men, Everman and Kline, in *Ornithologist and Oologist* and *Field and Stream* magazines, the references FMC sent him.]

I wish I had a photo to send you but the stock on hand was exhausted long ago. I intend to have some taken soon, however, when you shall be remembered. [It was the custom in the nineties for men to hang the pictures of respected colleagues on the walls of study and office.]

Thanking you for your kind attentions and with the hope that we put that Florida trip through and have lots of pleasant field adventures together, I remain,

Sincerely,
William Brewster

Will you please tell Mr. Allen [J. A.] that the Little Brown Crane was shot "the 8th or 9th of October by Benjamin Burlingam at Natick Hill" and ask him to make necessary additions to my note. I quote these data from a letter just received from Southwick.

[Just a week later Brewster wrote a second note to FMC and this one shows that both men were anxious to make the Florida adventure come true.]

Cambridge
Nov. 25, 1889

Dear Mr.Chapman:

Thank you for sending me the clipping. I sincerely hope that the scored sentence will not attract general attention. It would make a very big club in the hands of some people I know here who are hostile to all bird killing, scientific or otherwise.

I have been bird killing today. Found Redpolls very numerous and an *Acanthis rostrata* [Greater Redpoll]. I looked the flock (about one hundred) over carefully and picked out the *biggest* bird. There were three or four others that looked equally large and doubtless were of the same species but the flock whirled off out of sight over the woods and did not give me a second chance. I cannot help feeling a little proud of having picked out this bird on sight but it is probably an easy thing to do, after all. I wish I could find some way to distinguish *A. exilipes* [Hoary Redpoll] at gunshot distance. There must have been one or two of the latter in this flock.

Crossbills (*minor*) and Pine Grosbeaks are also numerous here now. Have they reached your country yet?

I hope the appearance of Ivory-bills, Black Rails and strange mammals in your dreams is a good augury of what we are to find in the St. Marks region. I mean to go if I possibly can and there are no serious obstacles visible yet.

> Sincerely,
> William Brewster

[The next letter from Mr. Brewster was written nearly a month later and is obviously an answer to one Chapman wrote outlining a tentative route and transportation possibilities as proposed by Florida correspondents. This letter also suggests that the Suwannee was not their destination originally.]

> 145 Brattle Street, Cambridge
> 21st Dec., 1889.

Dear Mr. Chapman:

Your correspondent's letter is certainly not too explicit but from what he says I should infer that the vessel will answer our purpose. I would ask him just what he means by "all things furnished at $15.00 per day," how many berths or beds the sloop has *in the cabin*, whether we can use his captain & cook as boatmen on our shooting trips, and what the draught of his vessel is.

How do you propose to get inland, that is up the rivers and winding creeks? Of course we can use the sloop only when there is broad water.

The two dingeys will probably answer for I shall take a canoe with me. I know the average Florida boat too well—leaky and clumsy.

I like your idea of starting early in March and believe that we should do better work during that month than later. What we want are the resident forms (and Bachman's Warbler), the migrants are of much less importance.

I saw Cory the other day and inadvertently mentioned our proposed trip. He expressed a wish to join us, not for the whole time, but merely "to have a talk and see us off!" I told him it was your expedition but promised to let you know of his wish. If you think there will be room for him to pass a night or two on the boat I shall be gratified to know that you will ask him but of course if there is not room, or if you do not wish, for any other reason, to invite him that settles it.

Your young friend's list [probably Hovey Bell's list of birds they could expect to find on the trip] is certainly suggestive of many tempting probabilities.

Sincerely,
William Brewster

[FMC as was his usual custom answered promptly and Mr. Brewster acknowledges his answer at once.]

145 Brattle Street, Cambridge.
25th Dec., 1889

Dear Mr. Chapman:

I am very glad that you authorize me to ask Mr. Cory to join our expedition which I will do at once by letter. He is probably at his place on Merritt's Island by this time. I do not think he has any idea of doing more than spending a day or two with us at the start. The working part of the trip will hardly be to his taste and we are going for *work*, not merely to have a pleasant time. I should be only too glad if he *would* go with us for, as you say, he could hardly fail to become interested but I fear, from what he said, that there is no chance of it.

I must still insist that it will be your expedition, not mine. You first conceived it and you will arrange all its general details. In so far as I can help I will do so cheerfully and after we start I am willing to share the "command" with you and decide on the movements of our fleet for formal councils of war in the cabin but I cannot take sole command unless, perhaps, if you wish it and it seems advisable after we start, in the matter of acting as a mouthpiece in giving orders to the men, etc. It is sometimes better to have one *ostensible* figurehead and I am of course willing to act in that capacity if necessary.

I will send you the M.C.Z. specimen as soon as I can get time to run over to the Museum.

Sincerely,
William Brewster

That Frank Chapman asked Brewster to be the leader of the group was to be expected. Courtesy and custom ordained that the oldest scientist was in "command" in any project, the senior author of any paper and all suggestions he made would be tantamount to orders. Hence the prompt invitation to Mr. Cory.

It is a pity that communication between FMC and Charles Slover Allen was all by word of mouth. As long as they were both in the

New York area they saw each other regularly at the meetings of the Linnaean Society, the New York bird club, and correspondence was unnecessary. Dr. Allen would have agreed as a matter of course, if FMC consulted him before asking Mr. Brewster to be the leader of the expedition and before extending an invitation to Cory.

These letters begin to illuminate the characters of the men involved: Frank Chapman earnest, enthusiastic, young ornithologist, deferential to his elders and considerate of his contemporaries; Dr. Allen cooperative, circumspect, and so self-effacing that he is rarely mentioned; and William Brewster, New England's *parfait gentil homme.* Charles Barney Cory, millionaire playboy, sportsman, collector, and amateur ornithologist appears, as he did off and on for years, at the fringes of Chapman's activities in Florida.

The first of January all plans were changed. FMC had not expected to go to Florida until late winter but he left for the south very suddenly and not in a way he would have planned. His superior at the museum, Mr. J. A. Allen, described his departure in a letter to a mutual friend: "Dr. M. saw FMC safely aboard the train in Jersey City and tucked the blankets around him and gave the carriage a shove." Dr. M. was Dr. Edgar Alexander Mearns, Medical Corps, U.S.A., noted ornithologist, on military leave doing volunteer work in the American Museum of Natural History.

A series of letters written by J. A. Allen to his young assistant during the next two months show solicitude and sympathy for FMC and great worry over his health. Mr. Allen spoke of necessary museum business but he also dwelt on an attempt to arrange with the director of the American Museum of Natural History for a salary for Florida field work and an out and out leave of absence to pursue it. The success of his efforts to obtain $100.00 (a generous amount in those days) and the two months leave is not confirmed in the letters we have, but as the subject was finally dropped we can assume that J. A. Allen was persuasive and the director agreed to his plan.

By mid-January the news of FMC's illness had reached William Brewster and his immediate response is this warm letter which completely ignores the Florida trip, probably because he feared that Mr. Chapman's health and his own family involvements might prevent it.

[In FMC's handwriting]
Ans. Jan. 31/90 (Copy)

145 Brattle Street, Cambridge.
19th Jan'y, 1890

Dear Mr. Chapman:

I am exceedingly sorry to learn of your physical breakdown but glad to know that you are able to start at once for the "land of peace" where you are sure to find speedy relief. It is a pity that you should have to do *any* museum work now for at your time of life you ought to be almost constantly in the field. That is where one gets the *bone & tissue* of ornithology and youth is so very fleeting. When one arrives at middle age it is not too easy to absorb new ideas and one tends to draw from the past. I speak from my own experience, largely, and I am thankful that I spent so much time in the field between the ages of twenty-five and thirty-five. I *enjoy* field work now as much as ever but in a calmer way and my senses are less keen and alert. In fact the intense enthusiasm and receptiveness of youth are dulled. Something in your letter led me to infer that you fear such a change in yourself. It will surely come and the time is not far off, probably. The more of active, vivid experiences you can crowd into your life now the more you will have to draw on later.

Pray forgive the personal character and application of the above gratuitous advice. It is prompted solely by the deep, friendly interest that I take in you and your work. I fear it may sound patronizing— but I do not mean it so in the least—if I add that I have been strongly impressed with your acumen and ability as an ornithologist and that I have great faith in your future.

The photographs came safely and I am glad to add them to my collection. But was it not just a little unkind to send them at a time when there is some doubt as to my being able to "see the gentle swaying of moss" and "hear the whistle of the Cardinal this year?"

However I don't despair yet and you may be sure if I *can* join you I *will*. But the future is uncertain, to say the least.

Cory has just written me from the Brock House, Enterprise, where you can doubtless address him safely for if he should go elsewhere they will be sure to forward his letters. He says he has four setters with him and is on the war path after the poor Quail and Snipe. I should like about five or six days after them myself; and then two or three *months* of good, earnest collecting.

Dwight [Jonathan Dwight, ornithologist] is here, knee-deep in Horned Larks. He seems to have a firm grip on them and promises to give us something very thorough and valuable as the final result of his labors. There will be two or three new names to learn, as might have been expected. He has examined about *seventeen hundred* specimens in all! [Article in *Auk* 1890, p. 136]

My winter has been wasted thus far. Family worries and business duties have taken up my time & thoughts to the exclusion of everything else. I have simply done nothing in ornithology.

Sincerely,

William Brewster

Before FMC answered this letter he received another solicitous note from Mr. Allen urging him to "remain idle and recover" but FMC did not remain idle. From his sick bed in "Cosy Corner Cottage" in Gainesville, he had arranged the itinerary of the trip and must have written to Brewster more than once in order to have settled the many details that had been taken care of in the three weeks that elapsed before the next letter was posted from Cambridge.

145 Brattle Street, Cambridge
10 Feb. 1890

My dear Mr. Chapman:

Mrs. Brewster's mother died the day I received your last letter and there were so many things that I had to attend to, that this is the first opportunity I have had for answering you. Even now I can only take up the practical points that you have raised, leaving the rest—in which I am deeply interested—for some other time, probably some evening when we are sitting on the deck of our house boat taking our after-tea smoke and listening to the hooting of the Barred Owls in the cypress swamps of the Suwannee.

You will gather from this that I am going to join you! It is now settled—as far as anything can be settled in a world where the unexpected too often happens—that I start about the 22nd of this month, take Mrs. Brewster to Charleston, go thence to Merritt's Island for a week's shooting with Cory, and get around to the Suwannee to meet you about March 10—certainly not *later*. I shall have to get back to Charleston early in April to take Mrs. Brewster north but I imagine that can be easily managed without curtailing our trip, for which three weeks should suffice!

As to your change of plan it more than delights me. By floating the Suwannee we shall see a lot of beautiful southern scenery in the easiest, safest, and most comfortable way (the latter consideration of *some* importance to an old "codger" like me), we shall thoroughly investigate what is supposed to be still a stronghold of the Ivory-bill and Parakeet, and we shall run no risk of sticking on mud bars or being weather-bound for days together as would be the case if we followed the coast. Accordingly I say "amen" to your decision and with all possible heartiness.

As to details of preliminary arrangements I must, perforce, leave all that to you, my sole regret at so doing arising from my reluctance to put all the hard work connected with the expedition on your shoulders. Were it not for my promise to visit Cory I would gladly join you a week or two before our start but this is now impossible. I can only promise to be with you on the 10th of March at latest.

As regards our food supply I will venture to suggest a few things which I have found useful if not necessary on similar expeditions. I can get them at Charleston and forward them to Branford if this will help you. They are: Olives, Crosse & Blackwell's pickles, sardines, Dutch cheese, canned crackers of several kinds (including graham or oatmeal crackers), dried ginger, breakfast bacon, and buckwheat flour prepared for griddle cakes. I shall also absolutely require a sufficient quantity of *safe* drinking water to last through the trip. I have found Apollinaris about the best and safest but cistern water will answer if it can be depended on to keep fresh and sweet. River, well, or spring water I dare not drink at all.

I may possibly take an assistant with me but at present I know of no really good man who can be had and I am inclined to undertake again the whole of my own work as I have so often done in the past.

Before leaving Cambridge I shall have to send a lot of loaded shells, some arsenic, cotton, etc., to our rendezvous, so you had better *telegraph* me (at Cambridge) on receipt of this letter, how they should be addressed. You had better write me, also, at Charleston, S.C. in care of C. K. Huger, 8 Legare St. Meanwhile I will push my preparations here and dream of not one, but *many* more, mornings on a Florida river.

I send you the C. Mus. [Cambridge] specimens of *Mimus saturninus* with this regretting that I have been unable to attend to your request more promptly.

Sincerely,
William Brewster

In the next few weeks the letters from J. A. Allen ran the gamut of a disheartened "I regret that you recuperate so slowly but trust at the end of a few more weeks you will recover lost ground" to an elatedly cheerful note. On February 27 he expressed his delight in FMC's improved health and spoke of Mr. Brewster, Dr. C. S. Allen, and the proposed Suwannee trip and went on to talk about field work and collecting, a sign that the patient was again in good health. Especially indicative was a sentence that was surely an answer to a letter from a recuperated Frank Chapman who had been out in the marshes, "The discovery of Round-tailed Muskrat at Gainesville shows how little we yet know about our mammals."

FMC had been corresponding with Dr. C. S. Allen, too, for probably in the same mail which brought Mr. Brewster's next letter was one from the Doctor enclosing a check for $30.00, his share of the cost of a houseboat. He asks FMC to act as treasurer for the group, to let him know when more money is needed and in closing says "I will see you next in Gainesville."

Mr. Brewster's communication was written at the house of William Elliott Huger at 34 Meeting Street in Charleston, South Carolina, where Mrs. Brewster visited while her husband was in Florida. In the letter, Mr. Brewster shows he is somewhat distraught, probably because of Mr. Huger's error and the unavailability of Apollinaris water in Gainesville.

Charleston, Feb. 26, 1890

Dear Mr. Chapman:

I have your letter of the 16th, but through a provoking mistake Mr. Huger forwarded Mr. Cory's letter to Cambridge just before we got here. Accordingly I am in complete ignorance of his plans as well as, also, of his present whereabouts. This is most unfortunate for I shall have to wait here until I hear from him instead of pushing directly on. Of course I shall telegraph him at once but I am hardly likely to get his answer before day after to-morrow if he is at his place on Merritt's Island. However I still hope to get around to Gainesville by the 9th or 10th of March. I could go to Titusville in the afternoon, spend the night at the hotel there and take the 5 A.M. train. I should prefer this to taking the 12:08 P.M. train & spending the night at Palatka. It is hardly worth while to say more about this, however, until I know whether I am going to Merritt's Island or not. Cory is very likely to elect to shoot Quail and Snipe at Enterprise instead.

I should think your darkey cook would do admirably. As to the stores we can, as you suggest, buy them together after I join you. Everything can be easily selected in an hour or less. The water question is the most serious. I think I shall take at least some Apollinaris but if Deep Rock will keep I had just as lief have it.

I sent a box by freight to your address before leaving home and a canoe was to follow on Monday. Both were to be shipped from

New York via the *Clyde* line of steamers, as these boats run up the St. John to Jacksonville and I was strongly urged to choose them in preference to the Ocean line of which no one in Boston knew anything. The canoe should be stored *in the shade* when it arrives & not taken from its crate of course as it will have to be put on the cars again for Branford.

I fear you will find this letter very unsatisfactory but I hope to send you more definite news soon.

Sincerely,
William Brewster

[If he had known of the delays to come he would have shown distress on the penny post card postmarked March 1 as well as on the letter which followed it.]

Charleston, Feb. 28/90

Have just heard from Mr. Cory. He wishes me to join him at the Brock House, Enterprise, whither I go to-morrow & where you had better address me until further notice.

Yours,
W. Brewster

Mch 6/90—Branford
 ans rec'd. [In FMC's writing]

The Brock House, Enterprise, Fla.
March 3rd, 1890 [Monday]

My dear Mr. Chapman:

Owing to a misunderstanding and missing connections I have lost two days & have only just joined Mr. Cory. He cannot carry out the plans he has laid unless I can stay with him until Wednesday of next week [March 12]. He agrees to put me in Titusville on Wednesday afternoon so that I can take the 5 A.M. train for Gainesville Thursday morning. I do not feel that I ought to press him to more than this for he has been at much trouble & expense in hiring horses, wagons, boat etc. for my use and as it is if I stay with him until Wednesday we shall get only four day's shooting together, two days at the Quail and two at Ducks. Accordingly if you can possibly spare me until the time above named I should like to be absolved from my promise to join you on the 10th.

Please write me at Titusville C/O Mr. Cory.

Sincerely,
William Brewster

Any letters you may have already sent here will be forwarded to Titusville.

While Mr. Brewster aggravated himself over Mr. Cory's cavalier treatment of times and dates and other people's plans, FMC was probably congratulating himself on having refused Mr. Cory's invitation to join the hunting party on Banana Creek, his duck preserve on Merritt Island, and to meet with him and his other guests at Titusville on March 3. Instead of a Cory hunting party, FMC was proceeding with the final preparations for the expedition.

This brings us to the story of the altering of a borrowed 30-foot scow into a houseboat, which is told in the *Autobiography of a Bird Lover*. The scow was the property of a lumber company operating at Branford, the spot where the railroad (from Palatka to Dupont, Georgia, via Gainesville) touched the Suwannee River. "I found an unsuccessful phosphate prospector whose inexperience in carpentry matched mine; we bought some tools and proceeded to turn the scow into a houseboat. Thought of the result still fills me with pride and surprise. At the end of four days we had nearly completed a house with kitchen, sleeping quarters and four berths, the upper pair folding, and a shelf-lined specimen room. A small open space was left aft for the steersman and a larger one forward, awning covered, served as deck, dining room, and work room."

This work was underway when Mr. Brewster's letter of March 3 was forwarded from Gainesville to Branford and was answered there on the sixth. I believe that by the time Mr. Brewster's next letter arrived FMC was back at "Cosy Corner Cottage" and probably with his mother, welcoming Dr. Charles S. Allen; then William Brewster's final letter arrived from Cory's headquarters.

Titusville—6th March, 1890

Dear Mr. Chapman:

Mr. Cory and I have just finished our Quail shooting and start to-morrow for his duck preserve. As your letter indicates a probable delay in getting the boat ready and as such tasks always exceed the time one allows for them I will venture to settle my plans as follows:

I will stay at the island [Merritt] until Wednesday, return here Wednesday night, take the 5 A.M. train Thursday morning (March 13) and join you on the evening of that day whether the boat is ready or not. We can then make final preparations together.

I have already bought a supply of Apollinaris & ordered it sent to you at Gainesville. It is about what I shall need for myself so you and the others will have to make your own provision in this respect. You can get Apollinaris at Jacksonville if you wish.

Mr. Cory has decided *not* to go on the Suwannee trip. I doubt if he even goes to Gainesville with me but he may decide to at the last moment.

Sincerely,

W. Brewster

Dr. Charles Slover Allen came to Gainesville early in March of 1890. He and FMC traveled together by train to Branford. They brought with them the Negro hunter named Allison who was to cook for the group. Another hunter, referred to by William Brewster as a backwoodsman named "du Bose," or as Frank Chapman speaks of him "DuBoise," was also a member of the expedition. The unsuccessful phosphate miner, Myers, who helped the self-described "inexperienced carpenter" FMC build the house on the scow was an additional crew member. The expedition left Branford on March 11 and William Brewster joined it on March 19, on the Suwannee. Mr. Cory characteristically had not put him in Titusville on the thirteenth as promised.

The "house-scow" was named the *Coota*. Long sweeps aided by a three-mile current moved it slowly down the river. The trip was leisurely. The expedition stopped to collect and observe birds and explore. At night they tied up at the river bank. Side trips up the creeks and branches were made in three canoes.

The high point of the trip was the discovery that Bachman's Warbler migrated up the Suwannee. This warbler, described in 1833 by Audubon from two specimens collected in summer near Charleston, South Carolina, was not seen again until a plume hunter found seven near Lake Pontchartrain, Louisiana, in 1886, just fifty-three years later. Then for the next three years a few Bachman's Warblers were collected each year at Key West. When Frank Chapman and William Brewster collected forty-six of these birds they were, of course, sure that if they had not solved the riddle of the migration route they had perhaps found a breeding territory. The next year Arthur T. Wayne of Charleston collected fifty more on the Suwannee, but the species has never been reported in such numbers anywhere again, and it has not been seen in Florida since 1909.

Except for announcing that he was with them, no mention of Dr. Charles Slover Allen is made in the Brewster report or in FMC's

Autobiography of a Bird Lover. In 1893 Charles Slover Allen died after a brief bout with typhoid. In addition to ornithology one of his major interests was snakes.

All together, specimens of sixty-four species of birds were collected and fifty-two more species of birds were observed.

☆ ☆ ☆

WILLIAM BREWSTER'S JOURNAL

THE MOST COMPLETE STORY AVAILABLE OF THE FIRST ORNITHOLOGICAL
EXPLORATIONS OF THE SUWANNEE RIVER

MAR 19, 1890   Cloudy with high S. wind. Heavy showers about sunset. Yesterday morning at 8 A.M. I started down the Suwannee River but the steamer in turning around struck her paddle wheel against a snag and tore about one-third of the "buckets" out. The captain ran her ashore a little below the landing and the remainder of the day was spent in repairing the damage. I worked on my canoe. Saw a few common birds on the shore.

This morning at daybreak we made another start. The day was cloudy and windy and there were almost no alligators seen. The river was broader than I had supposed and not nearly as beautiful. The banks for the first thirty miles were high and wooded with a mixed growth. River Birches growing along the water's edge in places with palmettoes, live oaks, water oaks, etc.

Saw a good many birds. Anhingas were exceedingly numerous; a dozen in sight at one time. Wood Ducks almost equally common. Many Black Vultures but few Turkey Buzzards. Three species of Herons, Wards, Little Blue, and Green, the last not common. Kingfishers very numerous.

Found Chapman and party on their houseboat a few miles below Ft. Fannin [just below Old Town, more than halfway between Branford and the Gulf]. Soon after the steamer left us the twilight fell and the Barred Owls began to hoot in the Cypress Swamps. We rowed down to Clay Bluffs before dark.

MAR 20, 1890   Clear and warm. A dense fog at daybreak. Chapman and du Bose (the cracker hunter) started out at dawn and found a heronry of Ward's in some cypress ponds about ¾ mile inland. There were about 100 nests with young. They also started about 25 Snipe, heard some Sand-hill Cranes and shot four Pine Woods Sparrows in the pine woods between the ponds and the river.

After breakfast I went out with Chapman crossing the river and landing a little below the point opposite the Bluffs. Found a larger cypress swamp separated from the river by a narrow, dry ridge wooded with water oaks, sweet gums, red maples, hackberry, etc. The deciduous trees just leafing out, many of them badly scorched by the recent frosts.

Cardinals, Carolina Wrens, Tufted Tits, Parulas, and Yellow-throated Warblers were in full song on every side. Pileated, Red-bellied and Red-headed Woodpeckers were drumming and calling far and near. We soon started a Barred Owl which flapped heavily off a few rods and alighted again when I shot it (I was unable to skin it afterwards for lack of time). Chapman then left me and I turned my attention to the ridge along the river. Found a large mixed flock of Warblers chiefly Yellow-rumps and Parulas with a sprinkling of Black and White Creepers, Gnatcatchers and a Solitary Vireo or two, catching flies in a sunny opening. Among them I soon made out a bird which I at once suspected to be Bachman's Warbler and on shooting it found that my suspicions were correct. I was a long time in finding it for it caught in a hanging bunch of moss fifteen feet or more above the ground. It was a female.

Shortly after this Chapman rejoined me. He had shot a ♂ Bachman's Warbler. While we were comparing notes a large flock of Warblers came along keeping high up in the tops of the cypresses. By shooting at all that made show of movement and hung head down at the ends of the terminal twigs we got three more Bachman's Warblers in the course of a few minutes sacrificing several Parulas also.

Gray Squirrels were surprisingly numerous and tame in this swamp. I must have seen a dozen.

Returned to our houseboat about noon. Just before dinner I slipped out among the oak scrub in the "Bluff" and hearing a Warbler making a fine wiry scraping sound went to the spot and discovered two ♂ Bachman's Warblers chasing one another. I quickly shot both with my auxiliary.

Skinning birds all the afternoon putting up our table under a live oak on the bluff. At frequent intervals we heard the "gobbling" of the Sand-hill Cranes in the cypress ponds nearly a mile away. At that distance the sound reminded me of the distant lowing of cattle. Chapman compared it to cowbells.

MAR 21, 1890   Clear and warm. Spent most of the day at the

Bluffs casting off our mooring late in the afternoon and drifting down stream two or three miles.

Had a rather early breakfast after which Chapman and I started for the Heronry. The way led through open pine woods where Blue-birds, Pine Warblers, and Flickers were singing and Palm Warblers flitting from shrub to shrub alighting frequently on the ground.

Reaching the Heronry we found a series of small, shallow ponds bordered by small, stunted cypresses with a few of these trees also scattered singly or in groups well out in the ponds. These isolated trees all had nests, large structures of sticks, some in their tops others on their lateral branches. Each nest held several young Herons, most of them full grown and well feathered. They were standing erect in the nests or out on the neighboring branches as we approached but as soon as they discovered us they all took to the nests and squatted down in them. Chapman killed two with his auxiliary, (first throw-ing one of them down from the nest).

We started several Snipe about this pond and I heard a Robin calling. On the way back through the pine woods heard two Bach-man's Finches singing divinely. I shot one of them. After getting back to the boat I crossed the river in my canoe to the place where I shot yesterday. There were many Warblers in the trees but they kept high up and were hard to identify. I shot several Parulas on suspicion and then got a fine pair of Bachman's Warblers. The ♂ was sitting motionless rather low down with a green background of foliage behind against which his yellow underparts and black throat showed distinctly. I had a long shot at a Swallow-tail Kite which came directly over me but as high as the tops of the tallest trees. I fired and at first thought I had him for he turned completely over and then towered beating the air incessantly with his wings. He must have been shot through the head. He finally drifted off out of sight before the strong south wind.

Late in the afternoon we cast off our moorings and floated down stream a few miles making fast to a point on the west bank about dark. After supper a pair of Barred Owls came about us. Chapman hooted and they approached nearer and nearer until finally they alighted directly over us within fifteen feet. They hooted every few minutes and several times went through their caterwauling perform-ance. I did not see them while thus engaged but repeatedly saw one of them hoot by throwing the light of a jack on him. He sat erect crouching down to his perch and did not move perceptibly while

Right: Frank Chapman. Photograph may have been taken when he graduated from Englewood Academy at the age of sixteen.

Center: Black vultures in Gainesville. Chapman's first bird photograph (1888).

Bottom: Chapman and his mother at "Cosy Corner Cottage." Perhaps a self-photograph (found in her scrap book).

Above: Professor W. P. Jenks (white beard), of Brown University, at the Latham's "Oak Lodge" in 1889. "Ma" Latham is at his right. Loggerhead turtle skull at base of palm (right foreground).

Left: A typical county road in the 1890's.
(P. K. Yonge Library of Florida History)

Below: The cabin FMC used when hunting parakeets on the upper Sebastian River in the spring of 1889. Note wing-tipped parakeet perched at left of entrance. *(From a watercolor by Tappen Adney, after a photograph by FMC)*

making the sound. One bird had a hoarser voice than the other and regularly hooted in a lower key. This difference I afterwards found to be common to all the pairs heard on the river. The birds tonight flapped audibly when they flew. The night was very dark.

MAR 22, 1890   Alternately cloudy and clear. Wind strong from S.W. Rained heavily through the night.

Started out after breakfast taking my canoe and paddling up river about 300 yds. landed on the west bank. It was a bad day for birds and I found but few, these in the tops of the tallest trees as a rule. Saw a Water Thrush, probably northern. Chapman shot a Swainson's Warbler and after joining we started and killed another on the ground where I had been spending most of the morning. I got absolutely nothing save a few Parulas. The locality was a cypress swamp separated from the river by a narrow ridge of hard ground wooded with oaks and hackberry (?) trees. There were a few Towhees (all white-eyed), Brown Thrashers, and Cardinals near the river and many Parulas in the tree tops.

After dinner crossed the river and tried the swamp on the other (east) bank. As I entered it I heard Blackbirds singing in medley —a great troop of them. Found Red-wings, Florida Grackles, and Rusties about equally represented in the flock. Killed two Rusties at one shot. Saw a Winter Wren which plunged into a fallen tree top and disappeared. Next came on a very large flock of Warblers fully 100, chiefly Parulas with a good many Yellow-rumps, one Prairie, some Gnatcatchers, and a Red-eye or two. After following them for some time I picked out and shot a ♀ Bachman's. Chapman and du Bose then came up. They had killed two Bachman's. We went on together and soon struck a new flock from which we each got a Bachman's.

The wind blew a gale all the afternoon and the dead branches came down on all sides, one striking the ground within a few feet of me. I also heard a tree fall not far off.

Just before sunset a large flock of Little Blue Herons with a few Louisianas intermixed passed us going down river. Also saw a few Night Herons. No Barred Owls hooting tonight. Red-shouldered Hawks screaming in the woods in every direction. Their cries are much harsher and more cracked than those of the northern bird.

MAR 23, 1890   Clear and cool with a moderate N. wind. Scarcely a cloud in the sky all day, the sun warm at noon.

Du Bose left us this morning in a huff and started for home on foot. Immediately after breakfast Chapman got the scow under way and ran her before the wind all the forenoon, making about eight miles. I paddled this distance in my canoe shooting by the way. I landed first directly upon our last night's camping place in the swamp where we shot yesterday afternoon. Found a large flock of Warblers and killed two Bachman's very quickly and was after an Orange-crowned. Heard a Warbler song new to me, most like Parula's but less guttural and all on the same key (not rising at the end like Parula's). Discovered the bird in the top of a sweet gum, no other bird near. Saw him sing, then shot him and found that I had a ♂ Bachman's. Heard another but could not find him. Paddled down stream a mile or more and seeing Dr. Allen on shore landed again. Found a beautiful spot, a bluff with a hard sand beach behind open dry oak woods with sunny openings and wood patches. These woods were literally alive with birds, chiefly Warblers with several Vireos of three species (Red-eyed, Blue-headed, and one Yellow-throated), Red-bellied and Pileated Woodpeckers, Cardinals, etc. Gray Squirrels were very numerous and were uttering their choking barks on every side. Butterflies sailed through the openings or flapped their broad wings lazily as they clung to the leaves of the magnolias. Several times a Swallow-tailed Kite glided past just above the tree tops.

It was comparatively easy to identify the Warblers in these woods for they chiefly haunted the deciduous oaks on which the leaves were just beginning to unfold, the trees having that delicate salmon pink tinge seen in our northern oaks at the corresponding season. The Warblers fed at the ends of the twigs hanging head downward like Titmice. I shot six Bachman's Warblers here in about two hours.

After lunching with the Doctor, our canoes floating side by side, I started down river again and rowed steadily until I overtook the scow which had anchored at a sandy beach at a landing on the east bank. The river was very beautiful most of the way. I saw several Anhingas, seven Wood Ducks, and two Swallow-tailed Kites. One of the latter went through the beautiful diving evolution. Also saw a flock of seven Pied-billed Grebes.

After skinning my birds we pushed off the scow and floated down river half a mile or more and tied up for the night to the west bank. Saw about forty Black Vultures after it had become nearly dark roosting in the top of a tall dead tree. A few Barred Owls hooting in the distance.

MAR 24, 1890   Clear and rather cool with stiff N. wind. After breakfast we all started out in our canoes, Chapman leading. He went down river about a mile and had the rare good luck to kill an Ivory-billed Woodpecker with his first shot, hearing it pounding and calling in the cypress swamp only a few rods from the river and stalking it easily enough.

I landed about half a mile down and found a number of Warblers among which I shot a ♀ Bachman's. Prothonotaries were rather common along the river but I heard none singing. I then went further down landing by chance at the very place where Chapman killed his Woodpecker. There were many birds here, also, but I found nothing worth shooting. In the swamp I heard a loud, harsh cry repeated every few seconds. I suspected that it might be an Ivory-bill and stole cautiously in keeping a sharp look out in the trees but at length discovered the author of the sound at my *feet.* It was a small frog which a small garter snake was trying to swallow *feet* first. Every little while the snake would open its mouth wider and try to suck the frog in further when he would cry out as already described. I finally put my foot on the snake when he let go his hold and the frog went off with long and doubtless joyful jumps.

Chapman joined me in time for lunch which we ate on a point at the mouth of a creek. After a short smoke we then paddled up this creek together. Started a pair of Wood Ducks and Chapman found a dead one, a drake, whose head had been eaten off by some bird or mammal of prey. He also shot a Water Thrush. I got a fine ♂ Bachman's Warbler which I shot from my boat dropping it into the water. We saw a dead oppossum at which a dozen or more huge cat-fish were tugging, dragging it about with much splashing.

I went ashore at one place to look at some Warblers in the tree tops and nearly stepped on a huge moccasin which was lying on the bank. It tumbled clumsily into the creek before I could shoot it.

We are now within the influence of the tide which rises and falls a foot or more daily but the water is still fresh.

Late in the afternoon they got the scow under way and picking us up on their way down we tied to the bank for the night at a landing where many red cedar logs lay piled and which is probably "Cedar Landing." Carolina Wrens, Cardinals, and Tufted Tits singing at sunset. Heard Barred Owls in the distance. Several Gulls are around. Night Herons flying about at twilight—their *quak* is similar to that of our bird, but higher pitched and more cracked or harsher.

MAR 25, 1890   Clear and warmer with light S.W. wind. Chapman
and I started down river in our canoes after breakfast. He took a
creek on the west side and went up it some distance getting nothing
but a ♂ Wood Duck.

I took the left bank and followed it a mile or more seeing Anhingas and Ospreys. Then came to a creek at the mouth of which I
shot an immature Florida Red-shouldered hawk (?) which I did not
skin. Met a native here who told me that deer and Turkeys are numerous in these swamps, panthers and bears fairly common. Ivory-
billed Woodpeckers he says are scarce. He is in the woods daily and
covers a good deal of ground looking after his hogs, yet he has not
seen an Ivory-bill for three months or more. Last year several "used"
in a "deadening" near his house. He has not seen a Paroquet for
eight or nine years.

We started up the creek together. After going a little way we
started a Yellow-crowned Night Heron which flew up to a branch
over the water where it stood motionless, its neck stretched up, the
yellow on the forehead showing very distinctly. I shot it, of course.
Going still further up I killed four more of these birds in the course
of a mile. They would usually rise out of range, fly a little way, and
alight on branches over the water. Normally the second time they
alighted and invariably the third, they would allow me to paddle
within shot. I saw several of their nests on branches over the creek,
rather large structures of rough pine twigs, rather neatly arranged.
Two of my birds were females which would have laid in another
week or so.

I started five Wood Ducks in this creek but they all flew in such
a way that I dared not shoot from my cranky little canoe.

This creek was narrow and winding with deep, dark-colored waters. Fish, probably bass, were numerous, jumping on all sides of
my canoe at times. On some of the larger floating logs rows of turtles lay sunning and I saw one large alligator which rolled off the
banks with a great splash as I rounded a turn. Prothonotary Warblers were exceedingly numerous along the banks. I heard a few sing.
Parulas were everywhere in the tree tops. Saw one Flicker, the first
for several days. Started two Barred Owls. They are shy alert birds
in the daytime here. Red-shouldered Hawks screaming incessantly.
Cardinals and Carolina Wrens singing.

Got in to our camp boat by noon and worked on birds and letters
all the afternoon. A pair of Ospreys at their nest on the opposite

side of the river whistling and calling. Have seen no Blue Jays for several days. Floated down stream about two miles and tied to the east bank for the night. After dark Dr. Allen fired off a rocket when a Panther (?) yelled loudly in the bushes within twenty yards. Out with Chapman in the evening taking a jack. Saw nothing but some large bass swimming past.

MAR 26, 1890   Clear in the morning, afternoon cloudy. Wind S.W. We cast loose the scow early this morning and drifted down into the East Pass where we tied to the bank before breakfast. The scenery changed considerably after we passed the mouth of Gopher River, the cypresses becoming lower and more scattering, the country more swampy with wide belts of tall grass along the water's edge. Narrow creeks debouched from the main river at frequent intervals. On every side a boundless wilderness without clearings, boats, or other signs of man's presence.

The birds changed somewhat also. We began to see more Redwings and to hear more Yellow-throated Warblers. The Swallow-tailed kites disappeared while Anhingas and Wood Ducks became more scarce.

After breakfast we all started out in our canoes. Chapman went down the Pass to the Gulf finding extensive marshes which were apparently barren of bird life. I took a creek which entered on the east side and followed it about two miles. Saw nothing of interest except five Wood Ducks, two males and three females. They were paddling idly about in mid stream and I watched them for several minutes through the glass at about 80 yds. In swimming they oscillated their heads and necks forward and back at each stroke of the feet.

There were a few Prothonotaries along this creek and countless Parulas and Yellow-throated Warblers singing in the cypresses. Heard a Pine Linnet [Siskin] distinctly and also saw the bird fly from one cypress to another. Turtles numerous as usual. Saw three alligators, one a rather large one. Came upon three men cutting cedar and visited their camp. They say there are no Limpkins on this river.

Came back to dinner. Three Bank Swallows passed the boat. Dr. Allen and Chapman came in, neither of them having fired a shot.

In the afternoon I started out again, taking a creek on the west side and going up it a mile or more. Heard a great crashing in the brush and sawgrass and the next moment a Ward's Heron started out within fifteen feet of me. I did not shoot. Shortly afterwards a Florida Cormorant tried to pass, coming from downstream, and I killed it. At the report of my gun an Osprey dropped a fish it was carrying. An eagle (adult) tried to pick it up when the Osprey and its mate attacked him fiercely and drove him off, but they did not attempt to recover their fish.

My creek proved very beautiful, narrow winding with palmettoes, cypresses, and sweet gums arching over its glassy surface. The swampy woods, silent and impervious. Occasionally a gray squirrel barked, a Log Cock called or a Cardinal or Carolina Wren sang. Mullet were jumping freely. Came back in the twilight, frogs croaking, a bullfrog bellowing. Yellow-crowned Night Herons flying about quaking in cracked tones.

MAR 27, 1890   Fair with alternating cloud and sunshine. Very warm. Off with Chapman for the entire day taking the main channel of the Suwannee and going down to the outlet. The distance is about five miles, the last two miles being through open marshes which stretch as far as the eye can reach. On the way down we heard the usual birds in the woods along the river. There were few water birds, four Anhingas, two Dusky Ducks (doubtless *fulvigula*), five or six Cormorants, and several Great Blue and Green Herons. Ospreys were numerous, mostly in pairs at or near their nests which were usually in large cypresses along the banks of the river.

On reaching the marshes we began to hear and see Boat-tailed Grackles, but there were not many of them. There were absolutely no gulls or terns. Two Brown Pelicans passed over the Gulf. A male Scaup Duck was swimming in the river. Saw a Louisiana Heron alight in the grass on an island at the mouth of the river and paddling to the spot flushed and shot it. Finding this island rather high and dry land we landed and lunched. On the next island above us we heard Clapper Rails calling at frequent intervals so we crossed the channel and fired the grass. After several failures we finally got a good blaze started and then lay off in the river in our canoes to see what would come out. Chapman got a shot at a rail that appeared on the edge of the water but missed it. We then landed and watched a bare muddy flat ahead of the fire but nothing came out there. I then returned to my canoe and quickly killed a Clapper Rail (which proved to be *R. scottii*) and a Marsh Hen, both of which ran out a hundred yards or more ahead of the fire. I also shot a perching Swamp Sparrow. Started three Snipe on the island and missed a fair shot at one of them. Besides the Clapper I saw a

Virginia Rail distinctly but failed to get a shot at it. There were several pairs of Red-winged Blackbirds on this island; also some Long-billed Marsh Wrens in a growth of low cane brake.

The river is fresh water quite to its mouth and indeed, as far out into the Gulf as I went in my canoe (a hundred yards or more). Nevertheless several huge porpoises were rolling and puffing in the channels among the outer islands. There were no beaches or sand bars visible, a fact which may account for the absence of Gulls and waders generally.

We started up river early in the afternoon, sailing most of the distance home before a fresh southeast wind locking our canoes together.

Mar 28, 1890   Morning clear, clouding over at noon. A heavy shower early in the afternoon. Wind strong from the S. all day. Starting off alone at 10 a.m. I paddled down the west pass for about a mile then entered a large creek on the W. side. Just before reaching it I had a long shot at an Anhinga, a ♀ which was sitting on a stake. She fell at the shot and when I reached her was lying on her back apparently dead, but as the bow of my canoe struck her she dove, came up once, then down again, and I saw her no more. For the first mile up the creek I saw nothing save two Little Blue Herons. At length as I rounded a bend I came suddenly on a huge alligator (at least 11 feet long) lying well up on the bank. As he plunged into the water the surge caused the canoe to rock violently. The noise he made startled three Herons and an American Egret and a pair of Black-Crowned Night Herons, which flapped out from the trees out of range. I started all them several times afterwards but failed to get a shot. Twice I saw three large gar fish swimming together, the largest in the middle, a smaller one on each side. I think they were two males following a female. One trio swam with their bills out of the water.

My creek soon came to an end in a saw grass marsh and I turned back and tried a smaller one which entered it on the south side. From this I again turned into another and still smaller one over which the trees interlocked, their branches forming a perfect arch. I had not followed it far when I started a Yellow-crowned Night Heron and dropped it into the creek. A few rods further on two started and one alighted again when I killed it.

My creek finally led into a much larger one, a small river in fact, nearly as wide as the Concord [Mass.] and very deep. Here I saw two Green Herons and a very tame ♀ Anhinga which sat on a snag with spread wings allowing me to approach within 20 yds. and finally dropping like a stone into the water.

Rounding a bend a little further on I came suddenly on a flock of eleven American Egrets. They were sitting in green ash trees over the river and I never saw as beautiful a picture of the kind before. I was within eighty yds. and looked at them several minutes through my glass. They reminded me of the group of Herons in one of Brehm's plates. One superb fellow had plumes which extended an inch or two *below* his feet as he stood erect on his long legs. Their attitudes were marvelously easy and graceful. Finally they flew one by one, going only a little way and realighting in the tops of some tall cypresses. Without any care whatever I approached them to within 60 yds. and picking out a bird at random (for I could not make out their plumes at that height) I shot it. It fell into the river and proved a fine bird, but not the finest one of the flock. Saw a few Prothonotaries and two Wood Ducks. Back to the scow boat early in the P.M. having to put on my rubber coat and hug the shore during a brisk shower.

MAR 29, 1890   Clear and cool with light N.W. wind. A brilliant day without a cloud.

Spent the first part of the morning at work on birds. At 10:30 started for the same creek where I spent yesterday. On the way down the main river I shot a Carolina Grebe that was swimming among the bonnets and an alligator seven feet long. The latter was lying in the grass asleep and I got within about 15 yds. of him. I shot him in the ear with no. 4 shot from the little 20 gauge. He tore madly through the reeds in a circle returning to nearly the spot whence he started and settled down apparently dead. I then shot him again behind the foreshoulders but he did not move and when I returned later in the afternoon he proved to be stiff and cold. Dr. Allen took his head and skin.

Entering the creek I had paddled only a little way when a fine Ward's Heron started from a tree and I dropped him into the water. A little further on I started two Green Herons and killed one of them. I passed a very tame Yellow-crowned Heron, an immature mottled bird.

Turning into the left branch I stopped under the shade of a water oak and lunched. Then I continued on and took the second left hand turn into the narrow Vista Creek. Here I started three Yellow-crowned

Herons and shot one of them as it sat on the branch of a cypress back from the water.

Coming out on the broad creek beyond I started a large White Egret. It flapped on ahead of me for some distance, frequently alighting. I could have shot it easily enough but it had poor plumes and I did not care for it. I killed another Yellow-crown on this creek. Going only a short distance beyond where I stopped yesterday I came in sight of the Suwannee into which this large creek proved to flow.

I then returned by the same route. Shot at a Yellow-crowned Heron at the entrance to Vista Creek and missed or only wounded it. The report of the gun started an Ivory-billed Woodpecker which uttered its trumpet note a dozen times or more. It was several hundred yards off apparently. I turned back and paddled hard but it stopped calling and I failed to find it.

Near the lower end of Vista Creek a White Ibis flew from a cypress uttering a course rough call (*cr-r-r-r*). And alighted again in another cypress. I paddled to within about 50 yds. and fired just as it opened its wings to start. It flew out of sight up the connecting creek. I followed and found it floating dead in mid stream.

On the way down to the main creek I started three Yellow-crowned Herons and heard a fourth crying out every few seconds *squaw* in harsh piercing tones. It proved to be my tame gray bird which was sitting in an ash over the water.

Paddling down the creek I found Dr. Allen near its mouth and just outside, Chapman. King Rails (?) calling in the marsh where I shot the alligator.

MAR 30, 1890   Clear and cool with S.E. to S.W. wind. At 10:30 A.M. we all started together for the mouth of the West Pass of the Suwannee. The tide was running out strongly and we sped swiftly and easily downstream stopping occasionally to rest under the shade of the overhanging trees. During one such halt a number of birds collected about us, a pair of Cardinals and Tufted Tits, two Parula Warblers, a Solitary and Red-eyed Vireo, and a Great Crested Flycatcher. Saw an Osprey hovering above its nest with the peculiar butterfly flight whistling shrilly very much like a Duck Hawk. The next moment it dropped with closed wings and through the glass I could see it copulating with its mate which was sitting on the nest. Lower down we saw another pair at their nest. They are probably laying now.

We saw only one duck on the way, a ♀ Shoveller. On reaching the mouth of the river heard Widgeons calling and found three of these ducks swimming near the last island. Landed on the island that we burnt partially on the 27th. Started three Snipe, doubtless the same seen on that day. Chapman shot one of them and I missed another. I also shot a ♀ Redwing and upon going to pick it up flushed a very black Florida Clapper Rail and killed it.

We then separated and fired the island at three different points. Only one of these fires proved a success but that fairly raged for an hour or more burning quite across the island with a width of 100 yds. or more. We all took stations on the leeward side but saw only four or five Rails of which I shot one and Dr. Allen another. They rose a hundred yards or more ahead of the fire and flew long distances seeming much alarmed. One, however, came out of the grass directly in front of the fire. Swamp Sparrows and Marsh Wrens also came and I shot one of the latter, a Short-billed, as it was flying over the water. Saw a single Sea-side Sparrow and shot it but failed to find it.

We next crossed the river and fired a long narrow island on the west side. The grass was dryer here and the fire ran madly making a great roaring and, when it got into an extensive bed of cane, sending up flames 15 to 20 ft. and filling the air with black smoke through which the sun shone dimly. The Rails were thoroughly alarmed and began to show themselves at frequent intervals, some flying, others walking over the beds of lodged grass or sneaking under the banks. Yet they were very shy and instantly disappeared when they saw us, turning back towards the fire. I shot four, one sitting, three flying, losing one of the latter. Many Marsh Wrens (Short-billed) singing *sotto voce* on this island.

At sunset saw hundreds of Herons (chiefly Little Blues and Louisianas) assembling to roost on a marshy treeless island near us. Night Herons (Black-crowned) flying about at dusk. Paddled back by moonlight reaching camp at 8:30. A flock of 50 White Ibis passed over us at about 8 P.M. looking in the dim light like a band of ghosts or a wandering moon beam in a dark cellar. Their wings made a strong rushing sound.

Mar 31, 1890   Cloudless and warm. Wind N.E. to S.W. Spent the entire morning at work on birds. After dinner we started out in our canoes. Chapman went up Gopher Creek and brought back a Yellow-crowned Heron and a fine ♂ Wood Duck. We heard a Turkey gobble just before he started and he heard it again later but could not come up to it.

I crossed the river and entered a small creek that came in from the west about a mile below the Gopher. It was narrow, very crooked and proved to be less than a mile in length, rising in an extensive saw-grass savanna. Soon after entering it I heard a continued outcry of loud, harsh voices which I did not recognize. Rounding a bend I discovered the authors in some Ward's Herons, young birds mostly big enough to fly which were standing in their nests calling for food. There were three nests, all in cypresses over the creek. Three adult Herons were sitting among the branches, one very near a nest, the others above the nests in the tops of the trees. The old birds at once flew off upon discovering me and the young squatted so closely in the nests that I could not see any of them from below.

A short distance above this I started two Yellow-crowned Herons, one very shy, the other tame. Shot at the latter wounding it badly but it flew out of sight among the trees. I followed on after it until I came to a place where my creek virtually came to an end in a saw-grass savanna, or rather split up into several small branches only two or three feet wide. I pushed the canoe up one of them for about 100 yds. when a deer that had been lying on the bank probably asleep, suddenly rose to its feet within 4 yds. of me and giving one terrified look tore off through the saw-grass at a great pace making a loud plumping sound as it drew its legs from the soft mud at each bound. It stopped about 100 yds. away but I could not see it. I heard another start a moment later on the other side. The one I saw was a large animal, probably a full grown buck, but of course without horns. There were a few Prothonotaries among the scattered cypress trees on the edge of the savanna but none along the creek below. The males were singing in low tones. I also heard a Downy Woodpecker and some Parulas.

Returning to the Suwannee I kept down river for about half a mile and entered a large creek on the eastern side which Myer partially explored a few days ago. It proved very beautiful, winding about through a fine forest of cypresses, sweet gums, red maples, and green ashes with palmettos along the banks. For the first mile it was broad with frequent large deep pools bordered by dense beds of bonnets but higher up it became so narrow that the trees arched over it interlocking their branches for hundreds of yards at a stretch where the growth was of hardwoods or old cypresses, where of younger or more stunted cypresses and bay trees forming a nearly straight vertical wall on each side, the path of the stream looking in places like a narrow wood road walled in by straight cypresses hung thickly with dark Spanish Moss. In places the bay trees formed almost the sole growth. Their roots washed clean by the overflows or perhaps growing naturally above, instead of under, the surface literally covered the ground so thickly that one could walk on them in slippers as on a dry floor. They resembled nothing so much as great beds of snakes lying stretched at full length in loose coils, or entwined together in masses. Their general color was a plain stone gray mottled with darker very like that of a cotton-mouth moccasin and their bark was in texture not unlike that of the skin of a large serpent. In fact the general resemblance, or perhaps I should say suggestiveness, was so strong that I could not walk on them without a shrinking sensation. It would be next to impossible to discover a real snake among them. Along the sides of the creek they formed in many places a clearly defined vertical bank or wall. They did not seem to extend under water or to encroach anywhere on the bed of the creek.

On the lower reaches of the creek I saw few large birds. A solitary Great Blue Heron, an Osprey sitting above its nest whistling shrilly and eyeing me suspiciously as I paddled past, a Red-shouldered Hawk, and a Kingfisher or two. Small birds were numerous, especially Prothonotaries of which I passed a dozen or more, several of them females. They haunted bushes which hung low over the stream where they flitted about among the terminal twigs, their yellow heads gleaming like gold among the foliage or showing in strong contrast against the dark water. I shot one fine orange headed male. Parulas and Yellow-throated Warblers were numerous as usual. Saw a pair of Crested Flycatchers as I was paddling slowly and silently across a broad pool where the sunlight brought out a sand bar beneath with great distinctness I suddenly discovered a huge alligator gliding slowly under the canoe at nearly a right angle. As I had not time to shoot ahead and escape him I suspended my paddle and sat perfectly still until he passed out of sight into deeper water on my left. His back must have nearly grazed my keel and he was not less than twelve feet in length with a bulk nearly equal to that of a small pony.

In the overarched portions of this creek I found several pairs of Yellow-crowned Herons and saw several of their nests. On one which was placed on a branch of an ash low over the creek a bird was sitting but on climbing above the nest I found it empty. I shot a bird here and another on my return down the creek.

As I turned back twilight was settling over the swamp and it was nearly dark before I reached the river. Barred Owls were hooting on every side and the Yellow-crowned Herons squawking and yelling far and near. Several of the latter came close past me and one alighted within ten yards. A few Rail voices (probably King Rails) in the marsh at the mouth of the creek.

APR 1, 1890   Cloudless and warm with a pleasant breeze. Spent the day in packing and made no observations of interest. The steamer came down at about 8 P.M. and we quickly got our things on board and started for Cedar Keys which we reached at 11 P.M. This practically ended our trip.

[It is only ten miles from the mouth of the Suwannee to Cedar Key. At this period in history a steamer regularly left Branford on the Suwannee River and traveled down it into the Gulf of Mexico, landing at Cedar Key. An 1883 advertisement of the "Peoples Line" said the Caddo Belle left New Branford at 4 A.M. Fridays and made the return trip from Cedar Key on Mondays. The Florida Railway and Navigation Company operated trains from Cedar Key to Fernandina Beach which stopped at Gainesville.]

APR 2   Cloudy and warm. Left Cedar Keys at 8:30 A.M. and reached Gainesville at 3 P.M. At the Keys saw a flock of twenty-seven White Pelicans flying in a long line through the channel between the islands. They flapped and sailed alternately in the usual manner and (this I have not seen before) undulations were continually passing down the line as the leader rose and lowered his flight and each bird followed him. They were flying at a height of about 40 ft.

As the train passed over the marshes inland we saw a good many Gulls, all apparently Laughing Gulls, and a few Green Herons but no blue or white Herons.

(I left Gainesville on the morning of the 3rd, spent that night at Jacksonville, reached Charleston on the evening of the 4th, started for Washington on the afternoon of the 6th, reached New York on the 10th and Cambridge on the afternoon of the 12th.)

List of Species on Suwannee River, Florida
(March 19–31, 1890)

Turdus pallasi [Hermit Thrush]
Mimus carolinensis [Catbird]
M. polyglottos [Mockingbird]
Merula migratoria [Robin]
Harporhynchus rufus [Brown Thrasher]
Sialia sialis [Bluebird]
Polioptila caerulea
 [Blue-gray Gnatcatcher]
Regulus calendula
 [Ruby-crowned Kinglet]
R. satrapa
 [Golden-crowned Kinglet]
Parus bicolor [Tufted Titmouse]
P. carolinensis
 [Carolina Chickadee]
Anorthura hiemalis [Winter Wren]
Cistothorus palustris
 [Long-billed Marsh Wren]
C. stellaris
 [Short-billed Marsh Wren]
Thryothorus ludovicianus
 [Carolina Wren]
Seiurus notabilis
 [Northern Waterthrush]
S. motacilla [Louisiana Waterthrush]
S. aurocapillus [Ovenbird]
Mniotilta varia
 [Black-and-white Warbler]
Helminthophila celata [Orange-Crowned
 Warbler]
H. bachmani [Bachman's Warbler]
Parula americana [Parula Warbler]
Dendroica dominica
 [Yellow-throated Warbler]
D. palmarum [Palm Warbler]
D. discolor [Prairie Warbler]
D. coronata [Myrtle Warbler]
D. pinus [Pine Warbler]
D. hypochrysea [Yellow Palm Warbler]
Protonotaria citrea
 [Prothonotary Warbler]
Helinaia swainsoni
 [Swainson's Warbler]
Sylvania mitratus [Hooded Warbler]
Geothlypis trichas [Yellowthroat]
Setophaga ruticilla [Redstart]
Vireo noveboracensis
 [White-eyed Vireo]
V. flavifrons [Yellow-throated Vireo]

V. solitarius [Solitary Vireo]
V. olivaceus [Red-eyed Vireo]
Piranga rubra [Summer Tanager]
Collurio ludoviciana
 [Loggerhead Shrike]
Cotile riparia [Bank Swallow]
Ampelis cedrorum [Cedar Waxwing]
Spinus pinus [Pine Siskin]
Chrysomitris tristis [Goldfinch]
Tachycineta bicolor [Tree Swallow]
Cardinalis cardinalis [Cardinal]
Ammodramus maritimus
 [Seaside Sparrow]
Melospiza palustris [Swamp Sparrow]
Peucaea aestivalis
 [Bachman's Sparrow]
Pipilo erythrophthalmus
 [Red-eyed Towhee]
P. alleni [White-eyed Towhee]
Agelaius phoeniceus
 [Red-winged Blackbird]
Quiscalus major [Boat-tailed Grackle]
Q. agelaeus [Common Grackle]
Molothrus ater [Cowbird]
Scolecophagus ferrugineus
 [Rusty Blackbird]
Chaetura pelasgica [Chimney Swift]
Trochilus colubris
 [Ruby-throated Hummingbird]
Ceryle alcyone [Belted Kingfisher]
Cyanocitta cris. florincola [Blue Jay]
Myiarchus crinitus
 [Crested Flycatcher]
Corvus americanus [Common Crow]
Picus pubescens [Downy Woodpecker]
P. borealis [Red-cockaded Woodpecker]
P. audubonii [Hairy Woodpecker]
Hylotomus pileatus
 [Pileated Woodpecker]
Sphyrapicus varius
 [Yellow-bellied Sapsucker]
Melanerpes erythrocephalus
 [Red-headed Woodpecker]
Campephilus principalis
 [Ivory-billed Woodpecker]
Colaptes auratus [Flicker]
Centurus auratus
 [Red-bellied Woodpecker]
Tyrannus carolinensis [Kingbird]

Syrnium nebulosum [Barred Owl]
Nanclerus forficatus
   [Swallow-tailed Kite]
Buteo lineatus alleni?
   [Red-shouldered Hawk]
Buteo borealis [Red-tailed Hawk]
Pandion carolinensis [Osprey]
Haliaetus leucocephalus [Bald Eagle]
Catharista atrata [Black Vulture]
Cathartes aura [Turkey Vulture]
Meleagris gallopavo [Turkey]
Ardea egretta [Common Egret]
A. caerulea [Little Blue Heron]
A. ludoviciana [Louisiana Heron]
A. virescens [Green Heron]
A. wardi [Great Blue Heron]
A. candidissima [Snowy Egret]
Nyctiardea nevaea
   [Black-crowned Night Heron]
Nyctherodius violaceus
   [Yellow-crowned Night Heron]
Ibis alba [White Ibis]

Gallinago wilsoni [**Common Snipe**]
Tringoides macularius
   [Spotted Sandpiper]
Totanus semipalmata [Willet]
T. melanoleucus [Greater Yellowlegs]
Rhyacophilus solitarius
   [Solitary Sandpiper]
Rallus virginianus [Virginia Rail]
R. scottii? [**Clapper Rail**]
Grus fraterculus [Sandhill Crane]
Fulica americana [Coot]
Anas fulvigula [Mottled Duck]
Fulix affinis [**Lesser Scaup**]
Aix sponsa [**Wood Duck**]
Mareca americana [**American Widgeon**]
Spatula clypeata [Shoveller]
Pelecanus fuscus [Brown Pelican]
Plotus anhinga [Anhinga]
Grauculus floridanus
   [Double-crested Cormorant]
Podilymbus podiceps
   [Pied-billed Grebe]

A sequel to the Suwannee trip are two letters Mr. Brewster wrote to his friend Frank Chapman, one in May and one in September of the same year. We learn from them that Chapman somehow earned the nickname "Fiend of the Suwannee." Until his death in 1919, William Brewster's personal letters to FMC always started "Dear Fiend." What fun it would be to know how this came about and why Frank Chapman in after years addressed Brewster as "Dear Sahib" and Brewster signed his to FMC, "Sincerely, The Sahib."

An entry on March 7 in Chapman's 1891 Journal tells of a meeting with Allison, cook on the scow, and hints at the reason for the title "Fiend." I have found no hint about the title "Sahib" unless Brewster's personality and character as it emerges in his and Chapman's writings is one.

It is easy to understand why Frank Chapman treasured Brewster's letters and laid them away. In 1933, more than 40 years later in *Autobiography of a Bird Lover*, he wrote, "On July 12, 1919, I lost my friend William Brewster. For twenty years that had passed since we descended the Suwannee together, he had held a unique place in my esteem and affection. Thirteen years my senior, a past master in the art of observing and recording what he saw, he came into my life at a time when, by example and constructive criticism, he exercised a profound influence on my development as an ornithologist. He was my ideal both as a man and as a student of birds."

A touch of hero worship probably prompted Chapman to save all of Brewster's letters. Although the friendship of the older man for the younger grew with the years, Brewster would have had no reason in 1890 to treasure the words of a promising young assistant curator of birds.

This letter written two months after the Suwannee trip is the only typewritten document in all the journals and letters used in this book.

DICTATED

Cambridge, Mass., May 2, 1890

Mr. F. M. Chapman,
    American Museum of Natural History,
      New York City.
Dear Mr. Chapman:

This is not to be understood as an answer to your kind and very interesting letter of April 27, to which I will reply more informally as soon as I can find time but I must send you a few words with regard to the set of photographs which will go to you with this. They all relate to our trip on the Suwannee river excepting a very few taken at the market in Charleston, S.C., to show the Black Vultures which, as you doubtless know, congregate there daily. I am having an enlargement made of the best of these Buzzard pictures, the one with the four birds in the street, two of them squabbling over a piece of entrail. If it comes out well, I shall probably get a number of copies, one of which I shall be happy to send you, if you would like it. As to the Suwannee pictures, you probably will not recognize all or indeed many of them; but, when I am in New York, I will look them over with you, and tell you just where each was taken. I shall send a similar set to Dr. Allen, Charles Slover, and hope to get some from him when he has developed and printed the contents of his camera. I hardly know when I shall visit New York, but I hope to do so some time this month. Can not you run on to spend a Sunday with me? It would give me the greatest pleasure in the world, and it is a beautiful time now to see the country here.

Yours sincerely,
/s/ William Brewster

Early fall brought another communication from Mr. Brewster, a combination of Suwannee nonsense and ornithological business.

Robertson's place on Newnan's Lake photographed by FMC, 1889.

A view of the "Coota" on the Suwannee River (1890).

Chapman and Tom Barbour
(c. 1933) at FMC's Coconut
Grove outdoor study.

Above: Putnam House and its interior, 1887. From *Palatka Daily News.* *(P. K. Yonge Library of Florida History)*

Left: Frank Chapman and his mother in New York, probably in the late 1890's.

145 Brattle Street, Cambridge
16th Sept., 1890

My dear Fiend:

Shades of Allison ("all pisen")! You and the Doctor [C. S. Allen] must be stark, staring mad. He coolly (possibly (?) with kind intentions) offers me a baby moccasin which, he says, is already quite up to biting. I have declined the offer in the most emphatic manner. Will it trouble you too much to ask Mr. Allen [J. A. Allen, then editor of the *Auk*] to cross out from the proofs of my article on *Totanus s. cinnamomeus* [western race of the Solitary Sandpiper, therein newly described] the sentence or clause relating to the spotting on inner webs of primaries? It is not in the diagnosis, I think. If it *ever* occurs in *solitarius* it had better not be mentioned for it is not always well marked in cinnamomeus. I am going to so remote a place that the proofs may not reach me.

Yours sincerely,
/s/ William Brewster

Dr. Allen holds out some hopes that I may have the pleasure of seeing him in Nov. Cannot you arrange to come too? We could then have a Suwannee reunion!

To Brewster's intense disgust Frank Chapman had skeletonized the one specimen of the Ivory-billed Woodpecker collected on the Suwannee expedition. Skeleton specimens of birds are used to identify remains of prehistoric birds, the bones found in archeological digs, and to study the evolution and relationships of birds to one another. Skeletonized specimens of recently extinct birds are invaluable to present day research. Only five skeleton specimens of Ivory-billed Woodpeckers exist today, four in the National Museum in Washington, D.C., and the one Frank Chapman collected on the Suwannee River on March 24, 1890, in the American Museum of Natural History in New York.

Mr. Brewster deplored the destruction of a beautiful bird skin, but 413 skins are scattered through our museums today, a great plenty to show the world the beauty of one of our vanished birds. Mr. Chapman did not waste the feathers of the skeletonized Ivory-bill. At Christmas they greeted Mr. Brewster on a card, forming within a pen and ink outline a feather portrait of an Ivory-billed Woodpecker (see *Frontispiece*).

One final amusing note closes the Brewster-Chapman correspondence. The congeniality and comradeship between the two men is evidenced by their gentle teasing of one another.

145 Brattle Street, Cambridge, Mass.
February 24, 1899.
Dear Fiend:

Mrs. Brewster and I are extremely sorry to know that Mrs. Chapman will not be able to come to us on the 4th but we shall try to make the most of her "fiendish" husband. There is a small boy here —one of our neighbors—who has the singular taste of fairly worshipping him and who has had one of his letters framed. This misguided youth's name is Corruth. He is most anxious now to get a photograph of his idol and his mother is making my life miserable about it. Can you help me out? Strange to say I have no picture of you in your "store clothes"—only backwoods things like the one I took at the cabin. So you had better bring a couple of dressed up ones with you.

I am looking forward to seeing you with the greatest pleasure and with impatience for there are many things I want to say to you and then—I want to see that fiendish grin once more. We will discuss the nuthatch article when you are here and if you are very good I will draw another sketch for your magazine. I am delighted to hear that it is succeeding so well but I have little doubt that this fact is mainly due to my contribution to the first number.

Sincerely,
The "Sahib"

Telegraph me if anything prevents your getting the last train from Framingham. If I get no message I will sit up all night.

☆ ☆ ☆

The magazine spoken of is, of course, *Bird-Lore,* the first number of which had appeared only a few weeks before Brewster wrote this letter. I am quite familiar with *Bird-Lore* and I could not remember seeing any sketches in it nor could I remember that William Brewster had ever done any drawing of any kind. When I took the first number of *Bird-Lore* down from the shelves, this is what I found:

A COVER DESIGN

This interesting sketch was contributed by a prominent ornithologist as an appropriate cover design for this magazine at a time when it was proposed to call it "The Bird World." The appearance of a book bearing this title renders it necessary for us to abandon its use, but we do not, for the same reason, feel justified in depriving the world of this remarkably artistic effort, and therefore present it for the edification of our readers, and, we trust, to the delight of its author! (From *Bird-Lore,* vol. 1, no. 1, February 1899, page 25.)

A very old ornithological mystery has been solved! What is probably the only published drawing by William Brewster, the "Father of the American Ornithologists' Union" is preserved for posterity.

6

The Journals of 1891 - 1892

*W*E CAN PRESUME THAT AFTER THE Suwannee trip ended in April, 1890, Frank Chapman and his mother traveled north. Her scrap book indicates that Mrs. Lebbeus Chapman was in Englewood and FMC was concerned with his duties at the American Museum. In November of 1890 he attended the meetings of the American Ornithologists' Union held at the United States National Museum in Washington, D.C., from the eighteenth through the twentieth, and delivered a paper on neotropical birds. He did not, as he had on several occasions, proceed southward after the meetings but waited until March, 1891 (we hope they had a mild winter in New York and New Jersey that year) before returning to Florida. He spent a short time in Gainesville with his mother before going on to collect in Texas.

☆ ☆ ☆

EXCERPTS FROM FRANK M. CHAPMAN'S "FLORIDA—TEXAS" JOURNAL
Florida from March to April, 1891

MAR 1   Trip to Gainesville, Fla., via Atlantic Coast Line. Mar. 1-2, 1891.

February 28, at 9 P.M. I left New York on my fifth trip to Gainesville. At the time of my departure the weather was cold and windy and the ground was still white with the remains of the snowstorm of Feb. 26. Mar. 1 at 11 A.M. we reached Richmond. The day was cold, raw, and disagreeable. Ice of some thickness had formed the night before. On the morning of Feb. 28 the mercury had registered 22°.

Proceeding rapidly southward I commenced now to look for the first signs of spring. No indication of the advance of the season was seen, however, until we were about 20 m. south of Petersburg, Va. Here the willows, "weeping" variety, were just commencing to leave, wild plums showed the whiteness of incipient blossoms, and the maples had an indistinct reddish haze. There was a chorus of sparrows—principally Song Sparrows—from a hedge-row and Robins were calling in a meadow nearby. It was like the last of March or early April at home. As we stopped a sheet of ice slid from the car roof. Was it the greeting of winter to Spring? or did the train in this incident typify the new season's struggle to escape from winter's cold embrace?

Very soon the peach trees commenced to blossom but beyond this there was no appreciable change for the rest of the day.

MAR 2   We awoke in the early morning near Savannah. The train stopped just outside the City and we picked yellow jessamine from the side of the railroad. I have never seen this flower more abundant. The banks in places were yellow with it and the vines in full blossom covered some of the trees and thickets in the woods we passed. A small white blossom growing thickly on trees about twenty feet in height was also very common. There was no marked change in condition of the larger trees except that Cypresses were commencing to blossom.

Between Jesup and Waycross the China-berries commenced to leave and here Le Conte pears were in full bloom. On the whole the season here was about as far advanced as it is at home on say April 25.

After leaving Jacksonville and going south up the river to Palatka there was a decided change, many of the larger trees were in full foliage. To-morrow, March 4, I hope to get into the woods here and will be able to say more about the few trees I know.

The first whiff of *pine smoke*: how it peoples the mind with scenes and incidents of the past.

As we turn the leaves and each year brings us nearer the end of the book, how much more frequently we recall the earlier chapters. The odor of burning pines always reminds me of my Georgia experience in 1872. [He visited his maternal grandparents, Mary Johnson Parkhurst and Chester Parkhurst, M.D., at Milledgeville, Georgia, when he was eight years old.]

MAR 4   Gainesville, Florida. This morning with Wingate I left town about 9 A.M. and rode to the "Sink" via Oliver's Park [an amusement center and picnic ground southeast of town near Alachua Sink], returning through the English colony. The day was warm and partly cloudy with a fresh south-west wind. We were too late to see or hear many birds nor was the locality of the best. My object was to see the lake and I have never seen it lower. Four years ago the water was within fifty yards of the hammock, now a stretch of meadow at least six hundred yards wide intervenes. It was too boggy to ride near the water but I could see Coots and hear them calling and there were also a few Scaup Ducks (Lessers). Cardinals were very abundant and in full song. It was good to hear them. Their mellow, plaintive, whistle recalls many a pleasant morning in the woods.

It is the height of spring. The season is perhaps comparable with the middle of May at home, though of course the migration is by no means as far advanced. Yellow jessamine is almost entirely out of bloom, I could find very few blossoms. The "Carolina Cherry" or "mock orange" and the red trumpet flower are nearly out of blossom. The ashes and the prickly ash are fully leaved and in bud; the large sweet gums are fully leaved; the turkey oaks in the pines are in half *plumage,* the wild orange trees in full blossom. The cultivated orange groves are just commencing to bloom, their condition depending on their location as regards sun and soil and the care they have received.

MAR 4   In the afternoon I drove my mother and her friends to Rocky Point [near where today route 441 starts across Payne's Prairie on the north] about five miles. The road was new to them and they were amazed at the hilliness of it. We made ascents of a hundred feet in as many yards and from the summits could gaze away into the blue distance across the lake. We drove through "heavy" hammocks where the oaks, gums, and magnolias were from sixty to eighty feet in height. A slight shower had washed the leaves and the fresh new foliage of the gums was in striking contrast to the dark, rich green of the magnolias. Returning with the wind and sun at our backs the light was reflected from both surfaces of the magnolia leaves as they played in the breeze. The effect was a beautiful combination of dark green and shining reddish-brown.

We visited the market garden region. The prominent crop just now is cabbages. We saw hundreds of acres of this plant which now is just commencing to "head." One field continuously planted with the long straight, evenly grown rows, must have contained between 150 and 200 acres.

It is warm, but very pleasant and breezy. At noon today the mercury registered 80°.

There has been no rain for some time and everything is extremely dusty.

MAR 5   A ride of five miles to Robertson's point on Newnan's Lake

was full of interest. It is a beautiful spot and has always been favored ground with me. The point is grown with cabbage palms,
cypress, ash, oaks, and a few wild orange trees. There is a sandy
beach in places and a fine view of the lake, here about three miles
wide. It is a great resort for gators and I rode quietly down looking for a probable specimen of one on the shore. There was one
there with about half his body out of water. He was between seven
and eight feet in length and by riding cautiously I got within fifty
feet of him, then with a splash he went into the water and swam
rapidly out into the lake. There were several others lying out there
and their grunts, groans, snores, and bellows were frequently heard.
There were a group of warblers on the point, Yellow-rumps [Myrtles]
mostly with a few silent Parulas and Yellow-throated Warblers. The
few songs I heard from the last-named recalled the Suwannee River
more vividly than any incident which has occurred since we left that
ever-to-be-remembered stream. I could write a great deal just here—
but I won't. It was good to hear this song. While I was reviewing
these warblers with a possible Bachman's in my mind's eye I heard
in the distance the familiar *whoo whoo whoo*, etc., of a Barred Owl.
The water lapped the shore at my feet, the air was typical of Florida
and there was wanting little to complete the Suwannee illusion. I
responded to the old Barred Owl of course and after a few replies
from the distance there was a commotion among the small birds near
by and the owl flapped into a tree above me. In a moment he dropped
down to within fifteen feet. I called and he evidently misplaced the
first part of my address for he hopped around and turned his back
towards me. But before I had concluded he located me and turning his
head just half around looked down at me directly over and between his
shoulders. The position was very odd. Well, we had a long conversation
and he was evidently much puzzled, flying about from tree to tree in
search of this unseen friend or enemy. At last when I arose he was
startled and evidently intended to leave, but a call reassured him for
the time and he remained until I walked into plain view. This was too
much for him and he sprang from his perch and uttered a hoot of alarm
as he flew away through the forests.

I heard a Yellow-throated Vireo singing. (The song was too brief
and incomplete to make identification certain.) The bird does not winter
here, I think, and its presence may be taken as an indication that the
migration has commenced. Two Purple Martins seen March 1 confirm
this.

A brood of "blind mosquitoes" (males) had evidently been recently hatched at the lake. The shore for a width of twenty feet and I know not how long was swarming with them. I have never before seen any living thing in such numbers. They covered every blade of grass, limb, twig, and leaf. After several calculations I should say they averaged from six to eight individuals to the square inch. As they were quite large this practically covered a given surface. I killed fifty by crushing a leaf and a half between my hands. When they were disturbed they arose in myriads really interfering with clear vision. Their combined voices made a terrific sound. Surrounded by them I paused several times to see what I could compare it to and on each occasion decided it was as much like and fully as loud as the sound of steam escaping from a locomotive as anything I could think of.

There was a Pine-Wood Sparrow singing in the pines. He was not a very good singer but good enough for me. It is a divine chant. So pure, so leisurely, so composed, certainly this bird is at peace with the world.

No small part of the day's pleasure was the ride itself. I had a fine black mare, full of spirit but gentle and an excellent saddle horse. I gave her the rein once, and we flew through the pines. Is anything more exhilarating than riding a horse at full speed? It brushes the cobwebs from one's mind.

The flowering dogwood blossoms are past the prime and the trees are commencing to leave. The scrub palmetto is in blossom.

MAR 7   Yesterday was an off day. I wrote letters, packed odds and ends, read and slept.

This morning, with Hovey Bell, I rode to the lake [Alachua Lake, now Payne's Prairie] at the mouth of "Sweetwater Branch" and there along the shore to and up Bivins Arm. I was in search of *Neofiber* [Round-tailed Muskrat] signs but I found only the remains of what was probably a nest. I wore shoes and did not go out into the deeper mud near the present border of the lake, the territory now suitable for the animal's occupation, but I thoroughly searched the drier ground which must recently have been as boggy as the ground which now bounds it. There were a number of possible places and if *Neofiber* was at all common here signs of its habitations could be easily observed.

Although the water in the lake is so low the islands in Biven's Arm are still islands, and therefore probably floating but I had no means of getting to them. We found three snakes, two "racers" and a King snake.

They were lying concealed in clumps of grass where we found them in poking around.

On returning Allison saw me riding through the town and as I dismounted I saw him in the distance, approaching. Before he came within hail I could hear him chuckling; his delight at meeting me was evidently too sincere to be questioned. He laughed all over, his eyes shone and he had so much to say in greeting that he fairly stuttered in his eagerness to say it. And I was so glad to see Allison. He was a living reminder of the ever glorious Suwannee days. I played Suwannee with him and said, "Allison, I have been over to the lake, let me show you one of the snakes I caught there"—motioning toward my pocket. Sure enough it was Allison and no one else. With a pleading, "No, sah," he beat a hasty retreat to the center of the road, saying, "Doan yer do it, now Mr. Chapman, doan yer do it," and returned only when I had assured him it was a false alarm. This was "fiendish."

I showed him some Suwannee pictures I had with me, and among others two in which he figured. His pleasure was childishly sincere. His remarks and manner must be seen and heard to be appreciated. He recoiled abruptly from the one of Dr. Allen skinning a snake and the action was too quick to be assumed. No one I am sure remembers the Suwannee trip with more pleasure than Allison does. It was with real regret I told him there was no possibility of our going again this year. He had just returned from a camp hunt west of the Suwannee at Fort Fannin, reaching the Gulf near the Steinhatchee. His party killed twelve deer, a wild cat, and a rattlesnake. He says Turkeys were common and he saw a number of Ivory-bills. He has marked the region so that he could take us to it. Of the rattlesnake he said, "I looked at der *rattles,* but I diden *tech* 'em."

No gun; no specimens; no skinning! This afternoon I wrote letters, read, packed trinkets, and studied ant-lions. They are interesting insects. Their lives are marked by constant deceit, their days stained with the blood of many victims. They live in ambush, a never-ending lying in wait. With wide open jaws they are ever on the alert to grasp their unfortunate prey. I watched one through a glass tonight as he caught a small ant I dropped in his pit. The ant seemed aware of danger and made haste to run up the slippery slopes, but the old villain below saw him and immediately shot up a tiny shower of sand. They were like good sized stones to the poor ant and, struck by several of them, he lost his footing and tumbled down the steep incline into the hungry jaws at the bottom of the pit. The struggle to escape was exciting and prolonged. The glass magnified both the contestants and the battle. It was a real tragedy. Several times out of pure pity I was tempted to interfere. Slowly the ant was drawn downward; the treacherous sand gave him no footing, he clasped and bit at small straws and sticks, but they too failed him. Finally his body disappeared, then his fore-limbs, and at last only his head was left above the surface. He seemed to be gasping, his antennae waved in the air, then he became quiet. There were only occasional movements and a few minutes later I took him out and he was dead.

I wish I had time to make a careful study of these ant-lions. Their life-histories are tales of murder, and intensely tragic. They are abundant in the undisturbed sand under the house. The largest pit I measured there was three inches in diameter at the surface and one and a quarter inches deep. The average was about two inches by three-quarters of an inch. I crawled under and captured a number which I have placed in a box of sand in order that I may easily watch them.

It is 11 P.M., more of the ant-lions anon—as I write the mocking-birds are singing disconnectedly. Half songs and snatches of song, no full-voiced inspired performances.

MAR 10   Gainesville to Corpus Christi. Today I left Gainesville en route to Corpus Christi, via Jacksonville and Montgomery, etc. At Waldo both umbrella and China trees were fully leaved and commencing to blossom. Orange trees were full of blossoms. We saw one tree 30 feet in diameter and of about the same height. At Jacksonville the season was not so far advanced as at Gainesville. The live-oaks showed no signs of new growth. March 11 at 10 A.M. we reached Montgomery, Ala.

[Frank Chapman spent the next seven weeks traveling to and from, and in Texas, collecting there.]

MAY 1   Pensacola to Jacksonville. I awoke this morning shortly after 6 o'clock at Pensacola. The town is apparently on a bluff which borders the bay. We skirted the bay for several miles, the pine-grown bluff arising (at our left) abruptly 20 feet. There is a wide sandy beach. I saw three gulls and two snipe, no other water birds and no tracks in the sand. We crossed the bay on a trestle about two miles long. On the east shore there are some marshes and some heavy growth, near Milton, a very pretty place.

The country from this point to within about twenty miles east of Tallahassee may be briefly described as a rolling and frequently hilly pine-land, a clay alternating with a sandy soil, numerous "bays" or "heads" of low growth mixed with the fine and heavy timber along the rivers and creeks and in the bottoms. From the Suwannee to Jacksonville there are flat pine lands.

De Funiak is in hilly pine-lands with a sandy soil. The "spring" is simply a "clear water" lake, perhaps ten acres in extent. There are a large hotel and some modern cottages here.

The Choctawatchee River bottom is half a mile or more in width. The river's banks are ten feet above its present level. The river is about one hundred yards wide. At Coryville the soil is red clay. There is a heavy forest growth with frequent beeches.

Chipley is a lumber town in the pines. At Cottondale there were pines and forests with some cypresses.

At Marianna there is a mixed growth of pines, cedars, and deciduous trees. I saw a few beeches. The soil is red clay, the country decidedly hilly and quite unlike anything I have ever seen before in Florida. Marianna is a very attractive place. Chipola creek, a short distance beyond, is a beautiful little limewater stream. I saw a limestone quarry near here. The bottoms are wooded and evidently wide. Cotton was about one inch above the ground. The Chattahoochee was ten feet below its banks but there were recent water-marks on neighboring trees ten feet above the ground. A wide river bottom with a fine growth of timber and creeks to the eastward. There is a heavy growth of timber on the west shore of the Ocklockonee, on the east, the town is situated on a pine-bluff. There are lumber mills here. The river is about seventy-five feet wide.

At Tallahassee there are red and yellow clay hills and an abundance of fine timber. The country here resembles that at Marianna and is equally unlike the peninsula of Florida. This region is well worth investigating during the breeding season. It differs so greatly from anything in the same latitude I think a corresponding change may be found in the fauna. Probably a southern extension of more northern breeding birds, if nothing else. Tallahassee and Marianna are the most beautiful places, in their way, that I have seen in Florida.

Several miles east of Tallahassee there is a wide hill-surrounded "prairie," traversed by small streams and later with a growth of young cypresses. I saw a few Little Blue Herons there and a flock of six adult and one immature White Ibises.

Twenty-five miles east of Tallahassee we have apparently passed the hilly country and are in flat or slightly rolling pine-lands.

At Lloyds there are fine old oaks and a mixed pine growth.

The Aucilla is about thirty feet wide with low banks grown with cypresses and pines.

The dear old Suwannee at this part of its anatomy is about seventy feet wide. The banks are rocky ledges of limestone and about ten to fifteen feet above the water. It really seemed as though this stream should make some sign of recognition as I crossed. The rest of the journey was through the pines.

[This journey ended in Gainesville where Frank Chapman again spent some time with his mother before escorting her to their New Jersey home and returning to his work at the Museum. He did not keep a journal of his activities, but we know he collected the Florida mole on May 4 and other mammals during his stay, so as usual he was not idle.

Of special interest in this journal for 1891 is the description of the level of water in Alachua Lake in the March 4 entry, particularly when compared with descriptions of the same lake in his 1886-87 journal and what he found on February 16, 1892, when he was again in Gainesville preparing for his first foreign expedition, a collecting trip to Cuba.]

EXCERPTS FROM CHAPMAN'S "FLORIDA — CUBA" JOURNAL
February — April, 1892

FEB 12　　At 9 P.M. on the 10th I left New York on my sixth trip to Gainesville. The journey was far less interesting than that of last year, first because the season in Florida had been an unusually severe one; second, the date is nearly three weeks earlier; third, it was comparatively warm when I left New York and comparatively cold when I reached Gainesville. All these causes and my familiarity with the route made the journey uneventful and the change of scene not especially noteworthy.

Feb. 11 at Richmond ice formed on pools of still water. Beyond a slight swelling of the buds of the larger trees in southern North Carolina, no signs of a new season were observed.

Feb. 12 maples, plums, and yellow jessamine were blooming near Jesup, Ga.

Feb 13   The mercury went to 32° this morning. Mockingbirds, which my mother says commenced to sing on the first, are nearly silent. I have heard only half-hearted performances. Ground Dove are cooing softly in the orange trees, and Blue Jay and Shrikes are heard. The Dove came to me when I imitated his call of four coos and I watched as with a slight swelling of the throat and forward movement of the head he answered me. The Shrike has the same old guttural whistle, changing to an ungreased squeaky note.

Woodcock are said to have appeared here in unusual numbers this year. They are generally rare.

Feb 16   Gainesville. A cold and bad weather have kept me quiet. Today with Wingate, drove to the "Sink." A great change has occurred there since my last visit; the subterranean opening, the closing or "clogging" of which in 1872 created Alachua Lake, has become clear and the Lake has disappeared. In its place is a prairie containing thousands of acres, dotted with grazing herds and bisected by a small stream which flows into the pool forming the sink. Here water marks show that the water has fallen about 12 feet leaving perhaps half an acre of water in the "sink" proper, and exposing some peculiar extensively water-worn limestone. This limestone is honey-combed and tunneled, in some places large blocks being supported by columns, and when these gave away there would result a cave-in. Two sinks are made by under ground streams.

The wild orange trees on the bluff are laden with buds two or three of which had opened. The dogwood is just coming into bloom, the red bud is blooming, maples are budding, yellow jessamine is at its height, prickly ash and gum are leaving.

Feb 17   What I supposed to be a large flock of grackles heard singing in the distance reminded me of escaping steam as the sound comes to one fitfully on the wind. A nearer approach proved it to be escaping steam. It is cold and unpleasant.

Feb 18   I left Gainesville this morning at 8 o'clock en route to Havana via Tampa, reaching the latter place at 7:30 after an uneventful journey.

The following notes of the character of the vegetation were made along the way.

Palatka bounded on west by pines with hammock and cypress growth along St. Johns. Satsuma, Sisco, Pamona, Crescent City and Seville are in the pines. At De Leon Springs is a zone of dense live?

oaks. Beresford pines. DeLand hammock for a mile. Sanford and Lake Monroe pines and palms. Altamonte pines. Kissimmee, pines, "open prairies" and cypress islands in the distance. Davenport, creek region, palm hammocks and cypress swamps. Lake Lock pines pine mouse. Davenport rolling pines and cypress on the creek. Haines City, rolling pines, lakes, prairie openings. Barton Junction [Now Lake Alfred], high rolling pines and lakes, then mostly pines to Tampa.

At Port Tampa, nine miles from Tampa, I boarded the steamer Olivette, 1400 tons, and at 10:30 P.M. we cast off and headed down Tampa Bay.

FEB 19   After a good night's rest I awoke this morning to find myself out of sight of land for the first time. A stiff breeze is blowing from off the port bow, and the intensely blue waters of the Gulf are capped with foamy, white crests. The sun shines brightly and in the distance these white caps look like a fleet of small sails. We have not sighted a single vessel, I have seen only one bird, a gull, and beyond an occasional bit of seaweed, or rollicking, jumping school of porpoises, the sea is apparently without life.

At 3 o'clock we sighted land, a small Key to the eastward of Key West and shortly after the spires and steeples of the city itself appeared on the horizon. Key after key came into view and I soon counted about 30 stretching in a broken line from east to west. Ringbill and Laughing Gulls, Royal Terns, Cormorants and Pelicans were not uncommon. We were boarded by a pilot and a man in a small cage-like affair which projected from the deck below the wheel-house made soundings as we passed over bars and shallows. From 12½ to 16 feet were the figures he called. We made fast to a pier where was an odd looking crowd of natives, Cubans, Conchs and Negroes, and hiring a victoria were driven about the town. Key West Island is seven miles long and two wide, the city with a population of twenty thousand is situated at the eastern end. There is very little soil and the hard uneven streets are natural coral-limestone. There are some substantial, handsome government and state buildings and a number of fine residences, but most of the houses are of one or two stories with single or double balconies. Cigar-making and sponge-fishing are the principal industries. The prevailing tree is the cocoa palm: these have been introduced and are seen everywhere. Other trees are Chinaberry, date-palms, sapodillo, gumbo limbo, mango, tamarind, banyan, and banana. Some of the houses are embounded with a luxuriant vegetation and have a truly tropical appearance. All these trees have apparently been introduced and the little I saw of indigenous growth was mangrove, prickly pear, and other low bushes and plants. Returning from our ride I called on and was very cordially greeted by Mr. J. S. Atkins whom I have long known through correspondence. We had a three hour talk on matters ornithological and I found him an intelligent and enthusiastic naturalist, whose time, unfortunately is much restricted by the duties of his position as cable operator. Mr. Atkins thinks that with some birds, e.g., Parula Warblers and Redstarts, the young come first in the fall; with others, e.g., Bachman's Warblers, young and old come together; and with others still; e.g., Black-throated Blue Warblers, the adult comes first. This of course is based solely on his experience here. I urged him to publish his observations and he expects to do so.

I was much surprised to learn from him that Mr. Cory passed through here a week ago en route to Havana and the Isle of Pines. While I was talking to Mr. Atkins a young man came to the counter and introduced himself as O. H. Tuthill of Rockville Centre, L. I., and stated that he had been there five years before while on a "taxidermist's" (!) trip in southwest Florida during which he had secured 130,000 birds! but that the fashion went back on him and he had been unable to dispose of them all. These birds were largely Terns and plume-birds Atkins says, and this man was connected with Batty. [J. H. Batty was a well-known plume hunter responsible for the wholesale slaughter of millions of Florida birds.]

We are casting off and will soon be on the last stretch for Havana. As we got from under the lee of the island and rounded its western end we encountered a strong easterly wind which blowing on our beam soon caused us to roll heavily in the trough of the sea. My room-mate Mr. Bailey who had been "taking notes" shortly remarked he "guessed he would omit taking notes this evening," and although he was "fortified with ginger cakes" the sea was too much for him and he passed a miserably sick night. It was my first experience with a rough sea and I thoroughly enjoyed it, strangely enough exulting when a more than usually prolonged roll sent all movable articles tumbling about the ship.

[For the next two months Frank Chapman collected in Cuba. He reported his experiences in some detail in *Autobiography of a Bird Lover.*]

CHAPMAN'S RETURN TO
FLORIDA FROM CUBA
April 1892

Apr 18   We passed Sandpoint Light, which turned to red as we crossed the shoal, at 8 p.m. and an hour later made fast to the pier at Key West. Our electric search-light was thrown on the two or three hundred people who came down to see the boat arrive, making them appear as though illuminated by a ray of some hidden sun. I at once went ashore and had a very pleasant two hour chat with Mr. Atkins whom I found, as before, at the Cable Office. He says the migration is backward and that there have been no real rushes as yet. He has taken two and observed six Bachman's Warblers.

Apr 19   We passed Sanibel Light this morning at 8 a.m. I was at breakfast and unfortunately did not see it. The Florida coast was about four miles off our starboard beam and with a glass I could see the shore distinctly. For a long distance south of Sarasota it is all pines with a fine white beach. A few old Brown Pelicans were the only birds observed.

At 1 p.m. we sighted Egmont Key Light and the Quarantine Station east of it. There were more water-birds in Tampa Bay than I have seen elsewhere; Laughing Gulls in adult plumage were common, one to two hundred being observed while a few were in immature dress. All the buoys and stakes were crowned with either Brown Pelicans or Cormorants and some were on the wing. Some of the channel posts have cross pieces nailed to them making five or six steps and occasionally each step would have its Cormorant. Half-way up the Bay to Port Tampa we sailed through a scattered school of devil-fish. There were at least fifty in twos, threes, or fours distributed over an area two hundred yards in width and six hundred in length. They were all near the surface, some with the back out of the water and the tips of the wings were frequently thrown up showing the white undersurface.

We reached Port Tampa at four o'clock and after a most cursory examination by the custom-house officers were passed and then with a Mr. James Gale of Palatka whom I met on board, I went to The Inn for dinner and to wait for our train which left at 7:20.

The steamer warehouses, the Inn and several smaller buildings are placed at the end of a pier a mile in length. There are many covered walks and lounging places, in fact the place has been made very attractive. The water is clear, about six feet in depth below the hotel, with a smooth sand bottom. Schools of fish, principally mullet, were almost constantly passing below us, a flock of fifty Laughing Gulls were actively feeding within thirty yards of me, sometimes hovering over the water or lightly dropping to pick up food from the surface, and about thirty Lesser Scaup Duck showed the confidence born of protection by swimming fearlessly around within easy gunshot. The sun was setting, a few white sails dotted the Bay, and it was very pleasant to sit down to an excellent dinner amid these natural surroundings.

In diving the Scaup Ducks gathered headway by jumping half out of the water and describing a semi-circle before they went under. I watched one flock of six feeding alone and sometimes they were all under at the same time.

Throwing some broken bread on the water it floated from the pier for thirty yards to five or six ducks feeding there. They snapped it up eagerly and by their rapid actions at once told their companions for a hundred yards around of the presence of food, with the result that they all flew in to partake of the feast.

Dr. George Trowbridge, whom I met at St. James [Pine Island] a few years ago, came in a small schooner and took the train for the north. He has been cruising for three months on the west coast as far south as Cape Sable and says he notices a marked increase in the number of bird-rookeries as compared with last year. There are, according to his observations, but five men engaged in shooting for milliners and these are natives.

Apr 20   At 5:30 A.M. the train left me at Palatka where I had five hours to wait before starting on the last stage of my journey to Gainesville. The first part of this time was passed in the woods north of the town, bordering the St. Johns. I thus had an excellent opportunity to make a superficial comparison of Florida's flora and fauna with those of Cuba. In the pines there was of course no chance for comparison, while in the hammocks the things which impressed me most were the absence of palms and the presence of magnolias, "Spanish" moss of which I saw only four bunches in Cuba, and the fresh, green foliage which many of the trees, leafless in the winter, had now assumed (e.g., cypress and maples).

As for the birds I heard only one voice which reminded me of Trinidad, the call of the Red-bellied Woodpecker. This was not so loud and continued as that of the West Indian Red-bellied Wood-pecker, and the Florida bird's *chuh, chuh,* is not uttered by the Cuban bird.

It was pleasant to hear songs again, the medley of the Mocker, the mellow whistle of Cardinals, the ripple of House Wrens, and the vigorous *Sweet William* of the Carolina Wrens never sounded better. Birds were abundant for Florida, but not more common than for Cuba. Besides the species mentioned I saw or heard one Great Blue Heron, two Ground Doves, one Flicker, one Hairy and one Pileated Wood-pecker, six or seven Crested Flycatchers, one Blue Jay, two Bobolinks flying over, several Redstarts, one Prairie Warbler, several Yellow-throats, two Swamp Sparrows, many Purple Martins, three Rough-winged Swallows, one Shrike, and two Catbirds (one singing). These were nearly all observed in one locality.

It is good to get back home. I took them somewhat by surprise. One of the pleasantest things about going away is coming back.

APR 21   I passed the day about home saying "Howdy" to my friends here, and dining at Dr. Phillips.

APR 22   I have had a delightful ride to my favorite haunt here, the cypress point on Newnan's Lake. It is very dry, there has been no rain for three months, but nevertheless the woods are at their best. The turkey-oaks in the pineries are clad in new suits of delicate green, the cypresses are fully feathered, and the vegetation denser than a winter's view gives one an idea of. In the pines were Blue-birds, Great-crested Flycatchers, Kingbirds, Red-bellied Woodpeckers, Pine Warblers, Summer Tanagers. I heard the *tree, tree* of a Brown-headed Nuthatch and the devout song of Pine Woods Sparrows. In the ham-mocks were Red-eyed Vireos, their song is not so loud or emphatic as that of the Black-whiskered Vireos, but quite as leisurely. There were several Acadian Flycatchers and a few Wood Pewees. I did not meet any flocks of migrants but they have never been common here so far as my experience goes, but that the migration has gone on just the same is evident. Down at the point I called for my friends the Barred Owls and they soon responded, alighting in the cypress over my head. A pretty picture they made sitting on a crooked limb within a few feet of each other, the lace-like foliage behind and moss dropped about them. The great black eyes looked human as they peered in-tently down upon me.

Doubtless they have a nest near by. Once they went through the laughing performance.

There were signs of a great swarm of mosquitoes similar to the ones I saw here last year, but now I record another page in their history, for attracted by this easy and abundant prey, numerous spiders of different species had woven webs of death over the shrubs and tree-limbs, and these gauzy mazes were filled with the remains of mosquitoes placed there as food for the young (eggs as yet) in the cocoons attached to suitable parts of the web.

I found my friend Mr. Robertson working in his new orange grove which shows, as do many of the trees, the effects of the recent frost. I asked him about the rookery of Little Blue Herons which was established near by last year and together we went to the spot. It is, or was, a button-bush pond in a dense hammock. Here there is very little water and the rookery is confined to the small space, about 100 feet square, where water still remains. Here there are at least fifty nests, some with as many as four eggs while others are not yet completed. The birds, about 100, were entirely blue except one which was pure white. Robertson says all the young birds are white.

With very few calls these birds circled about or alit on the tall trees; pines, magnolias, maples, near by and waited for us to withdraw.

Last year when there was more water there were five times as many birds there.

Not far away, Robertson tells me, is a nesting Great Blue Heron with young ready to leave, and also a nest of the Anhinga.

APR 23   I went over the same ground today repeating the experiences of yesterday.

The owls came down as before. The laughing performance seems to be merely the result of excitement and was accompanied by no unusual motions.

When I approached the Heron Rookery, I could hear a low grunting as the birds talked to one another.

APR 25   Today I went to Sugarfoot Prairie. It was very warm, but the sun's rays are not so intense as in Cuba.

I have never seen the Prairie so dry, in fact there is no water at all, while in only one of the surrounding ponds was there any water, this was the one to the westward where there was about quarter of an acre.

Six young Ward's Herons were the only herons seen. The absence of water in their old nesting places has evidently driven the numerous Little Blue Herons that used to breed here to a more favorable resort.

A flock of 30 male Bobolinks was feeding on the Prairie. Beyond the *chink* note they were silent.

A Florida Yellowthroat was singing in the thicket at the road side. The song seems to me to be clearer and more musical than that of the Northern Yellowthroat; it is a low ventriloquial particularly at the beginning when the bird seems to be far away, but comes out louder at its conclusion.

The song of the Summer Tanager so closely resembles that of the Robin that I could not be sure which of the two species was singing. The Tanager, however, does not sing so continuously, its song is disconnected.

I saw one female Robin. It was apparently in good condition.

MAY 1   I reached Washington at 11 P.M. Apr. 29. The next day was passed at the Departments and today I have been with Mr. Ridgway all the morning at his new home three miles from the city and from there went to Dr. Merriam's with whom I dined.

MAY 2   Left Washington last night at 11 and reached the museum at 8:30. My vacation is over.

7

Progress, Programs, & Pelicans

URING THE SUMMER OF 1892 the American Museum of Natural History planned an experiment. Beginning in January, 1893, they proposed to present to the people of New York City a series of lectures, free to the public, on the natural sciences. The lectures were so favorably received that they have been repeated annually ever since.

Frank Chapman gave the first series of lectures, four talks on the birds of the New York area, and they were his introduction to the lecture platform. From then on for the rest of his life FMC was in demand as a popular lecturer. His enthusiasm for his subject ignited response from the most lethargic audience and his simplicity of delivery made the most complicated facts easy to understand. The man who held the attention of a group of erudite scientists could also hold a group of children spellbound. I know because I heard him. The success of the afternoon lectures for adults encouraged the museum to introduce morning lectures for children. At one of them I first saw Mr. Chapman and his wonderful lantern slides, I think in the winter of 1912 or 1913.

FMC filled speaking engagements from one end of the country to the other and as far west as Minneapolis and St. Louis during the years before World War I speaking to his audiences of familiar and exotic birds. Always, until adequate laws and the means to enforce them were a fact, he asked for help in rescuing and conserving birds whose very survival was endangered by the craze of the women of the so-called civilized world for wild bird feathers on their hats. The illustrations for the lectures were lantern slides made from his own photographs, many of them taken in Florida.

The 1890's were a busy time for FMC. Traveling by ship, train, horseback, muleback, and various horse and mule drawn vehicles he traveled and collected in Texas, Trinidad, Mexico, and Florida, and spent allotted time at the Museum in New York. During these ten years he also published seventy-three scientific papers and two books, *Handbook of Birds of Eastern North America, with Keys to the spe-*

cies and Descriptions of their Nests and Eggs (12mo, 427 pp., D. Appleton and Co.) in 1895, and *Bird Life: A Guide to the Study of our Common Birds* (12mo, 269 pp., D. Appleton and Co.) in 1897.

The first of these books was also the first practical field guide to birds in America. Written in simple, non-technical language, the *Handbook of Birds* was the most noteworthy contribution to the popularization of bird study ever made. For the first time anyone who knew how to read could, by following a simple key, identify the birds he saw and learn something of their habits and distribution. This book was the forerunner, the prototype, or one might say the "type-specimen," of all the nature guide books to come. First, "The Reed Guides," then Roger Tory Peterson's wonderful "Field Guide" series, the Audubon Guides, and even the little "Golden Guides" are sincerely flattering Frank M. Chapman by imitation. These more modern guides had an enormous success because FMC's *Handbook of Birds* broke the trail for them. It aroused a popular interest in birds which has grown to be today's major American sport of bird watching.

The *Handbook of Birds* was the standard equipment of every bird student, lay or professional, for forty years and is still used for reference some seventy years after the first edition appeared.

Frank Chapman and Fannie Miller Bates Embury were married on February 24, 1898, and he took his bride to honeymoon at Ma Latham's place, Oak Lodge, opposite Micco on the Indian River. It was his first return to the lodge since the spring of 1889, but he remembered it as an ideal spot for a naturalist's wedding journey. Charley Latham's old sloop, the "Lida," met the Chapmans at Titusville and they cruised around Merritt Island where Mrs. Chapman prepared her first specimen, a Long-billed Marsh Wren, soon followed by the "rare and delicate" Dusky Seaside Sparrow. Mrs. Chapman started her lifetime of assisting her husband in field work and exploration during the two days they spent at Merritt Island before proceeding south to Oak Lodge, and during the weeks that followed.

Brown Pelicans were nesting on Pelican Island nine miles south of Oak Lodge. The Chapmans took the "Lida," anchored off the island, and began the most thorough study of the home life of the Brown Pelican ever made.

The object of this first trip was a series of pelicans from egg to adult to show the development of the birds in a display at the American Museum of Natural History. So Frank Chapman approached the birds and the island he protected for posterity with a gun in one hand,

"Snap Shots at Prominent Ornithologists. No. II."

(Cartoon of FMC by Walter K. Fisher [1878-1953] from *Condor*, March 1901.)

but he used it only when the light was insufficient for the camera he carried in the other hand. In only four days and four nights he collected the series needed by the Museum for a habitat display, and the pictures, remarkable for the 1890's, were published in *Bird Studies with a Camera*. This book gave hints and instructions to bird photographers. It was published in 1900, and while the photographic equipment recommended is obsolete, the Pelican pictures could have been made during this year's nesting.

In 1900 FMC returned to Pelican Island with a new battery of cameras and no gun. He took more pictures showing Brown Pelican flight and wrote for *Bird-Lore* (Vol. III, 1901) an article on Pelican Island which ends:

To yield to the temptation to redescribe the wonders of Pelican Island would only result in a repetition of what I have already written. I may, however, state that this second visit fully confirms my opinion that Pelican Island during nesting time is by far the most fascinating place it has ever been my fortune to see in the world of birds. But this estimate of its charms only serves to increase the desire that this colony of remarkable birds may be preserved. The land is very accessible, the Florida law affords Pelicans no protection, and a party of quill-hunters might easily kill practically all the inhabitants of Pelican Island within a few days. The loss would be irreparable, and it is to be especially noted, would not be confined to the vicinity, but would affect the whole east coast of Florida, there being, so far as is known, no other breeding colony of Pelicans on the Atlantic coast of the peninsula.

There is doubtless no area of similar extent in the world so well adapted to the wants of certain aquatic birds as Florida; and if today it were inhabited by even one-tenth of the myriads of Herons, Egrets, Spoonbills, and other large and conspicuous birds which animated its lakes and marshes thirty years ago, the marvel of its wild life would be known the world around and prove of greater interest to tourists than any existing attraction in the state. If Floridians doubt this valuation of birds which they have been accustomed to regard as worthless, or at so much per plume, let them observe the excitement occasioned among the tourists on a St. John's or Ocklawaha steamer by the now rare appearance of White Herons within a short distance of the boat.

The birds have gone, and what has the state received? Proportionately nothing. Here and there a poor hunter, or a curio dealer, has made a few dollars, but most of the killing has been done by, or under the immediate inspiration of, northern dealers, and Florida's loss has been their gain.

There are still scattered colonies of these birds in the less accessible parts of Florida, and if the natives of the state ever open their eyes to the indisputable fact that a living bird is of incalculably greater value to them than a dead one, they may perhaps take some steps to defend their rights, and by passing and enforcing proper laws, put an end to the devastations of the northern plume agents, who have robbed their state of one of its greatest charms.

In April, 1905, Frank Chapman made his third visit to Pelican Island. This time he moved in with the birds. He had developed a blind from which he could observe and photograph without being seen. Under a large umbrella on a stick like a beach parasol with a ventilation hole in its top and a slit denim bag that fell to the ground draped over it, Frank Chapman watched and used his camera through peek holes. He made day and night observations in 1905 and returned in March of 1908 to repeat the experiment and add to his data and take the first cinematograph or moving pictures of Pelicans.

In *Camps and Cruises of an Ornithologist* FMC gives a very complete account of life in a Brown Pelican colony. The book was published in November, 1908, by D. Appleton and Company. No one before or since has made such an exhaustive study of Brown Pelicans, and Frank Chapman's intimacy with them and interest in their welfare bore far reaching consequences. As a result of his published and publicized distress over their welfare, in 1900 every effort was made to gain control of Pelican Island and have a warden appointed to guard the birds. Frank Chapman appealed to his friend, Theodore Roosevelt, and thus came into being the first "Federal Bird Reservation" by declaration of the President of the United States. It was the forerunner of hundreds of wildlife reservations throughout this country.

The following is an excerpt from Frank M. Chapman's mother's scrap book of newspaper clippings:

THE PRESIDENT'S BUSY DAY

Has Six Guests at Luncheon—Five More in the Afternoon

Oyster Bay, Aug. 7.—President Roosevelt had many visitors today. In addition to Secretary of War Wright, Colonel Hugh L. Scott, superintendent of the Military Academy at West Point, and National Chairman Hitchcock, H. L. Higginson and John Perkins, both of Boston, and Gerritt Forbes, a big game hunter, arrived. All were the President's guests at luncheon.

During the afternoon Mr. Roosevelt expected Father John C. York and Messrs. Heckscher, Conklin and Vernon of Huntington, Long Island, who were to drive over to Sagamore Hill to pay their respects to the President.

Frank M. Chapman, ornithologist and author, was expected to reach Sagamore Hill late in the afternoon and be the guest of the President overnight.

Jenesse Richardson (1857-93), preparateur and taxidermist at the American Museum of Natural History from 1886 until his death, worked with Frank Chapman to create realistic displays of birds and mammals in their natural backgrounds with their young. After Richardson's death the work continued with John Rowley's cooperation. They were not the first museum people to try habitat groups. A primitive attempt was made by Rembrandt Peale (1778-1860) in his Philadelphia Museum, and the British Museum in London had also done something of the kind.

William H. Werner of Nazareth, Pennsylvania, a highly skilled taxidermist, made some very primitive groups of birds as early as 1868 and in 1870 created a habitat group. He displayed a number of such groups at the Philadelphia Centennial in 1876.

Mr. Frazer, Keeper of Zoology at the British Museum, said in a letter to me on September 14, 1964, "Probably the first pictorial mounting of birds was done at Ludlow at about 1870 and the first man who produced what we now know as habitat groups was E. T. Booth of Brighton."

I do not know if Mr. E. T. Booth's groups still exist, but William Werner's work may be seen at the Regar Memorial Museum of Natural History in Anniston, Alabama.

The first modern habitat group reproducing an actual scene from the wild was the brain child of Frank Chapman. Acting as his own photographer and collector he brought from the field the materials and pictures which with the cooperation of John Rowley, head of the taxidermy department of the American Museum of Natural History, and Bruce Horsfall, the artist, recreated parts of the American wilderness in museum halls.

A section of Bird Rock in the St. Lawrence with its nesting birds and a reproduction of Pelican Island, Florida, with Pelicans in all stages of development were the first of the modern habitat groups of North American birds. These and other groups have backgrounds painted by Bruce Horsfall. Later display backgrounds were painted by Louis Agassiz Fuertes. Recreating an actual scene in nature with the cooperation of artist, photographer, scientist, collector, taxidermist, and preparateur is a normal procedure in museum techniques today, but was an innovation at the turn of the century.

Other groups from Florida followed in the displays of the American Museum of Natural History. The 1930 guide leaflet listed:

1. Anhinga, or Water Turkey in Florida, site Bonnet Lake with surrounding cypress and palmettoes 17 miles west of Lake Lucie.

2. A Florida Rookery, Egrets at Cuthbert Rookery in the Everglades.

3. Sandhill Cranes on Kissimmee Prairie.

A Florida Great Blue Heron was also listed but without a site. It was the oldest of the groups and was not done with the camera, reproducing an actual Florida landscape.

Frank Chapman was the first man who ever produced an entire hall devoted to habitat groups. This historic hall suffered from the ravages of time, but it has been renovated and many of the old groups have been preserved and restored.

To celebrate Frank Chapman's hundredth birthday, the Museum opened the Frank M. Chapman Memorial Hall of North American birds in June, 1964. On display are twenty-seven habitat exhibits.

From Frank M. Chapman's mother's scrap book as it appeared in the *Gainesville Sun* [circa 1903]:

"A SMART YOUNG AUTHOR"

"Son of a Gainesville Lady Receives
Recognition as a Fine Writer"

The *Nashville American* of January 18th contains a very interesting sketch of Frank M. Chapman, author of *The Color Key to North American Birds*, which appears as follows:

Frank M. Chapman, author of *The Color Key to North American Birds*, just published by Doubleday, Page and Company, more than any other man, perhaps is teaching people to know birds. One of the foremost living ornithologists and a curator in the American Museum of Natural History, New York City, going to some obscure corner of the world each year to get new birds, photographs and information, he is also one of the most delightful literary writers and lecturers on the subject, finding time with it all, to edit a magazine about birds —the illustrated *Bird-Lore*. His private collection of photographs of American birds in their natural haunts is the largest and most remarkable in the world. The new Color Key, which is issued by the publishers of *Country Life in America*, to which also Mr. Chapman is a contributor, is a sort of illustrated dictionary, ingeniously arranged so that one may learn a bird's name with the least possible difficulty.

Mr. Chapman is a son of Mrs. M. A. Chapman of this city. He is a young man of wonderful talent, and is connected with the Museum of Natural History in New York City. His wife and family are now here, and he is expected some time during the season.

An article printed in the *Gainesville Sun* in 1905, which was found in Frank Chapman's mother's scrap book:

APPRECIATED GIFT TO THE LIBRARY
From Frank M. Chapman, the Eminent Ornithologist.

PUBLIC LIBRARY FORTUNATE

The Recipient of Popular Works on
Bird Life From the Author—Also
Many Gifts From Mrs. Chapman,
Who is a Winter Visitor Here.

Frank M. Chapman of New York, the distinguished ornithologist, associate curator of the American Museum of Natural History, has done Gainesville the honor of presenting to the Public Library his popular work, *Bird-Life, A Guide to the Study of Our Common Birds,* and his latest work, *Color Key to North American Birds.* Than these books no more practical guides to bird identification are before the public, and they are increasing greatly their author's already wide-reaching influence in the study of ornithology. It is Mr. Chapman's idea in these works to create a popular interest in our common birds, and to help the bird-lover to name birds amid their natural surroundings. This first step taken, the delights of the resulting acquaintance with our feathered friends are never-ending.

Florida may well be grateful to Mr. Chapman for the attention he is drawing to the State through his interesting lectures on Florida bird-life, which he is delivering throughout our own country and abroad. A Massachusetts paper comments on the rare and beautiful views of Florida scenery, of the moss-hung live oaks, of the pines and palms and tropical growth which were thrown upon the scene as he lectured in Springfield for the tenth time on his recent platform tour in New England.

Mr. Chapman's extensive knowledge of birds is founded on close observation of them in their haunts, and studying with camera and blind he penetrates farther than any other into their surroundings and brings away accurate information of their habits and life. His lectures are illustrated with many lantern slides from photographs which he thus obtains, and the coloring of these slides is most exquisitely done by his mother, much of it at her Florida home here. The rare excellence of these slides is a matter of press comment.

The volumes mentioned were presented to the library through the influence of his mother, Mrs. M. A. Chapman, long a winter resident of Gainesville. The many friends she has made here by her charming personality quite claim her as one of the city's own. She, herself, has given to the library complete volumes of *Bird-Lore,* the magazine devoted to ornithology, originated by her son. This is the official organ of the Audubon societies of America, and it is edited by Mr. Chapman. He is also president of the Linnaean Society of New York, and one of four American members of the British Ornithologists' Union.

An article from the *Springfield Union* found in Frank Chapman's mother's scrap book. Undated—probably circa 1905:

SIGN SCARED BIRDS

Frank M. Chapman Describes Great Blue Heron and Brown Pelican

In his stereopticon lecture in High School hall last night, under the auspices of the Museum of Natural History, Frank M. Chapman, the noted ornithologist and naturalist, again demonstrated his ability to attract an audience far larger than attends other scientific lectures in this city. For those who love bird life and the woods Mr. Chapman will always have something fascinating to say, for he is full of his subject, has a happy manner of expression and spares neither time nor hardship to get first-hand information about his feathered friends.

In the lecture last night Mr. Chapman presented the results of his recent investigations among the birds of Florida, with particular attention to the hitherto ill-understood brown pelican. No small part of the success of the naturalist's lecture was due to the lantern slides with which he illustrated his subject. These were not only very clear in outline as all good slides must be, but they had the rarer excellency of portraying color schemes in a manner which was most realistic.

Mr. Chapman found it necessary to preface the main part of his lecture with a description of the geography and scenery of Southern Florida, which he rightly presumed were not well known to the majority of his hearers. He portrayed the innumerable quiet streams and lagoons of the Central region of the State and described the flora without becoming tiresome. Then he was ready for the birds.

He gave most of his time to descriptions of the great blue heron and the brown pelican. He proved himself familiar with the home life of these birds which most Northerners have barely heard of, and amused the audience with a narration of the process by which the parent birds feed their young, it developed that these birds had employed the predigested food idea in their nests long before the chemist had dreamed of it in his laboratory.

The great home of the brown pelican, the so-called Pelican Island, Mr. Chapman most vividly described. His sketch showed the birds in every stage of growth and in all their occupations. An interesting incident mentioned by him related to the result of President Roosevelt's order to make Pelican Island a Government reservation. It seems that as soon as naturalists obtained the grant from the President they lost no time in having a huge "No Trespass" sign hung up in front of the accustomed landing place on the island. The result of this sign was to scare away the birds completely, so that the island was perfectly bare the next year. At the beginning of the second season somebody by observation saw that the sign had been taken too literally by the birds. Upon its removal the birds returned to the island again in their thousands and ten thousands.

Frank Chapman recorded another somewhat sad visit to Pelican Island in April 1914 in *Bird-Lore*. Surrounded by 1,600 (as counted by the warden) dead and dying young of the year, FMC watched a thousand healthy adults heedlessly resting and bathing on the other end of the island. He spent a miserable day in mid-February trying to find out what had happened. Examination of the dead and dying showed that they were suffering from starvation. Why they starved is still an ornithological mystery.

Frank Chapman was to be troubled over the welfare of the Brown Pelicans again. During World War I the fishermen declared war on the Pelicans as competitors, and T. Gilbert Pearson was called in to analyze their food. It proved to be fish inedible to man and with the help of wardens the Pelicans were saved.

Today Frank Chapman would be very happy about the Brown Pelicans. They have their original home at Pelican Island and the Brevard Reservation at Mosquito Lagoon, which was declared a Wildlife Refuge on October 21, 1925, by President Coolidge. They are also nesting on the Halifax River and wherever they are, they are protected by law and also by custom because they are loved. They are so secure that in many places they have become outright beggars waiting on every wharf for a handout from fishermen.

8

Frank Chapman in the Twentieth Century

*B*ORN IN THE YEAR 1900 were a new century and Frank M. Chapman, Jr., as well as the annual Christmas Census, the Florida Audubon Society, the book *Bird Studies with a Camera*, and the first conference of state Audubon Societies which led to the founding of the National Audubon Society. Except for the twentieth century, Frank Chapman was more or less responsible for all these fledglings and all but Frank Jr. were announced in *Bird-Lore* which was celebrating its first birthday.

On page 192 in *Bird-Lore* for 1900, FMC wrote, "It is not many years ago that sportsmen were accustomed to meet on Christmas Day, 'choose sides,' and then, as representative of the two bands resulting, hie them to the fields and woods on the cheerful mission of killing practically everything in furs or feathers that crossed their path—if they could.

"These exceptional opportunities for winning the laurels of the chase were termed 'side hunts,' and reports of the hundreds of non-game birds which were sometimes slaughtered during a single hunt were often published in our leading sportsmen's journals, with perhaps a word of editorial commendation for the winning side. We are not certain that the side hunt is wholly a thing of the past, but we feel assured that no reputable sportsman's journal of today would venture to publish an account of one, unless it were to condemn it; and this very radical change of tone is one of the significant signs of the times.

"Now *Bird-Lore* proposes a new kind of Christmas side hunt in the form of a Christmas bird census, and we hope that all our readers who have the opportunity will aid us in making it a success by spending a portion of Christmas Day with the birds and sending a report of their 'hunt' to *Bird-Lore* before they retire that night. Such reports should be headed by the locality, hour of starting and of returning, character of the weather, direction and force of the wind, and the temperature; the latter taken when starting. The birds observed should then be added,

149

following the order in which they are given in the A. O. U. 'Check List,' with, if possible, the exact or approximate number of individuals of each species observed."

Twenty-seven people from twenty-five widely divergent places responded to the call for a Christmas bird-census in 1900. In 1964, thousands of people took part in 688 counts reported upon by the Audubon Society in *Audubon Field Notes* which, like *Audubon Magazine,* is a descendant of *Bird-Lore.* The subtitle of the April, 1964, number of *Audubon Field Notes* is "Sixty-Fourth Christmas Bird Count." In 1900 and for many years after, the annual report of the bird census was edited by Frank Chapman in Florida, first in Gainesville, and after 1912, at the Bretton Inn in Ormond Beach. In 1964, the hundredth anniversary of FMC's birth, the report of the bird census was edited by Allan D. Cruickshank at Cocoa, Florida. The National and the Florida Audubon Societies have grown mightily, even as the Christmas bird census, since the call to count and be counted was published in *Bird-Lore.* The counts have made a very real contribution to our knowledge of bird populations of the United States and Canada.

Another momentous event (in FMC's eyes) of the year 1900 was his appearance as a Lowell Lecturer in Boston. An invitation from the Lowell Institute to lecture was a sought-for honor and rarely was a lecturer asked to return, but FMC was invited to give a second series in 1907. His first series of eight lectures entitled "Birds in Nature" was given on Monday and Thursday evenings at 7:45 P.M. starting on March 19, 1900, and ending on April 12, 1900 (and FMC worked on Pelicans in Florida that year, too!). The second series of lectures called, "The Distribution of North American Birds" was given on Friday and Saturday evenings at 8:00 P.M. starting on February 8, 1907, and ending on March 2, 1907. Again the lectures were illustrated with lantern slides made from pictures FMC had taken himself, many of them in Florida.

In his *Autobiography of a Bird Lover* FMC made two errors in his account of his Lowell Lectures. After thirty-three years his memory for dates was shaky and he thought he had given his first series in 1897 and his second in 1900, but the Boston newspapers reported the facts and the *Boston Evening Transcript* cannot be denied.

In 1901, Frank M. Chapman was advanced to Associate Curator of the Department of Birds and Mammals at his beloved American Museum of Natural History. In 1908, he was appointed curator in charge of birds and in 1920, when birds and mammals were finally separated, he served as the first curator and chairman of the new division. He remained Chairman of the Department of Birds until he retired in 1942. During all these years a number of young men who were to be the distinguished scientists of the future did their first early work in ornithology under his tutelage. Dr. Robert Cushman Murphy who followed FMC as Chairman of the Department of Birds and Dr. James Chapin, authority on and curator of African birds, were among the first. Others who worked in the Department of Birds during FMC's administration are Dr. Austin Rand, now Curator of Birds at the Chicago Natural History Museum; Dr. Ernst Mayr, now Director of the Museum of Comparative Zoology at Harvard; and Dr. Dean Amadon, who as a youngster knew FMC only during his last five years as chairman and now holds that position himself.

Two books, *The Warblers of North America* in 1907, and *Camps and Cruises of an Ornithologist* in 1908, added to FMC's reputation as an author as well as a scientist. Ninety-six articles and papers, both technical and popular, were written between 1900 and 1912 when a revised edition of *Color Key to North American Birds* and a revised edition of the *Handbook of Birds of Eastern North America* appeared. At the time of his death in 1945 his bibliography included seventeen books and over 200 bulletins and articles without counting his editorials and other contributions to *Bird-Lore* and all the letters and journals in this book. The greater part of this prolific output was written in long hand.

An amazing man! Curating, lecturing, also publishing, editing, and managing a bi-monthly magazine, writing, campaigning for bird protection, creating exhibits, assisting fledgling ornithologists, pursuing photography in a professional manner, guiding the destiny of a number of professional organizations, and exploring at home and abroad. For relaxation FMC turned to music. Although his only performances were his perfect mimicry of birds and accomplished whistling, his perfect ear brought great joy to him all his life. This was enhanced in his later years when the musician was Frank Jr., a Metropolitan Opera baritone, or Mrs. Frank Jr., nee Gladys Swarthout.

FMC's visits to Florida in the early 1900's were necessarily short, even the 1900, 1903, 1904, and 1905 visits with the Pelicans, but the results of all were spectacular. His 1905 expedition with his wife and a guide named Adam Summerlin was, after Pelican Island, from St. Lucie westward toward Fort Bassenger on the Kissimmee River. Here were the nesting grounds of Anhingas and a cypress swamp heronry. They yielded material for two fine habitat groups and the first observations of the feeding and care of young Great Blue Herons. FMC would have contributed much more to the knowledge of their breeding and that of the Water Turkeys if the expedition had not ended in a blaze. A spark from the camp fire ignited the paraffin coated canvas tent and the Chapmans' entire camping outfit was enfolded in flames. Mrs. Chapman managed to snatch the exposed photographic plates from the open end of the tent and to carry them to safety. FMC does not say so but I'm sure a camera, a gun, and an umbrella blind were also saved for he was returning from his morning's work when the flames flared up. He had been photographing birds from the blind. He himself said he never moved about the heronry without a gun after his first morning among the herons when he found himself sharing an islet only six feet in diameter with a very large cottonmouth moccasin.

In 1907 Mr. Chapman was in the Bahamas in March (after finishing the "Lowell Lectures"), Florida in April, South Carolina in May, Saskatchewan in June, and in the Canadian Rockies in July. In each place he photographed breeding birds and made studies for habitat groups.

In 1908, FMC penetrated the "Great Mangrove Swamp" which separates the Everglades from Florida Bay and visited famed Cuthbert Rookery. His objective was material, photographs, and paintings for a habitat group of Roseate Spoonbills and Egrets. Cuthbert Rookery was, he believed, the last stronghold of these vanishing "plume-birds," made nearly extinct by plume hunters working to supply the millinery trade, as shown in the following account. This is a clipping in FMC's mother's scrap book, evidently from a New York paper, summer, 1908.

SNAPSHOTS OF RARE BIRDS

Frank Chapman Back From The Cuthbert Rookery

Last stronghold of the Snowy Egret and the Roseate Spoonbills and the Cause of the Murder of Guy Bradley—Moving Pictures of Pelican Life Shown.

Frank M. Chapman, the "bird man" at the American Museum of Natural History, has just returned from a visit to Cuthbert rookery, the last stronghold of the birds in the Florida forests. He saw there the first Snowy Egrets he has seen in twenty years and more Roseate Spoonbills than he ever saw before. But it is perhaps the last time naturalists will ever see it alive with birds. By the time it has been shot up a few more times it will be as silent and empty as all other unprotected rookeries have become. This is why Mr. Chapman and Mr.

Fuertes, the museum artist, visited it and spent some days in trees to secure sketches and photographs which will preserve in one of the museum groups a picture of the rookery of Florida.

The Cuthbert rookery has escaped so far because of its inaccessibility. To reach it the party was obliged to abandon the sharpie, a species of schooner-rigged craft drawing only two and a half feet of water, seven miles from shore on account of shoal water. Then by pushing and otherwise propelling a small boat they were able to reach shore in another five hours. From shore they could just see the sharpie's mast, so far away was it. They landed on Cape Sable, the extreme southern tip of Florida, covered with a waste of mangrove swamps.

It took them five hours longer to reach their destination, poling through little streams scarce wider than their boat and passing a series of six or seven lakes, which eventually brought them to Cuthbert Lake by a channel so effectually hidden that no one could ever reach it without a guide. The lake and the rookery were named after the "plumer" who discovered them. The first time he shot up the rookery he got $1,800 worth of plumes.

It became known to the naturalists and bird lovers that here was a wonderful primitive breeding ground of bird life, the last stand of the Snowy Egrets and Roseate Spoonbills, and they tried to protect it. From that ensued the most famous human tragedy of the war in which so many bird tragedies have been enacted. They employed Guy Bradley as warden to enforce the bird protection law in the Cuthbert rookery. There is no fresh water anywhere in the mangrove swamp, and at intervals the warden had to make a long and toilsome journey out to bring in his drinking water. One of his trips was watched and timed, and when he got back he was able to walk around the rookery on the bodies of the Snowy Egret mothers shot for the white marriage plume, which they wear at no other time but the breeding season, while the trees were full of starved or starving young birds.

Guy Bradley was a native of the nearest village, Flamingo, and well known and popular throughout the whole country. Nevertheless he was decoyed outside his house at Flamingo one night and shot at his own door, and a family of little children were left to grow up orphans. The National Audubon Society employed the best counsel and spent money freely to convict the murderer of Bradley, who did not deny the shooting, but it was impossible. No jury in the region would convict him. All the society could do was buy a home and furnish a pension for Guy Bradley's widow, which it did.

"No," said Mr. Chapman, "I don't think those people there are worse than anybody else, any more lawless, or any more dishonest. It is simply a question of no law enforcement. There is no law en-

forcing body in Flamingo; no police, no courts nearer than Key West,
ninety miles away by water, no mail route even. There is a post office,
but no regular delivery of mails. When a boat happens to be coming
over from Key West, it brings the mail bags; otherwise they don't
come. In such a condition as that each man is the regulator of his
own conduct. There is nothing to constrain him to obey the laws if
he doesn't want to. Egret plumes are now worth double their weight
in gold. There is no community sufficiently law-abiding to leave a
bank vault unmolested if it were left unprotected. This is just the
same. We have given up. We can't protect it and the rookery will
have to go."

Mr. Chapman spent several days in a tree, the ground being covered with water, photographing from his blind. One Louisiana heron,
in particular, posed for him most courteously. The bird lit directly
in front of his camera and preened and posed most enticingly in a
dozen different attitudes, every one of which was snapped. Unusual
photographs he secured also of the rare and exceedingly shy Roseate
Spoonbills, which in 1858 were so plentiful that the naturalist Bryant
said he saw plumers kill sixty a day on Pelican Island.

The photographs of these two birds which he secured are probably the best which have ever been made or can ever be made, for
at Cape Sable the visitors heard that a party of plumers was just ready
to go in and shoot up the rookery, but decided to wait till the naturalists got out. This expedition has probably already taken place, and no
one knows whether the rookery still exists or not. All the character-
istic vegetation was brought back, and the group will show the white
ibis, the little white egret, the large white egret, the roseate spoonbill,
the Louisiana heron and the little blue heron in their habitat. . . .

About the first of next month Frank M. Chapman's book *Camps
and Cruises of an Ornithologist* will be published. For the past eight
years Mr. Chapman has devoted all of each nesting season of the birds
to making the field studies from which he has constructed the series
of bird groups at the American Museum of Natural History. In pursuit of this object Mr. Chapman has traveled over 60,000 miles, from
the Bahamas to Canada, from the Atlantic to the Pacific, and even into
England. The story of those eight years of travel is told in the forth-
coming volume, which will contain besides over 250 pictures of bird
life taken from Mr. Chapman's photographs.

FMC had made three previous attempts to reach Cuthbert. In 1904
the Audubon warden, Guy Bradley, stopped him en route at Tavernier

Creek to tell him the rookery had been "shot-out" and the surviving birds had fled. In 1905 the fiery end of his Kissimmee expedition and an appointment to attend the International Ornithological Congress in England in June prevented him from going on to Cuthbert. This may have been fortuitous, for the man who put a bullet through Guy Bradley that year had been waiting his chance for three months, and had FMC lingered, his career might well have ended then and there. He might now be known as a "martyr to the habitat group" just as Guy Bradley is known as a "martyr to millinery." In 1907, FMC says he could not reach Cuthbert during the breeding season because he lingered too long in the Bahamas.

When FMC finally arrived at Cuthbert Rookery in 1908, he was guided by Guy Bradley's brother, Louis, and accompanied by Arthur Cleveland Bent who in 1903 was the first ornithologist to reach this last nesting place of plume-birds in Florida. A most important member of the party was Louis Agassiz Fuertes, one of America's greatest bird artists and FMC's well loved friend, colleague, and companion on many an expedition.

Louis Fuertes painted the backgrounds for the Cuthbert Rookery habitat group in the American Museum, which was created from photographs taken by FMC, but the birds themselves were not collected in Florida where so very few survived. The Roseate Spoonbills family was brought back in 1910 from Pajaro Island in Mexico where the birds were still plentiful.

In 1909, Frank Chapman had his last recorded contact with Ma Latham and Oak Lodge on the Indian River opposite Micco. In a letter to FMC from William Beebe dated May 24, the naturalist says, "Mrs. Latham's troubles have reached a climax," and goes on to explain that she is taking care of five little girls left by her daughter, Queenie, and her crops have failed leaving her in debt. William Beebe was raising money to send Ma Latham a surprise gift from all the artists and naturalists who had stayed at one time or another at Oak Lodge. Surely, the Chapmans made a generous contribution, but one cannot help wondering what became of Grandma Latham and her five little granddaughters and where was her happy-go-lucky husband, Charley, and did the Chapmans ever again visit the place where they spent their honeymoon?

Until World War I, FMC's travels extended farther each year into Central and South America, but Florida was part of the annual program and Gainesville a regular stop until the year 1912 when his mother died. The *Gainesville Sun* for August 23, 1912, reported, "Mrs. M. C. Bell [widow of Judge James Bell and mother of FMC's friend, Hovey] received a telegram Thursday [August 20] from Mr. Frank M. Chapman saying that his mother had died at his home in Englewood, N.J."

Mrs. Chapman had been a year-round resident of Gainesville for many years but in June of 1912 she traveled north to visit her son and his family for the summer and so never returned to her southern home. The paper speaks of her as a musician and "paintress" and a member of the Presbyterian Church.

The reasons for the move from Gainesville to Ormond Beach were many. The ocean and the broad beaches added shore and sea birds to the abundant land birds of the area, the climate was milder, the Inn most comfortable, old friends were near by, and the golf course was a major attraction. When Charles Cory introduced FMC to the game in 1901 at Palm Beach, he made a convert and the links of Ormond were FMC's playground winters until 1922.

Frank Chapman never admitted it, but I am sure the greatest attractions of all at the Ormond Beach–Daytona area were the famous and wealthy people who frequented it. Contacts which might bring financial support for expeditions, contributions to the museum, and donations of new habitat groups, new bird collections, perhaps even new wings on the building were probably in FMC's thoughts when he changed his winter *pied à terre.*

Whatever his reasons were, Frank Chapman left for Ormond Beach each winter as he once wrote to Roy Chapman Andrews, "with a bag of clubs in one hand and a bag of manuscript in the other." During ten winters he golfed and wrote books, edited *Bird-Lore,* carried on a voluminous correspondence, and hoped he would repeat the find of two early visitors to the resort and pick up a Great Auk bone on the beach. The winter community addressed him as Dr. Chapman, for in 1913, the degree of doctor of science was conferred upon him by Brown University.

For two years during World War I, FMC worked for the Red Cross. He volunteered and his natural abilities were put to work directing publications. Later he was appointed a special commissioner to Latin America and he traveled through the West Indies and South America lecturing in Spanish on the needs and aims of the Red Cross. In May of 1919, when his services were no longer needed, he returned to the Museum.

In 1923 largely through the efforts and financial backing of Dr. Thomas Barbour, naturalist and director of the Museum of Comparative Zoology at Harvard for many years, Barro Colorado Island in Panama was made into a laboratory for the study of plant and animal life. The island, once a tropical hilltop, was created by the flooding of Gatun Lake. Frank Chapman first saw it in December of 1925, after a winter or two in Coconut Grove of which no records remain except the date lines on a few letters and his editorials in *Bird-Lore*. He called his new winter home in Panama, "My Tropical Air Castle" and used this name as the title and part of it in a second title *Life in an Air Castle*, both books about the place which seemed to him the realization of boyhood castles-in-the-air, a naturalist's paradise. FMC deserted Florida for Barro Colorado Island; the winters of 1927-28, 1928-29, 1929-30, and 1931-32 were spent there and resulted in scientific studies and articles as well as in the two books.

9

The Journals from 1932 – 1934

THE WINTER AND SPRING OF 1932-33 and of 1933-34, the Chapmans returned to Florida and lived in a rented home at 921 Twelfth Street, Little River (now part of Miami) on Biscayne Bay. The place was originally selected as a quiet one in which to finish a book, most probably the *Autobiography of a Bird Lover*. The spot also appealed to birds and thus to Frank Chapman and his wife. His observations on the birds attracted to a feeding table and a water bath during the two periods they occupied it resulted in two articles published in *Natural History Magazine* in 1934, one called "A Season's Bird Guests" in the November-December number. Both are illustrated with photographs taken by the author.

In the first paper he describes the arrangements he made for wildlife entertainment and observation. "Our house is on 'made' ground, and all the vegetation about it is of recent growth. This means that it is thick and bushy and gives cover. Where the new ground ends the old ground begins. This is a red mangrove swamp with a margin of willows, and grassy openings partly filled with the debris of the last hurricane.

"Far enough within this swamp to ensure seclusion and concealment and at the head of an opening that gives an outlook, I built a little study. It measures six by seven feet and might better have been smaller. It is not beautiful, but I see it chiefly from within, and since the entire front and two large windows are of mosquito net most of the within is without. Behind this wire, when motionless, I appear to be invisible."

This is the only part of the articles that was not written from the notes in the journal, but he made many entries in his journal that he did not incorporate in the published papers. The first entry in the journal is conspicuous by its absence from the printed page:

DEC 8, 1932   At 4 P.M. I shot the Mockingbird (a male) that has dominated the food shelf.

At first glance this seems a very un-Chapman-like thing to do. On further thought, can you conceive of FMC spending months with a blind available, and birds around and about, and one bossy Mockingbird keeping every living thing away? I have watched many a Florida Mockingbird drive from its territory cats, dogs, every sort of small bird, and some large ones. There are well-authenticated records of Mockingbirds driving snakes off and away, so how could simple Catbirds withstand them? Clearly if the observation of FMC's " 'At home' to Furred and Feathered Inhabitants of Florida" was to produce any information or experimentation, the bossy Mockingbird had to go.

Having recorded his shooting of the Mockingbird, Frank Chapman continued to record the events of December 8, 1932, in the garden:

Within 20 minutes a Blue Jay was having his first square meal on the suet stand, a Catbird for the first time ventured out on the lawn ten feet from cover as Nonpareils (including 2 ♂ ads.) were feeding beneath the bath, 4 more than I had seen at one time before, and an Oven-bird came out from the shrubbery. It remains to be seen whether another mocker takes the valued throne. [Probably a perch slightly higher than the feeding table and in a position to dominate the scene.]

DEC 9 Blue Jays, Cardinals, a Catbird, Ovenbird, Myrtle Warbler, and at least 8 Nonpareils have fed on and above the stands the greater part of the day, undisturbed. There has been one Mockingbird, but it is not aggressive and I have not seen it attack. It has an upturned secondary and has been there all along. It was often pursued by the dead Mocker.

DEC 10 Still only the 'Secondary' Mocker, who is peaceful, but more birds of other species than have been before.

DEC 13 Secondary Mocker becoming aggressive. Has chased the catbirds for 3 days; now attacks Blue Jays. Not as vicious as first one, but bad enough. [This second Mockingbird became gradually less aggressive and was not shot.]

DEC 14 11:20—7 Quail—came in at bamboo and went to bath, then to end of shrubbery on road where apparently they stayed.

The record for the months of December and January goes on with entries every few days of the comings and goings of the resident forms with times of arrival and sometimes of departure, but these journals are very different from those of his youth. In his early years Frank Chapman followed the example of William Brewster and took as much pain in recording the day's happenings as he would if he were writing for publication. If he had only done the same in these journals, how interesting they would be!

Most of the entries in these journals are one short line or two, jottings of notes or impressions for his own later use. He did not spend much time in his little screened study, sometimes a late morning visit is recorded or an hour in the afternoon, and many days are skipped. In December he made twelve entries and in January fifteen. In several cases he lists human guests with his wild ones, leaving some confusion in one's mind at first reading as to whether or not they are new species of wild-life at the feeding table. Here are the high points of the 1932-33 and 1933-34 journals.

DEC 27   4 P.M. A wildcat walked the length of the log before my shack stopping at intervals to look around. It seemed wholly unaware of the fact that I was within 7-10 feet of it and showed no signs of nervousness or undue caution. When its head emerged from beneath the mangroves I thought for a moment I had been transported to Barro Colorado. It was a full-sized animal in excellent condition and doubtless looking for marsh hares.

The 4 ♂ and 1 ♀ Cardinals, 2 Blue Jays, a Redwing, Hermit Thrush, Ovenbird, Yellow-throat, Nonpareils and Red-bellied Woodpecker were all in sight within a few minutes of the cat's passage.

[NEXT ENTRY]
DEC 29   Wild cat again appeared at 3:30 just behind food table. No marsh rabbits on the lawn for several days and only one in the swamp.

JAN 2, 1933   7 Quail, 4 ♂, 3 ♀, under bamboos at 9:45.
[12 DAYS, NO ENTRY AND NO EXPLANATION]

JAN 14   Rockefellers here. Wild cat bounds over my doorstep. Redwings begin to call. Near 62°. [FMC played golf with John D. at Ormond. This could be any member of the family, even John D. himself who died in 1937.]

JAN 15   Three rabbits on lawn this morning. Cool N. wind, gray. 25 Redwings under the bamboo. They came to stay and eat continuously wing to wing with rarely a misunderstanding.

     11:45. 7 Quail, 2 Rabbits, many Bluebirds, Cardinals, Nonpareil, Catbirds. Many Tree Swallows coming apparently from the North. Is it the cold weather? They have not been here since the last cold snap. Willows blooming.

JAN 20 9:30—74°. Clear—still. Not a bird in sight when I place food, come as soon as my back is turned and within 5 min.—20 Redwings from sky—Catbirds, Cardinals, Yellow-throats, Nonpareil—1 Myrtle. 12 M. 4 Quail, 3 ♂ 1 ♀, conversational twitters and chuckles. Where is rest of flock.

JAN 21 9:56—75°. A Sharp-shin sweeps through and at the Cat-birds' sharp alarm note nearly every bird plunges for cover. It was 13 minutes before the first one reappeared. They had evidently been genuinely frightened. An incident of this kind explains why they ex-hibit so much caution. It may occur only once a month but if it does not teach a lesson it may never occur again. The false alarms must be obeyed.

Then came a single Nonpareil which may not have been one of the frightened birds. 19 min. 2 Catbirds, 1 Cardinal ♀, Hermit Thrush in mangroves! Half an hour before order was restored and business resumed as usual.

Strange attitudes of sunbath—plumage fluffed until bird seemed nearly twice its real size. Blackbirds, Catbirds, Mocker, Cardinal, Nonpareil, a frozen Finch. False scare, back in 10 to 20 sec.

Snake pours himself into hole. A sinuous stream of fluid flesh.

JAN 22 Quail and rabbits together, second rabbit on stand with Redwings and Catbirds, Jays, Cardinals, etc. 60°-70°.

JAN 24 Warm yesterday and today. Mockingbirds sing more freely. Stems, branches, growing downward as they disappear in crab-holes. [At least 20 blue land crabs (cardisoma quanhumi) lived in the garden.] Crab—a round, fat, pop-eyed baby being fed by its parents, one on each side of it. Cardinal raises his crest as one raises his eyebrows. Crested Flycatcher, first full call. Catbirds decreasing?

JAN 25 Mocker sings before sunrise. Blue Jay string of low beady notes like the rattle of a rattlesnake.

JAN 26 9:30—64°. Clear. Cardinal ♂ has been killed probably this morning and probably by a Sharp-shin. One hour before a bird came to log or suet. All keep to table in cover. *All* nervous. Take flight at frequent intervals and that's apparent cause. At the faintest squeak everything—even rabbits dash for cover. 11:30 Sharp-shinned dashes through, everything flees and remains hidden for 29 minutes.

JAN 28   49° Cl. Wind N. Fresh. Thousands of Tree Swallows toward lake.

JAN 31   Quail pictures. Fairchild frightens them into flight. [Dr. David G., botanist, agriculturist, and horticulturist for whom Fairchild Gardens in Miami are named.]

FEB 1   11 A.M. 88° Birds come out when I appear evidently associating me with food. All dive when mocker comes. He's alone because others fear him. Hermit is alone because he fears others. Polished shells of crabs shine in sunflicks.

FEB 2   Vogt here. [William, ornithologist and author of *Road to Survival.*]

FEB 3   Go to Royal Palm Hammock. Palms left but hurricane and fire have left few old trees up or untouched.

FEB 4   Barn Owls still come nightly but I rarely hear the food call of the young. Heard it once last night. 11:15 Cooper's ♂ dashes through from mangroves. Warning had been given but seconds before and all birds had disappeared. Black and white creeper.

FEB 9   Barbour [Thomas, of Harvard's MCZ] here. First day, cloudy and rainy.

FEB 16   Cardinals are singing more freely. Cardinals crest in expressing emotion. Yellow-throat gone. Starts alone? I miss him. What started him? More food here. [About this time, as explained in "A Season's Bird Guests" but not in the notes: "In order to observe a bird's reaction to its own image I placed mirrors on the ground and also behind the suet perches."]

MAR 4   Cardinal and Nonpareil attack image. Look behind glass? excited *chuck.*

MAR 8   Cardinal sings in mangrove over mirrors and is only one that attacks image. Pecks and flutters, always goes behind mirror after fighting image— ♂ answers ♂ singing. A ♀ Cardinal on perch at window and at ground feeding place utters *chuck* of male and with partly dropped wings rapidly vibrates her outer primaries—inner primaries and secondaries motionless.

     A Catbird for first time picks at image and flutters at it a bit— cat-call heard for first time. Redwings sing in chorus and alone but none show any interest in mirror. Birds even in sudden alarm flights rarely fly into mirror.

MAR 9   ♀ Redwing taking sunbath, twisting its body a half turn from right to left and back and repeating. Acts as though admiring itself in the glass. The feathers of the rump lifted perpendicularly exposing the oil glands.

MAR 20   Maryland Yellowthroat fights image for first time.

MAR 23   Maryland Yellowthroat continues at intervals to fight image.

MAR 24   Hermit back. Osgood here. Seem to be few Catbirds. [Dr. Wilfred, mammologist and ornithologist, Field Museum of Natural History, Chicago, Illinois.]

MAR 29   Pileated on owl tree—knocks off loose bark with side strokes. Blackbirds saturnine and mysterious. Mockingbird alights on roof. Pattering feet.

APR 15   Cardinal follows mirror. Makes long flight when glass is out of sight. Goes 108 feet from song tree. Turn glass showing pasteboard back. Still recognized the front and attacked.

APR 16   Place mirror 60 feet from log in about an hour male sees it, flies straight to it and attacks.

DECEMBER 1933

DEC 12   3 P.M. returned to #921 12th St., Little River. No marked change in surroundings. Shack as before. Table in position more concealed by vegetation. No water in bath. One green Nonpareil only bird seen. Owls heard at night a few times at long intervals. Cat lying under bush.

DEC 13   Got chick-feed out at 9 A.M. During day sat at intervals in the house. Have seen 2 ♂ ad. Nonpareils, 2 ♂ Cardinals, 1 ♂ Towhee, 2 Ground Doves, last two for first time. A Gnatcatcher, 1 Palm Warbler, 1 Phoebe, only other birds seen on place. 5 Killdeer in field. No songs. Mercury in 70's calm, clear. Barn Owls in tree but how many? Cat not seen.

DEC 17   Warm. Go to Bretts [cannot clarify]. They report no land birds about their place. See not one. 1 Wards, 2 Louisiana, 4 Little Blues.

DEC 20   Birds a little more evident, but still very shy. Catbird ascends suet stick first time. Doves go up on table—also Hermit. Twittering of Hummers only note. Crabs more common. Warm. First Red-wing, ♂ passed over yesterday. 3-4 Palm Warblers.

DEC 22   Cooler—60°—first rabbit—3 Redwings, 8 Nonpareils—Hummer hovers over paper flower but does not stop.

DEC 23   11:10 A Sharp-shin just dove for and apparently nailed a ♀ or juv. ♂ Nonpareil within 15 feet of me. The bird had just flown to a perch in a bush about 3 feet from the ground when the hawk plunged, then for nearly a minute remained motionless on the branch where it landed. I could not see whether it had the bird in its grip, but after remaining motionless it flew, whether with any-thing in its feet I do not know. Search showed 5 tailfeathers and 12 contour feathers. Perhaps the bird escaped. A ground Dove feeding below the Nonpareil flew and the Bunting may have gone with it minus half its tail.

11:39 before birds reappear, then a Catbird, ♂ and ♀ Nonpareil. It is amazing that a leaf-green bird in the cover of vegetation would not be free from hawk attack.

A pair of Ground Doves enter the drinking pan. They squat side by side nearly filling it and look like two strange immature swimming birds. From time to time they flutter a brief shower of drops. After three minutes first one then 15 sec. later the other gets out and walks rapidly away pausing every few feet to jump up in the air and rapidly clap its brown lined wings while a shower of drops falls from its body. 12:05. Ground Doves now lying down in the dust side by side as in one nest. She arranges his back plumage, cosily. ♂ Hummer hovers close over "flower" but does not stop. Second male dove appears and party is at once broken up. Newcomer pursues first male who retreats then all three walk rapidly away cooing briefly at intervals and creat-ing a situation I do not understand but one which has evidently opened the question of relations with the female who now seems equally in-terested in both suitors though she was apparently so content with one a few minutes ago.

FRANK M. CHAPMAN'S JOURNAL — 1934

FEB 5   Home from the hospital on Feb 2 at noon. I have been in my blind daily but have seen nothing not recorded today. There have been apparently no marked changes since I left in late December.

Several more Cardinals and one or two Catbirds, perhaps of last year's group. A Mocker has come, not, I should say, last year's. The Oven-bird seems to have disappeared. The willows were leaved when I returned and only a few 'pussies' remained.

FEB 7   Cardinals—one or two—now singing regularly. A musical song full of sweetness and sunshine. Perhaps as much or more than any other song it marks the beginning of a southern spring.

Six Catbirds at one look, more than I have seen together before. Something excited them and they mee-owed in various keys and notes all expressing degrees of annoyance. There were numbers of fluttery encounters. Why? Too early for sex to play a part. Doubtless just an exhibition of an irritable temperament to which their voice also gives expression.

FEB 8   The old cotton rat has but one eye, and half a tail and is evidently semi-crippled by age. He hobbles around stiffly and shows so little response to noises made to alarm him that I conclude he hears poorly. In all a badly handicapped animal long past his prime. Nevertheless he lives in the shadow of a Barn Owl's nest containing two nearly fledged young who after sunset make almost constant demands on their parents for food.

Suffering from a rather acute and prolonged attack of convales-cence, there was no serious work on my desk and I devoted the winter to an objectless contemplation of the birds at my feeding stands. Their companionship. Why? The birds brought with them a sense of com-panionship which in turn begot a sense of contentment in which the hours unmarked by incident passed happily and rapidly. I might spec-ulate idly and ineffectively on the significance of their color or their actions without reaching a conclusion satisfied alone by their presence.

Male Cardinals chase each other or one here chases trespasser, but there is no song or sign of courtship. Females seem also pugna-cious toward each other and utter a low *chuck*, but opposite sexes seem to pay no attention to one another.

FEB 9   Catbirds in a group all whine in various keys. I see no cause. One eating suet joins in. No excitement. No activity. What's it all about.

Cardinal here and one in the distance singing. Certainly spring has reached our shores.

Woman who whistled up her sparrows. That was a lesson for all young naturalists to remember. I was fortunately alone. Begin here.

[A reminder to use the following, published on page 530 of "My Florida Bird Guests."]

"Recalling an incident of a double-decade ago, I decided to see if I could not strengthen my relations with these independent acceptors of my bounty. At the time to which I refer a lady of mature years daily fed the sparrows and pigeons that lived on the Seventy-seventh Street side of the American Museum. Carrying a large paper bag containing bits of dried bread, she scattered this food at certain places and at the same time uttered the usually ineffective whistle of her sex while the birds quickly gathered about her. 'No doubt,' I said to myself with the always superior air of the professional, as I frequently witnessed this pleasing scene, 'the good lady believes that the birds are responding to her call, and does not realize that it is the conspicuously distributed food that attracts them.' But one day, as I was passing one of her feeding stations, association prompted me to repeat her whistle, when, behold! pigeons and sparrows at once came flocking about me in obvious expectation of food of which I had not a morsel. Nor could I believe that the birds were misled by any resemblance between me and their lady patron.

"I trust that both as a man and a naturalist I profited by that experience. At any rate, it remained green in my memory, and I determined now to see if I could not create at least a phrase of language which the birds would understand. Every morning, therefore, while I distributed food, I whistled loudly a bar from the Greater Yellow-legs' call. It required thirty-seven days to establish the association between sound and food."

FEB 12   Tuckers here. [Mr. and Mrs. Carll, patrons of American Museum of Natural History and fairy godparents to many young ornithologists.] Tree Swallows come at 55° but disappear at 44°.

FEB 13   Sanford here. [Dr. Leonard C., patron of American Museum of Natural History, instrumental in obtaining Harry Payne Whitney grant for Pacific exploration.]

FEB 16   First haircut since November! [Did he have a head injury?]

FEB 21   Catbirds calling in different time, and tone expresses different meanings with the same character of note. 2:48 P.M. Sharp-shinned Hawk [a mounted specimen] is in place in willow tree where nearly concealed by limbs and leaves. I cannot see it from the house without looking very carefully. It was obviously not seen by birds that fed from 2:48 to 3:15. At 3:45 I removed willow leaves making hawk more readily seen but still far from evident. Three ♂ and 1 ♀ Catbirds apparently discover it and chirp steely alarm note hopping about in neighboring oleander. I have not knowingly heard alarm note before. Males soon disappear and ♀ sits motionless until 3:58, then quietly disappears. A rabbit goes right under hawk 5 feet above and pays no attention to it. [This experiment and the mirror experiment were tried again and again in February and March and proved that birds recognized the hawk by sight.]

FEB 22   Catbird's alarm like breaking of fire dry twigs—several in quick succession. Rabbits' alarm—*chaw chaw chaw*—like an owl's note. What owl?

MAR 6   3 P.M. Catbird in oleander *sotto voce*. Fluent, melodious, continuous, varied, more even than normal, loud song. Lasted for ten minutes. Audible under wholly favorable conditions at 75 feet. The bird motionless. Other Catbirds in tree but no response.

I enjoy their companionship because I am a bird. That's my good luck, an asset that makes the world an infinitely more enjoyable place.

A bird's plumage usually fits it and most birds in nature look well kept. 4:15 Sharp-shin comes shooting like an arrow from the left past the house at a bird I think a ♀ Cardinal on the table. Catbird sounds *chick-chick* alarm and feeding bird springs for undergrowth above. Hawk swings up to follow but whether successfully I could not tell. I saw no feathers. This has obviously become a dangerous place for birds to feed; just as it has become a good feeding-place for bird-eating hawks. Small birds feed here, therefore, at unusual risk and show their realization of it by exercising unusual caution. Automatically I have been conducting a feeding shelf for Sharp-shins and the small birds that habitually feed here have through experience gradually developed excessive or unusual caution and do not expose themselves unnecessarily.

♂ Cardinal attacks mirror 3 times after I put it up in P.M. ♀ feeds on table but seems shy of mirror.

MAR 8   The stuffed Owl when placed in Hawk tree aroused no interest and excited no attention. Birds came and went as before. When I replaced it with the Hawk there was no reaction for nearly a minute, then the Catbird alarm was given and all the birds left hurriedly. 10:50 No birds return for 35 minutes.

MAR 9   Far back among the labyrinth of coiling mangrove roots I see fragments of motion as the rays of sky light hit here and there and reveal a back or claw or wing off stage. Or beyond that part of my surroundings I have made my stage.

10:50 The Ground Doves came. Cooing softly, running actively. Birds like plants bloom at different times. The Hermit starts north at one time, the Catbirds at another.

Two rabbits now at table. Their surprising call, heard last night as I watched the Barn Owls, was startling, very birdlike in tone.

As from the lawn I watched the young owls calling with a sudden sound like the sudden release of steam under pressure while the old ones screamed shrilly a passerby offered to loan me a gun to rid myself of so great a "nuisance." A "nuisance?" I replied. "Why I like it," which perhaps, was not exactly true for there are occasions during the night when I should like to spank these continuously vociferous Owlets vigorously.

But even then I like the idea of them. They give by their presence an endorsement to much I should find it hard to accept without them: to the vibrant roar of countless motor cars before which the ear shivers, the hum of airplanes near and far, the unspeakable irritating, unpardonable racket of an outboard on its unimportant errand or none at all. All these the Barn Owl has accepted as a part of his life, and in taking him into mine I must take them with him. Why then should I kill him because he makes one more noise when he makes it possible for me to endure the other noises which I cannot kill. (How gladly I would if I could.) [From this account in Frank Chapman's Journal developed this paragraph in the published article (page 537).]

Before the cardinal has finished his sunset song, the young barn owl, who, like his predecessor of last year, was born in the dead tree trunk above my blind, begins his food call; nor is his hunger appeased when the cardinal greets the rising sun. It must be confessed that his "peevish scream" is not a soothing sound, and there are occasions during the night when I should like to discipline this continuously vociferous owlet and his indulgent parents. But when I consider how his dreams are doubtless disturbed by the vibrant roar of distant motor cars, the hum of "blimps" and airplanes far and near, the unspeakably irritating racket of insignificant outboard motors, I feel that he, rather than I, has cause for complaint.

Rest time is when the bird needs its protective coloring for then it is off guard, perhaps actually asleep. When it is moving protective coloring does no good and then it must rely on its own alertness.

MAR 12   In Royal Palm Park with Tuckers. Cold, mercury 44°.

MAR 16   Rainy—9:15—all birds waiting and come to food immediately. I return to house. [The following is apparently an outline for the writing of the article]:

My Season's Guests. The second season.

Hiring of place—to remeet bird friends. Who is here? Changes. Have Blacks come? Are the Whites here? Me. Companionship. What do they do? Food and how they take it. Toleration. "Fear" and how they meet it. What else—Owl Hawk, difference from last winter. Color immaterial when bird moves for then alert. It is only when it rests and sleeps and is off guard that color is important. I want congenial companionship (kinship). It makes no demands and it is a pleasure to grant. Ground Doves exquisite little creatures. Perfect in line and plume and motion but nervous, restless, eager; pink feet patter rapidly; sleek, rounded little head with its coral bill nods to and fro with every step; their wing quills flicker; notes soft, dove-like coos. Fight with anything they encounter preferably a male of their own species but even a female may not be safe. Up goes their brown-lined wing shield, buckler and bludgeon in one. Between hunting sprees, they rest quietly side by side in each others arms, and then are loving dovelike creatures. In bath-tub together. Welcome addition to my season's guests.

MAR 17   White-mark on table of predator's presence with Catbird's body feathers in numbers, but 7 Catbirds.

MAR 18   For the first time birds appear to come to my whistle. I threw no food but stood at door of my house. Only one Catbird in sight when I came after less than one minute's whistling birds came in numbers, Cardinals, Catbirds, Nonpareils from apparently beyond immediate surroundings and evidently in response to my call. (Feb 9—begin, Mar 18—response /19/37 days).

Catbird's musical soliloquy with no distinguishable theme: a harmonious rambling improvisation without apparent motif but nevertheless varied and highly pleasing. Singing to himself: no territory, no mate, no audience, a reflection of his gradually awakening Catbird's awareness. Snake today and yesterday.

MAR 20   Four male Nonpareils moving about actively in the sunlight and shadow of the feeding-table is the most kaleidoscopic display of color I have ever seen in the world of birds. The colors are so pronounced and vivid the birds that wear them so active that strength of color and strength of bird combine to produce an unforgettable impression. The sense—one's color sense is immensely pleased—to the smiling point.

M AR 21   Awareness, alertness of Catbird, never a moment when he is on the move that he is not fully conscious of every significant detail in his surroundings, be it sight or sound. This is equally true of other birds but none of those about me here show it so plainly. His large black eye clearly defined in its gray setting expresses an alert intelligent perception of his surroundings, his caudal gestures are pronounced and no doubt appropriate, in short he is a bird of character. The Catbird is good company, he gives you due place in his immediate environment and acknowledges your presence. Cardinal tries lemon twice, Catbird once. Catbird eats grapefruit as freely as orange.

M AR 22   To have rabbits come loping toward you in response to your whistle gives one a distinct sensation of being on good terms with the animal kingdom. I think that St. Francis would have enjoyed this experience.

Nonpareils—bill to bill and claw to claw fluttering mount skyward. They present some form of undescribed avian pyrotechnic—a feathered firework. Lemon not touched all day. Orange slightly more favored than grapefruit.

M AR 23   9:15 Not a bird or bunny in sight this morning when I entered my house. Staying within I whistled the food call and at the end of about a minute birds began to come from every quarter and finally a rabbit appeared. They obviously came in response to my invitation. Grapefruit and orange disappeared from table during night, but lemon, practically untouched, remains. Several rabbits called at 5 P.M. yesterday loudly, repeatedly, the suppressed tang of a muted string. [The next paragraph is a note for the coming article.]

The period from Dec. 12-24 was passed in preparing for a season's work interrupted from the latter date to early February by laying the foundation for an acute attack of convalescence which lasted until May.

M AR 24   A mangrove swamp is not a good place in which to study the habits of birds. Too much goes on under cover to make it possible to understand a fraction of what you see.

M AR 27   No Catbird chums. Come 9:55—go 10:05—come 10:35. 11 A.M. Ground Doves come. Nichols for luncheon. [John T., Curator of Fishes at the American Museum of Natural History.]

MAR 29   Hermit here this morning. Last year he left, presumably for the North on this date. I look at him as he perches now within 6 feet of me, and ask if he will start tonight. Doubtless if he understood me he could not reply for he has no knowledge of the gradual growth of the impulse which when fully developed will lead him to begin his journey of over 1000 miles.

MAR 30   Hermit still here. Hot, close day.

MAR 31   Hermit not seen.

APR 1   Where is the Hermit this warm Easter Sunday? How far has he gone on his way north? Barn Owls still call, but much less frequently, at night.

APR 7   3:15 a heavy-bodied hawk struck a rabbit near the feeding-table, and rode on its back, fur flying for 25 yards, squealing loudly it reached the shelter of the dense pandanus where apparently the hawk could not follow. When I looked from my door the hawk flew and there were no signs of the rabbit. The hawk's back was brown. I did not see its tail. It was about the size of a female Cooper's. No wonder the rabbits cross the clearing rapidly. How will this affect their actions.

3:40 Buntings and Cardinals feed at pan. 3:45 Catbird at suet. 4:35 A rabbit from east eats at water pan. He seems unaware of recent occurrences. A second comes, from S.E. to table and dozes in the sunlight.

APR 9   One rabbit here at 9:30. One Blue Jay at 10. The first this winter. Dove (♀) comes at 10:50. 2:50 2 rabbits. Snake—bright yellowish brown—taffy brown with two indistinct blackish streaks and broken silver bands. [Probably a Chicken Snake.]

APR 11   Three rabbits present at one time and a fourth with a bare patch on his back may be individual hawk attacked.

APR 13   The Catbirds and Buntings apparently decreased. Redstart ♂ . Ground Dove—when walking—*whoo-whoo-too-coo.*

APR 14   Some Catbirds appear to have gone. Why should they go at different times? Enlargement of gonads has been developed as part of their organism and requires no annual stimulus to make it function like the molt.

With all birds the season of reproduction is annual. It is initiated under a wide variety of conditions: Light and temperature may decrease as well as increase or may not change perceptibly. In the tropics birds nest throughout the year, some species in the dry season others in the wet. But apparently there is as much individual regularity there as in latitudes where the date of the nesting season is governed by climatic conditions. At Barro Colorado, I found pairs and groups of birds nesting on or near the same time year after year.

Should we not therefore regard the enlargement of the gonads marking the approach of the season of reproduction as one phenomenon expressive of the physiological cycle and attribute its periodicity to cumulative influence of environment rather than to any one existing cause?

APR 27   Apparently only one Catbird left. It sings the *sotto voce* song and I assume is a male. The migration certainly began by April 12, perhaps earlier and has therefore extended over a period of two weeks. This indicates a corresponding variation in their reproductive cycle wholly unconnected with any external influence (light, etc.). Since they have all been living here under the same conditions. The fact that the remaining birds come in the morning when I whistle and act as they have all winter is to me proof that they are the same birds I have been watching and not new birds that have replaced them. The gradual reduction has occurred in Nonpareils. Note also that each bird evidently acts on its own initiative and not in response to the example set by the bird with which it has been associated during the winter.

The song of the Nonpareil! A faint, high, little trickling song suggestive of a warbler rather than a finch. Sung by a fully plumaged male about ten feet distant. It is of 3-4 seconds duration and repeated at intervals of about the same number of seconds. Whether it is a full-voiced or *sotto voce* song I cannot say. I should say the latter.

APR 29   A full moon last night, clear and still. Fine flying weather. Apparently my last Catbirds and Nonpareils (No ♂ 1 ♀) have left me and I have now only Cardinals, Ground Doves and rabbits. If light is the factor that acts on the organism why should it take 15-20 days more to send the last of these birds than the first?

The place seems deserted. In the presence of the fact of their absence one is impressed by the cumulative effect of influences active during untold years which starts them on an uncharted course to their unknown destination. Their departure seems much more remarkable than their arrival.

APR 30   No Catbirds yesterday or today. The Catbirds have gone and it is time for me to follow them. Tomorrow I will follow. We are to make essentially the same journey but what a difference in our methods! For days I have been packing, wrestling with the problems of packing—books, camera, field-glasses, clothing for summer and for winter—and tomorrow I board a steamer product of a century of man's designing, provisioned and fuelled, and our way will be directed by the use of chart, compass and sextant. But the Catbird with no thoughts of ways or means spreads his wings and flies into the night.

[Of course the last paragraph was used as the last paragraph in "My Florida Bird Guests."]

It was a nature of remarkable resiliency that created adventures and rewarding experiments in a bit of garden at the edge of a swamp. The span of forty-eight years between his first journal in 1886 and these notes in 1934 are affected by physical limitations. At three score and ten he did not go exploring in wild country and bring new birds and mammals to his beloved museum, but he planned a season of discovery among familiar creatures in his own back yard. His joy in whistling them to him shared with the friends that came readily to his door may not be so spontaneously expressed as the joy of the young Chapman when he caught his first *Neofiber,* but it is, nevertheless, still evident.

10

Epilogue

ORNITHOLOGISTS who become dedicated to their calling when they are children and remain so through their youth and middle years seem incapable of leaving their work. Even when one goes through the formality of retiring it is just a gesture, a retirement in name only. The day after the speeches and the ceremony, his profession, ornithology, is still his major concern. He retains an office, his work, and his scientific problems. He disposes only of those chores of administration that interfered somewhat with his pursuit of birds in the field.

Such would have been Frank Chapman's retirement as Chairman of the Department of Ornithology at the American Museum of Natural History had he retired in his late sixties or early seventies. And such was his retirement in fact, although he did not make the gesture until June, 1942, when he was seventy-eight years old.

Though old ornithologists, unlike old soldiers, eventually die, they never fade away. They keep right on producing, observing, and publishing. But being sensible men, they put their houses in order when they think their time is approaching. FMC's illness in the early winter of 1934, coupled with the celebration of his seventieth birthday the following June, may have instigated such a proceeding. Certainly the death of *Bird-Lore*'s able contributing editor, his old and valued friend Mabel Osgood Wright, in July, influenced his decision to turn *Bird-Lore* over to the National Audubon Society in December.

Bird-Lore lost money in its early years, but was a profitable property when FMC disposed of it. He gave it to the Audubon Society with the provision that they pay him $1500 per year for the rest of his life from the magazine's much larger annual profits. Thus though he received some compensation for the publication he had created, the Audubon Society nevertheless received a large and substantial gift. He remained a contributing editor and continued to write articles for it, the last appearing in 1943, three years after the Society rechristened the magazine *Audubon Magazine*.

FMC wrote his last two editorials for *Bird-Lore* a year apart for the fall issues of 1935 and 1936. Each urged Audubon members to join the American Ornithologists' Union and to attend the next stated annual meeting, the 1935 meeting in Toronto, the 1936 meeting in Pittsburgh. Reading these two editorials now, it appears that his last official words to his subscribers urged them to do what he no longer did himself. He had attended his last A.O.U. meeting before he wrote the editorials, when the organization celebrated its semi-centennial in November, 1933, at the American Museum of Natural History where it had been founded.

At this meeting FMC received the coveted Brewster Medal, awarded annually by the Union in memory of his old friend William Brewster, to "the author of the most outstanding work published during the past five years relating in whole or in part to the birds of the Western Hemisphere." The report of the 1933 meeting (*Auk*, 1934: 53) states: "The Brewster Medal for 1933 was awarded to Dr. Frank Michler Chapman for his *Handbook of the Birds of Eastern North America, 1932.*" This was the second revision of his first book, originally published in 1895.

Many honors came to FMC during his lifetime, including that honorary Doctor of Science from Brown University in June, 1913. This followed the presentation to him in December, 1912, of the first Linnaean Society medal "in appreciation of his invaluable services to ornithological science through his well known work in popularizing the study of birds." The National Academy of Science awarded him the first Daniel Giraud Elliot medal in 1918, for his report on the birds of Colombia.

In 1923, the Roosevelt Memorial Association awarded him the Roosevelt Medal for distinguished service in the promotion of the study of natural history, and in 1929, the John Burroughs Memorial Association honored him with their medal for the same reason. On October 26, 1937, he was elected an Honorary President by the National Audubon Society and presented with a silver loving cup in recognition of his services to the organization.

To be elected a Fellow of the American Ornithologists' Union is a measure of achievement all American ornithologists strive to reach. Frank Chapman joined the A.O.U. as an Associate Member in 1885, and was elected to full membership, then the highest class, in 1888. Like the Founders, he became a Fellow automatically when that class of membership was added by a change in the bylaws in 1902.

Between 1934 and 1937, FMC made several trips to Barro Colorado Island. In the fall of 1938, he returned to Florida and asserted, in correspondence with Dr. Thomas Barbour and others, that from now on Florida would be his home. But wanderlust apparently attacked him, so he traveled. And his travels in his last years seem to repeat his travels in '86, '87, '88, and '89—New York, North Carolina, Florida in the fall, the route reversed in spring—except that he no longer commuted to New Jersey, for the Chapmans stayed in New York City; and in North Carolina they went to Asheville, and in Florida to 3938 Leafy Way in Coconut Grove. In 1942 he notified the American Ornithologists' Union that this last address was his permanent one.

It is highly significant that Frank Chapman made no attempt to write again after 1943. Ill health had never stopped him before, but the illness of his wife, Fanny Miller Bates Chapman, and her death in Asheville, North Carolina, September 22, 1944, were another thing. He had written of her in his autobiography "when on February 24, 1898, I married Fanny Bates Embury, I acquired a helpmeet who ever since has made it the chief object of her life to advance the aims of mine."

When she was no longer by his side, the object of his life and the aims of hers were no longer important to him. For forty-six years she was his unfailing companion on all his journeys, from the heights of the Rocky Mountains and Andes Peaks to the lowland Florida prairies, from castles in England to camps in the Everglades, from the honeymoon on Pelican Island, through the winters at Ormond Beach, to the last years in Coconut Grove. It must have been a splendid adventure, and her share of it is amply acknowledged by FMC and by his colleagues. No ornithologist's wife before her was given the tribute of an obituary in the *Auk*.

Without his wife by his side, Chapman waited out World War II. He was still to have one great happiness come to him. Frank Chapman, Jr., a major in the U.S. Marine Corps, came safely home and perhaps was with his father on Nantucket on August 14, 1945, when the Japanese surrendered. Frank Chapman never returned to Florida. He was taken ill in New York and died there November 15, 1945.

"Everglades Islet," FMC's last paper on Florida, was published in 1943 in *Audubon Magazine*. It is illustrated by one of his own photographs and two of Allan Cruickshank's. It is a vivid description of Royal Palm Park, the state park that was created through the efforts of the Florida State Federation of Women's Clubs and was the forerunner and nucleus of what is now Everglades National Park. FMC tells of its fauna and flora, the only truly tropical flora in the continental United States. His essay was a plea for a National Park to conserve not only Royal Palm Hammock, but the surrounding glades and bordering keys for posterity. He did not live to see this come to pass, but his "Everglade Islet," like Marjory Stoneman Douglas' *River of Grass* and Thomas Barbour's *That Vanishing Eden,* helped make it happen.

CHAPMAN'S PUBLISHED WRITINGS

Exclusive of book reviews, notes, and editorials in Bird-Lore.

BOOKS

1895. *Handbook of Birds of Eastern North America.* With Keys to the Species and Descriptions of their Nests and Eggs. D. Appleton and Company, New York. 12mo. 427 pp.

1897. *Bird-Life: A Guide to the Study of Our Common Birds.* D. Appleton and Company. 12mo. 269 pp.

1900. *Bird Studies with a Camera.* D. Appleton and Company. 12mo. 218 pp.

1903. *Color Key to North American Birds.* With upward of 800 drawings by Chester A. Reed. Doubleday, Page and Company. 8vo. 312 pp.

1907. *The Warblers of North America* (with other ornithologists). D. Appleton and Company. 8vo. 306 pp.

1908. *Camps and Cruises of an Ornithologist.* D. Appleton and Company. 8vo. 432 pp.

1912. *Color Key to North American Birds.* With upwards of 800 drawings by Chester A. Reed. With bibliographical appendix. D. Appleton and Company. Revised ed. 8vo. 356 pp.

1912. *Handbook of Birds of Eastern North America.* Revised edition. D. Appleton and Company. 12mo. 530 pp.

1916. *The Travels of Birds.* D. Appleton and Company. 12mo. 160 pp.

1917. *The Distribution of Bird-Life in Colombia.* Bull. Am. Mus. Nat. Hist., 8vo., Vol. XXXVI, 729 pp.

1918. *Our Winter Birds: How to Know and Attract Them.* D. Appleton and Company. 12mo. 180 pp.

1920. *What Bird Is That?* — 301 birds in color by Edmund J. Sawyer. D. Appleton and Company. 12mo. 144 pp.

1921. *The Distribution of Bird-Life in the Urumbamba Valley of Peru.* Bulletin U.S. Nat. Mus., No. 117, 138 pp.

1926. *The Distribution of Bird-Life in Ecuador.* Bull. Am. Mus. Nat. Hist., Vol. LV, 784 pp.

1929. *My Tropical Air Castle.* D. Appleton and Company. 8vo. 417 pp.

1932. *Handbook of Birds of Eastern North America.* 2nd revised edition. D. Appleton and Company. 12mo. 581 pp.

1933. *Autobiography of a Bird-Lover.* Appleton-Century Company. 8vo. 420 pp.

1938. *Life in an Air Castle.* Appleton-Century Company. 8vo. 243 pp.

1966. *Handbook of Birds of Eastern North America.* Photo offset reprint of 2nd Revised edition. Dover Press. 12mo. 581 pp.

ARTICLES IN PERIODICALS

1886. Birds and Bonnets. Forest and Stream, vol. 26, p. 84.
　　　The Lark Finch in New Jersey. Auk, vol. 3, p. 136.
　　　The Barn Owl at Englewood, New Jersey. Auk, vol. 3, p. 485.
1887. Additional Captures of *Helminthophila leucobronchialis.* Auk, vol. 4, pp. 348-349.
1888. Observations on the Nocturnal Migration of Birds. Auk, vol. 5, pp. 37-39.
　　　A List of Birds Observed at Gainesville, Florida. Auk, vol. 5, pp. 267-277.
　　　Birds at Aiken, S. C. Auk, vol. 5, p. 324.
　　　Oidemia perspecillata in Florida. Auk, vol. 5, p. 319.
　　　List of Additions to the North American Avifauna and of Eliminations and Changes in Nomenclature Proposed Since the Publication of the A.O.U. Check-List. Auk, vol. 5, pp. 393-402.
1889. Preliminary Descriptions of Two Apparently New Species of the Genus *Hesperomys* from Florida. Bull. Am. Mus. Nat. Hist., vol. 2, p. 117.
　　　Description of a New Subspecies of the Genus *Sigmodon* from Florida. Bull. Am. Mus. Nat. Hist., vol. 2, p. 118.
　　　On the Habits of the Round-tailed Muskrat *(Neofiber alleni* True). Bull. Am. Mus. Nat. Hist., vol. 2, pp. 119-122.
　　　A Revision of the Genus *Xiphorhynchus* Swainson, with descriptions of Two New Species. Bull. Am. Mus. Nat. Hist., vol. 2, pp. 153-162.
　　　A Description of a New Species of Hummingbird of the genus *Amazillia.* Bull. Am. Mus. Nat. Hist., vol. 2, pp. 163-164.
　　　Further Note on *Amazilia aeneobrunnea.* Bull. Am. Nat. Hist., vol. 2, p. 182.
　　　Notes on the Birds of Aiken, S. C. Abstract. Auk, vol. 6, p. 197.
　　　Notes on the Mniotiltidae of Englewood, New Jersey. Abstract. Auk, vol. 6, p. 198.
　　　Remarks on the Northern Limit of the Carolinian Fauna on the Atlantic Coast. Abstract. Auk, vol. 6, p. 199.
　　　Helminthophila bachmani on the East Coast of Florida. Auk, vol. 6, pp. 278-279.
　　　Notes on Birds Observed in the Vicinity of Englewood, N. J. Auk, vol. 6, pp. 302-305.
1890. On a Collection of Birds by Mr. Clark P. Streator in British Columbia, with Field Notes by the Collector. Bull. Am. Mus. Nat. Hist., vol. 3, pp. 123-158.
　　　On the Eastern Forms of *Geothlypis trichas.* Auk, vol. 7, pp. 9-14.
　　　On the Winter Distribution of the Bobolink *(Dolichonyx oryzivorus),* with Remarks on its Routes of Migration. Auk, vol. 7, pp. 39-45.
　　　Note on *Cyanocitta stelleri litoralis* Maynard. Auk, vol. 7, p. 91.
　　　On the Changes of Plumage in the Bobolink *(Dolichonyx oryzivorus).* Auk, vol. 7, pp. 120-124.
　　　Annotations in "A List of Birds Observed at Santarem, Brazil," by C. B. Riker. Auk, vol. 7, pp. 131-137; 265-271; vol. 8, pp. 24-31, 158-164.
　　　The Song of *Helminthophila leucobronchialis.* Auk, vol. 7, p. 291.
　　　Notes on the Carolina Paroquet *(Conurus carolinensis)* in Florida. Abstract Proc. Linnaean Soc. N. Y., pp. 2-4.
　　　Remarks on a Trip to Brevard County, Florida, in the spring of 1889. Abstract Proc. Linnaean Soc. N. Y., p. 8.
1891. *Ictinia mississippiensis.* Orn. & Ool., vol. 14, p. 44.
　　　The Carolina Paroquet. Forest and Stream, vol. 37, p. 44.

On the Color-Pattern of the Upper Tail-coverts in *Colaptes auratus*. Bull. Am. Mus. Nat. Hist., vol. 3, pp. 311-314.

On the Birds Observed near Corpus Christi, Texas, during Parts of March and April, 1891. Bull. Am. Mus. Nat. Hist., vol. 3, pp. 315-328.

Note on *Junco hyemalis thurberi* Anthony. Auk, vol. 8, pp. 115-116.

Notes on the Birds of the Lower Suwannee River (with William Brewster). Auk, vol. 8, pp. 125-138.

On Two Birds New to Louisiana. Auk. vol. 8, p. 318.

Former Occurrence of *Spiza americana* in Northern N. J. Auk. vol. 8, p. 395.

Origin of the Avifauna of the Bahamas. Trans. N. Y. Acad. Sci., p. 54.

1892. A Preliminary Study of Grackles of the Subgenus *Quiscalus*. Bull. Am. Mus. Nat. Hist., vol. 4, pp. 1-20.

Notes on Birds and Mammals Observed near Trinidad, Cuba, with Remarks on the Origin of West Indian Bird Life. Bull. Am. Mus. Nat. Hist., vol. 4, pp. 279-330.

Birds of Central Park [New York City]. N. Y. Evening Post, I, June 18; II, June 25; III, July 2.

On the breeding of *Helminthophila pinus* with *H. leucobronchialis* at Englewood, New Jersey. Auk, vol. 9, pp. 302-303.

Melanism in a Caged Wood Thrush. Auk, vol. 9, pp. 303-304.

1893. Description of a New Subspecies of *Oryzomys* from the Gulf States. Bull. Am. Mus. Nat. Hist., vol. 5, pp. 43-46.

On a Collection of Mammals from the Island of Trinidad, with Descriptions of New Species (with J. A. Allen). Bull. Am. Mus. Nat. Hist., vol. 5, pp. 203-234.

Description of Two New Races of Mammals from Florida, with Remarks on *Sitomys niveiventris* Chapman. Bull. Am. Mus. Nat. Hist., vol. 5, pp. 339-341.

The Carolina Wren in the Lower Hudson Valley. Auk, vol. 10, p. 87.

On the Changes of Plumage in the Bobolink *(Dolichonyx oryzivorus)*. Auk, vol. 10, pp. 309-311.

Ornithology at the World's Fair. Auk, vol. 10, pp. 315-321.

Preliminary Descriptions of One New Species and Two New Subspecies of Birds from the Island of Trinidad. Auk, vol. 10, pp. 342-343.

1894. Remarks on the Origin of Bird Migration. Auk, vol. 11, pp. 12-17.

Birds of the Island of Trinidad. Bull. Am. Mus. Nat. Hist., vol. 6, pp. 1-86.

Remarks on Certain Land Mammals from Florida with a List of the Species Known to Occur in the State. Bull. Am. Mus. Nat. Hist., vol. 6, pp. 333-346.

Visitor's Guide to the Collection of Birds Found within Fifty Miles of New York City. Printed for the Am. Mus. Nat. Hist., pp. 1-100.

The Nocturnal Migration of Birds. Pop. Sci. Mo., 45, pp. 506-511.

1895. The Study of Birds Out of Doors. Pop. Sci. Mo., 47, pp. 664-670.

Further Notes on Trinidad Birds, with a Description of a New Species of *Synallaxis*. Bull. Am. Mus. Nat. Hist., vol. 7, pp. 321-326.

Notes on Birds Observed in Trinidad (with William Brewster). Auk, vol. 12, pp. 201-211.

History of a Wandering Albatross. Auk, vol. 12, pp. 291-292.

1896. The Changes of Plumage in the Dunlin and Sanderling. Bull. Am. Mus. Nat. Hist., vol. 8, pp. 1-8.

On the Changes of Plumage in the Snowflake *(Plectrophenax nivalis)*. Bull. Am. Mus. Nat. Hist., vol. 8, pp. 9-12.

Notes on Birds Observed in Yucatan. Bull. Am. Mus. Nat. Hist., vol. 8, pp. 271-290.

The Standing of *Ardetta neoxena.* Auk, vol. 13, pp. 11-19.

The Turkey Vulture in the Catskills. Auk, vol. 13, pp. 341-342.

The Wild Pigeon at Englewood, New Jersey. Auk, vol. 13, p. 341.

Feeding Habits of Purple Finches. Auk, vol. 13, p. 342.

Dendroica palmarum in New York City. Auk. vol. 13, p. 343.

Meteor or Bird. Science, vol. 4, pp. 316-317.

1897. Remarks on the Spring Molt of the Bobolink. Auk, vol. 14, pp. 149-154.

Preliminary Descriptions of New Birds from Mexico and Arizona. Auk, vol. 14, pp. 310-311.

Murres in Western New York. Auk, vol. 13, p. 202.

Critical Notes and Descriptions of Two New Species, in "Birds Observed on a Collecting Trip to Bermudez, Venezuela," by W. H. Phelps. Auk, vol. 14, pp. 367-371.

The Wearing of Heron's Plumes or Aigrettes. The Osprey, vol. 2, no. 1, pp. 8-9.

On Mammals from Yucatan, with Descriptions of New Species. Bull. Am. Mus. Nat. Hist., vol. 9, pp. 1-12.

On a Second Collection of Mammals from the Island of Trinidad, with descriptions of New Species, and a Note on Some Mammals from the Island of Dominica, W. I. (with J. A. Allen). Bull. Am. Mus. Nat. Hist., vol. 9, pp. 13-30.

On a Collection of Mammals from Jalapa and Las Vigas, State of Vera Cruz, Mexico. Bull. Am. Mus. Nat. Hist., vol. 9, pp. 197-208.

1898. Notes on Birds Observed at Jalapa and Las Vigas, Vera Cruz, Mexico. Bull. Am. Mus. Nat. Hist., vol. 10, pp. 15-43.

Origin of West India Bird Life. Nat. Geogr. Mag., vol. 9, pp. 243-247.

Golden Eagle in New Jersey. Auk, vol. 15, p. 54.

Probable Polygamy of the Great-tailed Grackle. Auk, vol. 15, p. 269.

Notes on the Black Seaside Finch. Auk, vol. 15, p. 270.

Nesting Instincts of Swallows. Auk, vol. 15, p. 271.

Kirtland's Warbler (*Dendroica kirtlandi*). Auk, vol. 15, pp. 289-293.

1899. The Distribution and Relationships of *Ammodramus maritimus* and Its Allies. Auk, vol. 16, pp. 1-12.

Further Notes on *Dendroica kirtlandi.* Auk, vol. 16, p. 81.

Descriptions of Five Apparently New Birds from Venezuela. Bull. Am. Mus. Nat. Hist., vol. 12, pp. 153-156.

Report on Birds Received through the Peary Expedition to Greenland. Bull. Am. Mus. Nat. Hist., vol. 12, pp. 219-244.

Descriptions of Two New Subspecies of *Colymbus dominicus.* Linn. Bull. Am. Mus. Nat. Hist., vol. 12, p. 255.

The Educational Value of Bird Study. Educ. Rev., March, pp. 242-246.

Bird Rock. Century Mag., vol. 58, pp. 329-339.

Bird-Lore, a bi-monthly magazine, 1899-1935. Numerous notes, reviews & editorials.

An Ornithologist's Experiences in Cuba. The Osprey, vol. 2, no. 5, pp. 59-62. Two illustrations.

Fauna of Porto Rico. Science, vol. 10, p. 419.

The Pelicans of Pelican Island, Indian River, Florida. Abstracts Proc. Linnaean Soc. N. Y., vol. 11, p. 3.

Pelican Island. St. Nicholas Magazine, Sept.

The Legend of the Salt. Bird-Lore, vol. 1, pp. 55-56.

Birds through a Telescope. Bird-Lore, vol. 1, p. 132.

The Surprising Contents of a Birch Stub. Bird-Lore, vol. 1, pp. 187-189.

Passing of the Tern. Bird-Lore, vol. 1, pp. 205-206.

1900. The Value of Birds to the Commonwealth. Rprt of Sec. of Dept. of Agriculture for 1900, pp. 1-41.

A Study of the Genus *Sturnella.* Bull. Am. Mus. Nat. Hist., vol. 13, pp. 297-320.

A Note on the Economic Value of Gulls, Bird-Lore, vol. 2, p. 10.

Obituary Notice of Elliott Coues. Bird-Lore, vol. 2, p. 3.

Description of the Nestling Plumage of *Falco islandus.* Auk, vol. 17, p. 387.

Proper Name for the Florida Yellow-throat. Auk, vol. 17, pp. 289-290.

1901. Economic Value of Birds to the State. Ann. Rpt. N. Y. Forest, Fish, and Game Comm. Albany, pp. 115-176.

A New Race of the Great Blue Heron, with Remarks on the Status and Range of *Ardea wardi.* Bull. Am. Mus. Nat. Hist., vol. 14, pp. 87-90.

Descriptions of Six Apparently New Birds from Peru. Bull. Am. Mus. Nat. Hist., vol. 14, pp. 225-228.

A Revision of the Genus *Capromys.* Bull. Am. Mus. Nat. Hist., vol. 14, pp. 313-323.

Pelican Island Revisited. Bird-Lore, vol. 3, pp. 3-8.

Bird Nesting with Burroughs. Bird-Lore, vol. 3, p. 88.

A New Device for Securing Birds' Pictures. Bird-Lore, vol. 3, p. 194.

How to Name the Birds. Bird-Lore, vol. 3, pp. 200-206.

Camera Hunter. Outing Magazine, vol. 38, pp. 255-257.

The Correct Name for the Florida Yellow-throat. Auk, vol. 18, p. 198.

The Local Collection of Mounted Birds. Am. Mus. Jour., vol. 1, pp. 27-28.

Hybrid Grouse. Am. Mus. Jour., vol. 1, pp. 62-70.

The Department of Ornithology. Am. Mus. Jour., vol. 1, pp. 102-104.

The Bird Rock Group. Am. Mus. Jour., supp. to No. 11, pp. 1-25.

1902. An Exhibit Designed to Illustrate Terms Used in Descriptive Ornithology. Am. Mus. Jour., vol. 2, pp. 33-34.

Collecting Flamingoes and Their Nests in the Bahama Islands. Am. Mus. Jour., vol. 2, pp. 78-83.

Natural History for the Masses. World's Work, vol. 5, pp. 260-270.

List of Birds Collected in Alaska by the Andrew J. Stone Expedition of 1901. Bull. Am. Mus. Nat. Hist., vol. 16, pp. 231-247.

A Hybrid Between the Cliff and Tree Swallows. Auk, vol. 19, pp. 392-394.

How to Name the Birds. Bird-Lore, vol. 4, pp. 20, 62, 88, 124, 155, 189.

The Great Auk in Florida. Bird-Lore, vol. 4, p. 97.

Flamingoes' Nests. Bird-Lore, vol. 4, p. 177.

How to Study Birds (first paper). Bird-Lore, vol. 4, p. 194.

Strange Experiences of a Blue Jay Family. Century Mag., vol. 64, pp. 405-422.

1903. How to Study Birds (second paper). Bird-Lore, vol. 5, pp. 25-27.

The Bird-Life of Cobb's Island. Bird-Lore, vol. 5, p. 109.

An Island Eden. Bird-Lore, vol. 5, pp. 175-182.

Pine Grosbeak at Englewood, N. J. Bird-Lore, vol. 5, p. 199.

Economic Value of Birds to the State. Ann. Rpt. N. Y. Forest, Fish, and Game Comm., 4to. Albany, pp. 1-66, 12 plates.

Hunting with a Camera. World's Work. vol. 6, pp. 3554-3560.

1904. The Black Tern at Home (with E. Thompson Seton). Bird-Lore, vol. 6, pp. 1-5.

The Warbler Book. Bird-Lore, vol. 6, pp. 61-63.

Climatic Variation in Color and Size of the Song Sparrow. Bird-Lore, vol. 6, pp. 164-165.

Birds' Nests and Eggs. Am. Mus. Nat. Hist. Guide Leaflet.

New Groups of Game Birds. Am. Mus. Jour., vol. 4, pp. 71-72.

Young Flamingoes. Bird-Lore, vol. 6, pp. 193-198.

A New Grouse from California. Bull. Am. Mus. Nat. Hist., vol. 20, pp. 159-162.

List of Birds Collected in Alaska by the Andrew J. Stone Expedition of 1903. Bull. Am. Mus. Nat. Hist., vol. 20, pp. 399-406.

A Flamingo City. Century Mag., vol. 69, pp. 163-180.

The Case of William J. Long. Science, vol. 19, pp. 387-389.

Flamingoes' Nests. Smithsonian Report for 1903, pp. 573-575.

1905. A Contribution to the Life History of the American Flamingo (*Phoenicopterus ruber*), with Remarks upon Specimens. Bull. Am. Mus. Nat. Hist., vol. 21, pp. 53-57.

What Constitutes a Museum Collection of Birds? Proc. 4th Internat. Orn. Congress, pp. 144-156.

Birds' Nests and Eggs. Am. Mus. Jour., vol. 4, pp. 5-31.

Note on the Migration of Warblers from the Bahamas to Florida. Bird-Lore, vol. 7, p. 140.

The Feeding Habits of the Northern Phalarope. Bird-Lore, vol. 7, pp. 273-274.

Photographing Flamingoes in their Rookery. Country Life, vol. 8, pp. 41-44.

Flamingo Outfit. Country Life, vol. 8, p. 84.

Intimate Study of the Pelican. Century Mag., vol. 71, pp. 198-211.

1906. List of Birds Found Within Fifty Miles of the American Museum of Natural History, New York City. Am. Mus. Nat. Hist. Guide Leaflet.

The Birds of the Vicinity of New York. Am. Mus. Jour., vol. 6, pp. 81-102.

Florida Bird Life, Pelicans and Paroquets. Abstracts Proc. Linnaean Soc. N.Y., Nos. 17-19, p. 3.

Bird Garden. Country Life, vol. 10, p. 74.

Bird Shelter. Country Life, vol. 10, p. 78.

Our New Bird Citizen. Country Life, vol. 12, p. 551.

American Impressions of English Bird Life. Scribners, vol. 39, pp. 705-720.

1907. The Eastern Forms of *Geothlypis trichas*. Auk, vol. 24, pp. 30-34.

The New Bird Groups in the American Museum of Natural History. Bird-Lore, vol. 9, pp. 168-170.

A Season's Field Work. Bird-Lore, vol. 9, pp. 256-262.

A Report on Expeditions Made in 1907 under the North American Ornithology Funds. Am. Mus. Jour., vol. 7, pp. 121-132.

1908. A Contribution to the Life-Histories of the Booby (*Sula leucogastra*) and Man-O'-War Bird (*Fregata aquila*). Carnegie Inst. Wash., Publ. 103, pp. 139-151.

A Bird Friend. Bird-Lore, vol. 10, pp. 14-15.

Home Life of the American Egret. Bird-Lore, vol. 10, pp. 59-68.

The Fish Hawks of Gardiner's Island. Bird-Lore, vol. 10, pp. 153-159.

The Use of a Blind in the Study of Bird-Life. Bird-Lore, vol. 10, pp. 250-252.

Cuthbert Rookery. Am. Mus. Jour., vol. 8, pp. 90-101.

Love-Making of the Prairie Hen. Outing, vol. 5, pp. 222-224.

Bird-Life and the Scenery of a Continent in One Corridor. World's Work, vol. 17, pp. 11367-74.

1909. The Feud of the Crows and the Owl. Bird-Lore, vol. 11, pp. 4-6.
The Bobolink. Bird-Lore, vol. 11, pp. 137-140.
Bird Motion by Cinematograph. Colliers, vol. 42, p. 20.

1910. Notes on the Plumages of North American Birds. A series of 95 short papers in Bird-Lore, 1910-1932.
Protective Coloration in the Habitat Groups of Birds. Am. Mus. Jour., vol. 10, pp. 195-198.
The New Loon Group. Am. Mus. Jour., vol. 10, pp. 260-261.
Marriage Customs of Birds. Colliers Mag., vol. 44, p. 34.

1911. Description of a New Oriole (*Icterus fuertesi*) from Mexico. Auk, vol. 28, pp. 1-4.
A New Oriole from Mexico. Am. Mus. Jour., vol. 11, p. 20.
Zoological Exploration in South America. Am. Mus. Jour., vol. 11, p. 52.
Same title as above. Bull. Panamerican Union, vol. 32, pp. 501-505.

1912. Diagnoses of Apparently New Colombian Birds. Bull. Am. Mus. Nat. Hist., vol. 31, pp. 139-166.
A New Ibis from Mt. Kenya, British East Africa. Bull. Am. Mus. Nat. Hist., vol. 31, pp. 235-238.
The Orizaba Group in the American Museum of Natural History. Bird-Lore, vol. 14, p. 97.
An Eighteen-Year Retrospect. Bird-Lore, vol. 14, pp. 141-144.

1913. Birds May Bring You More Happiness than the Wealth of the Indies. Nat. Geographic, vol. 24, pp. 299-714.
Remarks on a Recent Trip to Florida. Abstract Proc. Linnaean Soc. N.Y., vol. 21, p. 15.
Account of a Visit to Cuthbert Rookery. Abstract Proc. Linnaean Soc. N. Y., vol. 21, p. 17.
The Scientific Value of Bird Photographs. Auk, vol. 30, pp. 47-149.

1914. Diagnoses of Apparently New Colombian Birds—II. Bull. Am. Mus. Nat. Hist., vol. 33, pp. 167-192.
Descriptions of a New Genus and Species of Birds from Venezuela. Bull. Am. Mus. Nat. Hist., vol. 33, pp. 193-197.
Descriptions of New Birds from Ecuador. Bull. Am. Mus. Nat. Hist., vol. 33, pp. 317-322.
Diagnoses of Apparently New Colombian Birds — III. Bull. Am. Mus. Nat. Hist., vol. 33, pp. 603-637.
A Naturalist's Journey around Vera Cruz and Tampico. Nat. Geogr. Mag., vol. 25, pp. 532-562.
The Roseate Spoonbill. Bird-Lore, vol. 16, pp. 214-217.
Louis Agassiz Fuertes — Painter of Bird Portraits. Am. Mus. Jour., vol. 15, pp. 221-224.

1915. Descriptions of Proposed New Birds from Central and South America. Bull. Am. Mus. Nat. Hist., vol. 34, pp. 363-388.
Diagnoses of Apparently New Colombian Birds—IV. Bull. Am. Mus. Nat. Hist., vol. 34, pp. 635-662.
The More Northern Species of the Genus *Scytalopus* Gould. Auk, vol. 32, pp. 406-423.
Louis Agassiz Fuertes—Painter of Birds, Bird-Lore, vol. 17, pp. 277-284.
Bird Clubs in America. Bird-Lore, vol. 17, pp. 347-348.
Mysteries of Migration. Country Life, vol. 29, pp. 33-36.
Birds as Travelers. St. Nicholas Mag., vol. 43, pp. 171-174, 265-268, 366-369, 458-462, 552-554, 846-849.

1917. Descriptions of New Birds from Santo Domingo and Remarks on Others in the Brewster-Sanford Collection. Bull. Am. Mus. Nat. Hist., vol. 37, pp. 327-334.

In Memoriam; Daniel Giraud Elliot. Auk, vol. 34, pp. 1-10.

A Condor's Quill. Bird-Lore, vol. 19, pp. 5-8.

1918. One Year with the American Red Cross. Washington, D. C., 1 S., No. 2, pp. 1-40.

Notes from a Traveller in the Tropics: I. Down the Coastline to Cuba. Bird-Lore, vol. 20, pp. 393-397.

1919. William Brewster — 1851-1919. Bird-Lore, vol. 21, pp. 277-286.

Descriptions of Proposed New Birds from Peru, Bolivia, Argentina, and Chile. Bull. Am. Mus. Nat. Hist., vol. 41, pp. 323-333.

Descriptions of Proposed New Birds from Peru, Bolivia, Brazil and Colombia. Proc. Biol. Soc. Wash., vol. 32, pp. 253-268.

Notes from a Traveller in the Tropics: II. Cuba to Panama. Bird-Lore, vol. 21, pp. 11-15; III. From Panama to Peru, pp. 87-91; IV. Peru, pp. 157-164; V. Chile, pp. 333-341.

Nature and England. Bird-Lore, vol. 21, pp. 215-218.

The Study of Bird-Life in the Schools of New Jersey. Bird-Lore, vol. 21, pp. 257-258.

1920. Unusual Types of Apparent Geographic Variation in Color and of Individual Variation in Size Exhibited by *Ostinops decumanus*. Proc. Biol. Soc. Wash., vol. 33, pp. 25-32.

Description of a Proposed New Race of the Killdeer from the Coast of Peru. Auk, vol. 37, pp. 105-108.

1921. Over the Andes to Bogota. Nat. Geogr. Mag., vol. 40, pp. 353-373.

Descriptions of Apparently New Birds from Bolivia, Brazil, and Venezuela. Am. Mus. Nov., No. 2, pp. 1-8.

Descriptions of Proposed New Birds from Colombia, Ecuador, Peru and Brazil. Am. Mus. Nov., No. 18, pp. 1-12.

Descriptions of Apparently New Birds from Colombia, Ecuador, and Argentina. Am. Mus. Nov., No. 31, pp. 1-18.

John Burroughs, 1837-1921. Bird-Lore, vol. 23, pp. 119-123.

Our Christmas Bird Guests. Country Life Mag., vol. 41, pp. 41-43.

1922. The Distribution of the Swallows of the Genus *Pygochelidon*. Am. Mus. Nov., No. 30, pp. 1-15.

The Department of Birds, American Museum: Its History and Aims. Nat. Hist., vol. 22, pp. 306-318.

In Memoriam: Joel Asaph Allen. Auk, vol. 39, pp. 1-14.

Courtney Brandreth's Bird Paintings. Bird-Lore, vol. 24, pp. 1-6.

1923. Descriptions of Proposed New Formicariidae and Dendrocolaptidae. Am. Mus. Nov., No. 86, pp. 1-19.

Descriptions of Proposed New Birds from Venezuela, Colombia, Ecuador, Peru, and Chile. Am. Mus. Nov., No. 96, pp. 1-12.

The Distribution of the Motmots of the Genus *Momotus*. Bull. Am. Mus. Nat. Hist., vol. 48, pp. 27-59.

Mutation among Birds in the Genus *Buarremon*. Bull. Am. Mus. Nat. Hist., vol. 48, pp. 243-278.

1924. Criteria for the Determination of Subspecies in Systematic Ornithology. Auk, vol. 41, pp. 17-29.

The House Wrens of the Genus *Troglodytes*. (With Ludlow Griscom.) Bull. Am. Mus. Nat. Hist., vol. 50, pp. 279-304.

Descriptions of New Flycatchers from Colombia, Ecuador, and Peru. Am. Mus. Nov., No. 118, pp. 1-11.

Descriptions of New Genera and Species of Tracheophonae from Panama, Ecuador, Peru, and Bolivia. Am. Mus. Nov., No. 123, pp. 1-9.

Descriptions of New Birds from Ecuador, Colombia, Peru, and Bolivia. Am. Mus. Nov., No. 138, pp. 1-15.

Descriptions of New Birds from Colombia, Peru, and Bolivia. Am. Mus. Nov., No. 143, pp. 1-16.

The Andes: A New World. Nat. Hist., vol. 24, pp. 420-428.

Birds and Man. Bird-Lore, vol. 26, pp. 231-235.

Bird That Burrows. Worlds Work, vol. 49, pp. 192-196.

1925. Descriptions of New Birds from Colombia, Ecuador, Peru, and Argentina. Am. Mus. Nov., No. 160, pp. 1-15.

Descriptions of New Birds from Ecuador and Peru. Am. Mus. Nov., No. 187, pp. 1-9.

Remarks on the Life Zones of Northeastern Venezuela with Descriptions of New Species of Birds. Am. Mus. Nov., No. 191, pp. 1-14.

Descriptions of One Genus and Species of Birds from Peru and Ecuador. Am. Mus. Nov., No. 205, pp. 1-11.

The European Starling as an American Citizen. Nat. Hist., vol. 25, pp. 480-485.

The Relationships and Distribution of the Warblers of the Genus *Compsothlypsis:* A Contribution to the Study of the Origin of Andean Bird-Life. Auk, vol. 42, pp. 193-208.

Bird Gardening from Cosmos to Crocus. Garden Mag., vol. 42, pp. 109-110.

The Bird in Art. Country Life, vol. 39, pp. 34-37.

A Plea for the Evidence. Auk, vol. 42, p. 612; Ibis, vol. 66, p. 938-939.

1926. An Island Ark: An Unusual Wild Life Refuge near Panama. Worlds Work, November, pp. 60-66.

Darwin's Chile. Geogr. Jour., November, pp. 369-385.

Descriptions of New Birds from Bolivia, Peru, Ecuador, and Brazil. Am. Mus. Nov., No. 231, pp. 1-7.

Phibalura flavirostris Vieill. in Bolivia. Auk, vol. 43, p. 99.

Fate of the Passenger Pigeon. Country Life, vol. 5, pp. 49-50.

1927. Biographical Memoir Joel Asaph Allen. Mem. Nat'l. Acad. Sci., vol. 21, pp. 1-20.

Who Treads Our Trails? Nat. Geogr. Mag., vol. 52, pp. 330-345.

The Variations and Distribution of *Saltator aurantiirostris.* Am. Mus. Nov., No. 261, pp. 1-19.

Bird Haven: The Robert Ridgway Wild Life Sanctuary. Bird-Lore, vol. 29, pp. 1-4.

The Unveiling of the Roosevelt Memorial Fountain. Bird-Lore, vol. 29, pp. 225-226.

Address on the Unveiling of the Bust of John James Audubon in the Hall of Fame. Bird-Lore, vol. 29, pp. 223-225.

Roosevelt the Bird-Lover. Bird-Lore, vol. 29, pp. 309-313.

Louis Agassiz Fuertes: 1874-1927. Bird-Lore, vol. 29, pp. 359-368.

1928. In Memoriam: Louis Agassiz Fuertes. Auk, vol. 41, pp. 1-26.

Descriptions of New Birds from Eastern Ecuador and Eastern Peru. Am. Mus. Nov., No. 332, pp. 1-12.

Homes of a Hummer. Nat. Hist., vol. 28, pp. 284-289.

Mutation in *Capito auratus.* Am. Mus. Nov., No. 335, pp. 1-21.

The Nesting Habits of Wagler's Oropendola *(Zarhynchus wagleri)* on Barro Colorado Island. Bull. Am. Mus. Nat. Hist., vol. 58, pp. 123-166.

1929. Descriptions of New Birds from Mt. Roraima. Am. Mus. Nov., No. 341. pp. 1-7.
Descriptions of New Birds from Mt. Duida. Am. Mus. Nov., No. 380, pp. 1-27.
Relations of the Races of *Phaeoprogne tapera* and Their Probable Significance. Auk, vol. 46, pp. 348-357.
Common Sense and Nomenclature. Auk, vol. 46, p. 576.
Robert Ridgway: 1850-1929. Bird-Lore, vol. 31, pp. 173-178.
Presenting the Coati. Scribners Mag., vol. 85, pp. 292-300.
Conquest of Claudia. Nat. Hist., vol. 29, pp. 367-379.

1930. A New Race of *Phibalura flavirostris* from Bolivia. Auk, vol. 47, p. 87.
Nesting Habits of Wagler's Oropendola on Barro Colorado Island. Ann. Rpt. Smithsonian Instn. for 1930, pp. 347-386. (Reprinted from 1928 title.)
Habitat Groups of North American Birds. Am. Mus. Guide Leaflet No. 28, 5th ed.

1931. A New Race of *Brachygalba lugubris* from Northeastern Brazil. Am. Mus. Nov., No. 450, pp. 1-3.
The Upper Zonal Bird-Life of Mts. Roraima and Duida. Bull. Am. Mus. Nat. Hist., vol. 63, pp. 1-135.
Seen from a Tropical Air Castle. Nat. Hist., vol. 31, pp. 347-358.
The Trogons of Barro Colorado. Bird-Lore, vol. 33, pp. 105-107.
Columba squamosa at Key West. Auk, vol. 48, p. 116.
The Winter Range of the Chimney Swift *(Chaetura pelagica)*. Auk, vol. 48, pp. 119-121.
Northern Crested Flycatcher in Western Panama — A Correction. Auk, vol. 48, p. 603.

1932. Introductory notes and photographs in "Canvasback Ducks in Northumberland" by Viscount Grey of Fallodon. Nat. Hist., vol. 32, pp. 453-463.
From a Tropical Air Castle: The Courtship of Gould's Manakin. Nat. Hist., vol. 32, pp. 469-479.
Relation of Bird-Lore to the National Association of Audubon Societies. Bird-Lore, vol. 34, pp. 284-285.
An Eden where Man Spares Beast. N. Y. Times Mag., Dec. 4, pp. 6, 16.

1933. The Migration of Turkey Buzzards as Observed on Barro Colorado Island. Auk, vol. 50, pp. 30-34.
Obituary of Frederick J. Dixon. Auk, vol. 50, p. 153.
Introduction (with T. S. Palmer) to "Fifty Years Progress of American Ornithology." Am. Orn. Union, pp. 5-6.
Collections of Birds in the United States and Canada: Exhibition Collections in "Fifty Years Progress of American Ornithology," pp. 143-157.

1934. A Season's Bird Guests. Nat. Hist., vol. 34, pp. 16-30.
My Florida Bird Guests. Nat. Hist., vol. 34, pp. 523-538.
Letter on Grackles. Auk, vol. 51, p. 279.
Letter on excessive collecting. Auk, vol. 51, pp. 429-430.
Obituary of Mabel Osgood Wright. Auk, vol. 51, pp. 564-565.
Descriptions of New Birds from Mocha Island, Chile, and the Falkland Islands, with Comments on their Bird Life and That of the Juan Fernandez Islands and Chiloe Island, Chile. Am. Mus. Nov., No. 762, pp. 1-8.

1935. The Whitney South Sea Expedition. Science, vol. 81, pp. 95-97.
The Courtship of Gould's Manakin *(Manacus vitellinus vitellinus)* on Barro Colorado Island, Canal Zone. Bull. Am. Mus. Nat. Hist., vol. 68, pp. 471-525.

Further Remarks on the Relationships of the Grackles of the Subgenus *Quiscalus*. Auk, vol. 52, pp. 21-29.

Letter on alleged excessive collecting. Auk, vol. 52, p. 128.

Quiscalus quiscula in Louisiana. Auk, vol. 52, pp. 418-420.

José, Two Months from the Life of a Barro Colorado Coati. Nat. Hist., vol. 35, pp. 299-308.

The Making of a Cayuco. Nat. Hist., vol. 35, pp. 311-316.

Presentation of Daniel Giraud Elliot Medal to James P. Chapin. Science, vol. 81, pp. 415-416.

1936. Further Remarks on *Quiscalus*, with a Report of Additional Specimens from Louisiana. Auk, vol. 53, pp. 405-417.

The Composer. Bird-Lore, vol. 38, pp. 267-273.

José — 1936. Nat. Hist., vol. 38, pp. 126-135.

White-lipped Peccary. Nat. Hist., vol. 38, pp. 408-414.

Fuertes and Audubon. Nat. Hist., vol. 39, pp. 204-214.

1937. My Monkey Neighbors on Barro Colorado. Nat. Hist., vol. 40, pp. 471-479.

José — 1937. Nat. Hist., vol. 40, pp. 524-527.

The Phelps Venezuela Expedition. Nat. Hist., vol. 40, pp. 760-762.

Three Barro Colorado Birds. Bird-Lore, vol. 39, pp. 413-419.

Letter of thanks to Aud. Socs. Bird-Lore, vol. 39, p. 462.

Introduction to "Adventures in Bird Protection" by T. Gilbert Pearson. D. Appleton Century Co., N. Y.

Simorenops proposed for *Anachilis*. Auk, vol. 54, p. 208.

Swifts at Sea. Auk, vol. 54, p. 392.

1939. The Riddle of *Oxyruncus*. Am. Mus. Nov., No. 1047, pp. 1-4.

The Upper Zonal Birds of Mt. Auyan-Tepui, Venezuela. Am. Mus. Nov., No. 1051, pp. 1-5.

Quiscalus in Mississippi. Auk, vol. 56, pp. 28-31.

Nomenclature in the Genus *Quiscalus*. Auk, vol. 56, pp. 364-365.

Memories of Louis Fuertes. Bird-Lore, vol. 41, pp. 3-10.

1940. The Birdman. Nat. Hist., vol. 45, pp. 147-150.

Señor Sparrow. Nat. Hist., vol. 46, pp. 200-204.

The European Bullfinch in Milledgeville. Oriole, vol. 5, p. 37.

The Post-Glacial History of *Zonotrichia capensis*. Bull. Am. Mus. Nat. Hist., vol. 77, pp. 381-438.

Further Studies of the Genus *Quiscalus*. Auk, vol. 57, pp. 225-233.

Unknown Fuertes Painting. Bird-Lore, vol. 42, pp. 540-541.

1941. Mockingbirds in Panama. Auk, vol. 58, pp. 98-99.

1942. Birding in a City Museum. Univ. State of N. Y. Bull. to Schools, vol. 28, pp. 260-262.

1943. Birds and Man. Am. Mus. Nat. Hist. Guide Leaflet Series, No. 115, pp. 7-52.

Everglades Islet. Aud. Mag., vol. 45, pp. 19-28.

William Henry Hudson, American. Aud. Mag., vol. 45, pp. 264-267.

Presentation of Daniel Giraud Elliot Medal to Robert Cushman Murphy in 1936. Science, vol. 97, p. 434.

11

The Birds of the Gainesville Region, Then & Now

by

OLIVER L. AUSTIN, JR.

*F*RANK M. CHAPMAN'S FIRST MAJOR SCIENTIFIC PAPER, "A list of the birds observed at Gainesville, Florida," appeared in the *Auk*, the journal of the American Ornithologists' Union, in July 1888. A more accurate title might have been "The winter and spring birds of the Gainesville region" for, as its author states, the paper was "based almost entirely on observations made from November 27, 1886 to May 27, 1887." In this six-month period he collected 581 specimens and gathered notes on the occurrence of 149 species, no slight accomplishment for a young man not in the best of health and working alone in unfamiliar country.

The report is not only the first one published on the birds of north-central Florida, it is a sound, reliable, first-hand account of what birds were here and of their status three-quarters of a century ago. Evaluated in the light of what contemporary records and his own autobiography, journals, and letters reveal of the conditions under which he worked, the paper is manifestly the product of a skilled field ornithologist who was careful and conscientious as well.

To the young naturalist from the north, the Gainesville he came to in 1886 must have had great appeal. Essentially a rural trading center and county seat at the junction of the Florida Southern and the Transit Railroads, it was then the fourth largest city in Florida, exceeded in size only by Jacksonville, Pensacola, and Key West. It boasted, in addition to the East Florida Seminary and various shops and stores, six hotels, a cotton gin, an iron foundry and machine shop, and a lumber yard and planing mill. Its population totalled about 2500, among which the whites outnumbered the colored by slightly more than 100. The town proper, clustered around the county courthouse in the central square, extended barely a half mile between what are now East and

West Third Streets, and about a mile north and south from the rail-road station at Depot Road (now South Seventh Avenue) to about where North Fifth Avenue now runs. Thus a five-minute walk over its unpaved streets in almost any direction took the youthful Frank Chapman into wild open country, broken only by a few rutted sand roads leading to the scattered outlying farms and citrus groves.

The surrounding rolling sandhills and flatlands were largely dominated by the long-leaf and slash pines, which the local lumbermen were felling to meet the growing town's building needs. Richer soils in more protected spots boasted hammock growth of live, laurel, and water oaks, sweet gum, hickory, red bay, and magnolia, often with tangles of smilax and wild grape. The deeper swamps and lake shores still supported some stands of virgin cypress among the black gums, white bay, and red maple.

Traveling and hunting at first on foot, later on horseback, young Frank seems to have remained largely within about five miles of town, except for the three days in January he "passed in the pine barrens going to and returning from Jonesville, a settlement 16 miles west of Gainesville." He probably saw little need to push farther afield, for within an hour's ride of town lay productive stretches of practically all the major types of habitat in north-central Florida. His principal hunting grounds were the shores of Newnan's Lake four miles east of town, Sugarfoot Prairie, then surrounded by a fine expanse of hammock four miles west, and the banks of Alachua Lake south of town "two or three miles through heavy sand" between Alachua Sink and Bivins Arm. He occasionally got as far as the head of Alachua Lake, of which he commented: "the best [collecting] place I have seen but unfortunately distant 8 miles."

Though birds were plentiful within reach of town, the effects on them of man's expanding civilization were already evident. One reason for this which Chapman, and also T. Gilbert Pearson who was then doing his first youthful birding nearby in Archer, were later to be instrumental in changing, was the careless attitude of the general public toward wildlife. It was so plentiful few could foresee or conceive of any need to conserve it. Game laws were nonexistent. Men shot what birds they pleased whenever and wherever they pleased, for food, for market, or just for fun. The main criteria determining what birds were killed for food were their toothsomeness, size, and availability. Song and insectivorous birds—Robins, Blue Jays, woodpeckers, and even Nighthawks—were shot for the pot as readily as quail, ducks, doves, and the Wild Turkey that Chapman noted as already "rare" around Gainesville. Plume hunters had already broken up most of the heron-ries within easy reach of the settlements, as his notes attest all too clearly. The only Carolina Parakeet on record for the county was collected in Gainesville the year before Chapman arrived. The Ivory-billed Woodpecker was retreating before the lumbermen's axes and saws to the few distant stands of big trees remaining. The Passenger Pigeon was entering its last sad decade, and the Roseate Spoonbill was diminishing rapidly.

From Chapman's early records we can trace the changes in the bird life of the Gainesville region that have ensued since his day. Most of these have followed changes in the local habitat, the most immediate and striking of which after the winter of 1886-87, was the reappearance of Payne's Prairie with the fortuitous draining of Alachua Lake, which Chapman was the first to describe in his journal of 1888. Important though this was, it was not nearly so far-reaching as the man-made changes that were slower in coming but just as inexorable. As the pines were cut, the hammocks cleared, and the swamps drained for farming, the birds inhabiting those habitats perforce declined. On the other hand, new plant associations in the farm lands, the orchards, and particularly the fallow and abandoned "old fields" of broomsedge and other weeds attracted a few new species.

To Chapman's original list of 149 species, later workers have added 93 more, bringing the total known to have occurred in Alachua County through 1965 to 242 species, as shown in the appended annotated list. Almost three-fourths of the subsequent additions, 67 to be exact, are today and doubtless always have been at best uncommon, and many of these are of irregular or accidental occurrence, known by only one or two records:

SPECIES OF UNCOMMON OR IRREGULAR OCCURRENCE TODAY IN ALACHUA COUNTY NOT RECORDED BY CHAPMAN

1. HORNED GREBE
2. WHITE-TAILED TROPIC BIRD
3. BROWN PELICAN
4. CANADA GOOSE
5. BLUE GOOSE
6. FULVOUS TREE DUCK
7. CINNAMON TEAL
8. EUROPEAN WIGEON
9. REDHEAD
10. CANVASBACK
11. GREATER SCAUP
12. COMMON GOLDENEYE
13. BUFFLEHEAD
14. WHITE-WINGED SCOTER
15. RED-BREASTED MERGANSER
16. BROAD-WINGED HAWK
17. SHORT-TAILED HAWK
18. ROUGH-LEGGED HAWK

19. PEREGRINE FALCON
20. VIRGINIA RAIL
21. BLACK RAIL
22. GOLDEN PLOVER
23. WILLET
24. PECTORAL SANDPIPER
25. WHITE-RUMPED SANDPIPER
26. DOWITCHER
27. BLACK-NECKED STILT
28. BONAPARTE'S GULL
29. LAUGHING GULL
30. FORSTER'S TERN
31. COMMON TERN
32. SOOTY TERN
33. ROYAL TERN
34. BLACK TERN
35. BLACK SKIMMER
36. RINGED TURTLE DOVE
37. BLACK-BILLED CUCKOO
38. GRAY KINGBIRD
39. WESTERN KINGBIRD
40. VERMILION FLYCATCHER
41. ROUGH-WINGED SWALLOW
42. CLIFF SWALLOW

43. BROWN CREEPER
44. LONG-BILLED MARSH WREN
45. WOOD THRUSH
46. SWAINSON'S THRUSH
47. VEERY
48. GOLDEN-CROWNED KINGLET
49. SWAINSON'S WARBLER
50. TENNESSEE WARBLER
51. YELLOW WARBLER
52. MAGNOLIA WARBLER
53. NORTHERN WATERTHRUSH
54. YELLOW-BREASTED CHAT
55. YELLOW-HEADED BLACKBIRD
56. BULLOCK'S ORIOLE
57. BREWER'S BLACKBIRD
58. SCARLET TANAGER
59. BLACK-HEADED GROSBEAK
60. ROSE-BREASTED GROSBEAK
61. PAINTED BUNTING
62. DICKCISSEL
63. PINE SISKIN
64. SLATE-COLORED JUNCO
65. CLAY-COLORED SPARROW
66. WHITE-CROWNED SPARROW

67. FOX SPARROW

Two species not on Chapman's list were, as pointed out above, already rare and vanishing—the Carolina Parakeet and the Ivory-billed Woodpecker. Six more species were definitely present in the county, but slightly beyond the range of his travels: the Reddish Egret, Glossy Ibis, and Limpkin at Orange Lake, the Yellow-crowned Night Heron and Wood Stork at Ledwith Lake, and the Scrub Jay in the nearest scrub habitat just south of Cross Creek, 16 miles south of Gainesville. The following 13 species, now of regular occurrence in the county, have come in and become established since Chapman's day and probably were not here in 1886-87:

1. DOUBLE-CRESTED
   CORMORANT
2. CATTLE EGRET
3. MOTTLED DUCK
4. SANDHILL CRANE

5. HERRING GULL
6. RING-BILLED GULL
7. BURROWING OWL
8. SHORT-BILLED
   MARSH WREN

9. STARLING
10. HOUSE SPARROW
11. BLUE GROSBEAK
12. LECONTE'S SPARROW
13. HENSLOW'S SPARROW

This leaves only five species that, from all we can determine today, should have been plentiful here in 1886: Least Bittern, Greater Yellowlegs, Least Sandpiper, Rock Dove, and Barn Swallow. Chapman doubtless regarded the Rock Dove as a domestic bird, and no more to be mentioned than the farmers' chickens. The absence of the other four species from his list is difficult to explain though, under the circumstances, certainly easy to pardon.

Undoubtedly the most gratifying change in the Florida bird life that Chapman lived to see was the return, with the protection he worked so successfully to obtain for them, of the species that had borne the brunt of the persecution for their plumes—the egrets, herons, gulls, and terns.

ANNOTATED LIST

ALL FORMS RECOGNIZED as having occurred in Alachua County are listed and numbered at the species level; references to subspecies are included where pertinent in the textual comments under the species. Species difficult to identify in the field for which specimen evidence of occurrence is lacking are considered hypothetical unless based on at least two separate reports by observers of known competence. The hypothetical species and the several recorded erroneously are listed in their proper sequence, but are enclosed in square brackets and unnumbered. The scientific and common names used and the sequence of species followed are those of the American Ornithologists' Union "Check-list of North American Birds," 5th edition, 1957. Forms preceded by a star (*) were reported here by Chapman, and the quotes introducing them are his comments from his 1888 paper. The abbreviation "UF" signifies the University of Florida collections in the Florida State Museum, "PBC" the private collection of Professor Pierce Brodkorb.

*1. COMMON LOON. *Gavia immer.* "From March 31 to April 17 about fifteen were seen flying over at a great altitude." Though a common winter visitor to both coasts from late October to May or early June, the Common Loon is of uncommon and irregular occurrence inland in Florida, appearing most often during migration. Burns (1952) states "Single birds were observed regularly on [Newnan's] lake between December and February." Karraker (1953) recorded single birds on Lake Alice March 31, April 21, and November 21, 1952. Two Gainesville specimens in the PBC were taken April 3, 1948 and October 17, 1953.

2. HORNED GREBE. *Podiceps auritus.* A fairly common winter visitor to both coasts of Florida from late October to late April, this species visits inland waters irregularly. Doe (notes) lists one picked up dead at Bivins Arm January 21, 1939 and remarks "skin made," which is not traceable. Burns (1952) saw three on Newnan's Lake December 6, 1950. The Audubon Christmas counts report one on Lake

Alice December 27, 1959 and a pair on Bivins Arm December 29, 1962.

*3. PIED-BILLED GREBE. *Podilymbus podiceps.* "Common; none were observed after April 27." Had he remained into the summer, FMC would probably have discovered that the Pied-billed Grebe nests here, as Pearson (1890) first reported. In the UF is a nest with seven eggs Charles E. Doe collected in Alachua County April 13, 1938. The species is still far more plentiful here in winter than in summer, most of the wintering population leaving for more northerly breeding grounds in April.

[WILSON'S PETREL. *Oceanites oceanicus.* The bird Sprunt (1949) reported seeing on Bivins Arm July 10, 1948 could just as well have been a Leach's Petrel. The two are exceedingly difficult to differentiate without the bird in hand.]

4. WHITE-TAILED TROPIC-BIRD. *Phaethon lepturus.* A UF specimen taken in Alachua August 12, 1955 was a storm-driven straggler from off-shore waters.

5. BROWN PELICAN. *Pelecanus occidentalis.* Also a straggler from the coast where it is a common resident. A UF specimen was collected at Levy Lake January 10, 1918.

6. DOUBLE-CRESTED CORMORANT. *Phalacrocorax auritus.* A year-round resident, but commonest in winter and not known to breed in the county. Its absence from FMC's list is explicable only, as McClanahan (1935) suggests, by assuming it did not push into this region until later. Had it been present on Newnan's or Alachua lakes, FMC could hardly have overlooked it. That local hunting pressure could have driven away the inland birds seems unlikely.

*7. ANHINGA. *Anhinga anhinga.* "Three extremely wild birds wintered among the cypresses on the lake; April 12, two flocks of seven or eight each were seen passing over, and on the 26th a flock of six more." The species is now fairly common the year round and, as it is no longer persecuted, is not at all wild. Pearson reported it nesting near Archer in 1891. It now nests commonly on trees in Lake Alice and Bivins Arm. In the UF are eggs collected in Gainesville May 9, 1926, and April 1, 7, 16, and 30, 1936.

[GREAT WHITE HERON. *Ardea occidentalis.* Howell (1932) reports a sight record by O. C. Van Hyning near Gainesville May 9, 1926. The "30 Great White Herons" FMC wrote of seeing a mile away on Alachua Lake December 3, 1886 were undoubtedly Common Egrets.]

*8. GREAT BLUE HERON. *Ardea herodias.* "Common." Still a common resident, starting to nest in March. Though Ridgway had described *A. h. wardi* from Estero Bay on the southwest coast of Florida in 1882, Chapman was evidently unaware that the resident birds nesting here are referable to that form, rather than to the nominate race, *A. h. herodias,* he was familiar with at home in New Jersey. In fact the subspecies concept was by no means well understood or universally accepted in those days. That the northern subspecies winters here is attested by two Gainesville specimens in the UF taken January 13, 1928 and February 9, 1959, respectively.

*9. GREEN HERON. *Butorides virescens.* "One seen January 28 was the only one observed until April 4, when new arrivals were noted. They were common throughout May, and on the 25th of that month young just from the nest were taken." The Green Heron is still uncommon from October to March, though a few winter here fairly regularly. It nests commonly at Lake Alice and Bivins Arm. The UF has eggs collected in Gainesville April 21, 1900, April 12, 1930, April 19, 1935, and June 24, 1939.

*10. LITTLE BLUE HERON. *Florida caerulea.* "The most common Heron. The blue slightly outnumber the white birds, and but three in intermediate plumage were seen." Though still plentiful, the Little Blue Heron is now outnumbered in the Gainesville heronries by the Cattle Egret. The UF has seven sets of eggs taken here between April 12 and May 13.

11. CATTLE EGRET. *Bubulcus ibis.* First recorded in Florida in the Okeechobee region in 1952, seven birds appeared in the Lake Alice heronry the spring of 1954 and bred successfully (Rice, 1956). Since then the species has increased steadily and the main heronry, which moved from Lake Alice to Bivins Arm in 1964, contained an estimated 2,000 pairs that year. The Cattle Egret is now unquestionably the most plentiful heron in Florida.

12. REDDISH EGRET. *Dichromanessa rufescens.* Baynard (1913a) reported from the Orange Lake Heronry, which FMC never visited: "Abundant during 1907 and 1908. Found about 1500 pairs on Bird Island and many straggling pairs in many other localities. One pair only nested in 1911, and have only seen one pair this year." The species has not been recorded in this region since then.

*13. COMMON EGRET. *Casmerodius albus.* "Not uncommon during the winter, and frequently observed until its plumes were sufficiently grown to render them worthy the plume hunter's attention, when it became almost rare and exceedingly shy." The species today is resident, plentiful, and fairly tame. A clutch of eggs in the UF was taken in Alachua County May 18, 1894.

*14. SNOWY EGRET. *Leucophoyx thula.* "The same remarks [as for the Common Egret] apply to this species." Six clutches of eggs in the UF were taken locally between April 9 and May 12. The species is fairly common.

*15. LOUISIANA HERON. *Hydranassa tricolor.* "Not uncommon. Almost all those observed were adult birds." Resident and plentiful today, the Louisiana Heron nests in all local heronries. UF eggs March 25 and April 9, 1939.

*16. BLACK-CROWNED NIGHT HERON. *Nycticorax nycticorax.* "Locally common." It still is, and resident. Karraker (1953) records a nest with young at Lake Alice June 14, 1952.

17. YELLOW-CROWNED NIGHT HERON. *Nyctanassa violacea.* Doubtless scarce in the Gainesville region in 1886 when all herons were persecuted, Pearson (1892) reported it breeding in April 1888 on Levy Lake, which Chapman never reached. A set of three eggs in the UF was taken in Gainesville May 12, 1894. Today the species is resident but never as common as the Black-crowned, and more plentiful in summer than in winter.

18. LEAST BITTERN. *Ixobrychus exilis.* Not uncommon summer resident, rare in winter. The UF has eggs taken in Gainesville March 12, 1895, and April 21, 1901, and in Archer (by Pearson) June 30, 1887. McClanahan (1935) reports nests with eggs at Lake Alice April 28 and May 7 and 12, 1934. One was reported at Lake Alice on the Christmas census December 29, 1962.

*19. AMERICAN BITTERN. *Botaurus lentiginosus.* "Locally common." The Bittern is fairly common in winter, less so in summer, and probably breeds locally in small numbers. Baynard (1913a) records finding a nest near Micanopy June 15, 1911.

20. WOOD STORK. *Mycteria americana.* Pearson (1892) mentions seeing the species at Ledwith Lake, which FMC never visited. Baynard (1913a) states that in 1906 "they bred in numbers in a Cypress Swamp in the northeastern part of the county. This rookery of about 1500 nests was nearly exterminated by men and boys who shot the young from the trees, evidently just to see them fall. After nesting season they come here and feed all summer on our lakes. Fresh eggs about March 15." By mid-March, however, most of the young are usually well grown. No breeding colonies have been reported in this part of Florida since then, but the species is a not uncommon visitor in late spring, summer, and fall, and non-breeding individuals may be seen in winter.

21. GLOSSY IBIS. *Plegadis falcinellus.* Never plentiful, the Glossy Ibis was doubtless a rare bird here in the late nineteenth and early twentieth centuries. After a long absence the species appeared in the Lake Alice heronry in 1936, and Charles E. Doe collected 11 sets of eggs between April 23, and May 27. It last nested at Lake Alice in 1958, when five pairs were present. Some thirty pairs nested on Payne's Prairie west of route 441 in April, 1965.

*22. WHITE IBIS. *Eudocimus albus.* "March 4, 1887, and January

11, 1888. One observed each day." Pearson (1892) mentions the birds as common at Ledwith Lake in summer, but does not mention their nesting. In those days the young were esteemed for food and shot from their nests. Today the species is a fairly common resident, breeding locally and irregularly. Karraker (1953) states the birds started to nest at Lake Alice April 20-25, 1952. In 1954 the Lake Alice colony had more than 1,000 pairs, which had dwindled to about 200 in 1958. They deserted the area when the flood-killed trees they nested in disappeared in 1959.

*23. ROSEATE SPOONBILL. *Ajaia ajaja.* "None were observed by myself, but three were reported to me by my friend Mr. Bell on April 13, and Mr. Reynolds had a specimen in his collection." Pearson (1892a) mentions collecting one at Ledwith Lake. These remain the only county records.

24. CANADA GOOSE. *Branta canadensis.* Small numbers appear sporadically in winter. Burns (1952) reports a flock of 27 on Newnan's Lake November 8, 1950. J. C. Dickinson, Jr., saw three on Bivins Arm November 6, 1953, and Dale Crider found a lone bird foraging with a small flock of Sandhill Cranes on Payne's Prairie November 24, 1965.

25. BLUE GOOSE. *Chen caerulescens.* A white-phase specimen in the UF was shot November 24, 1927 on Payne's Prairie, where Dale Crider and Lovett Williams saw two more December 28, 1965. Dark phase birds have been reported on Bivins Arm January 26, 1939, February 1, 1941 (2), and December 13, 1946; Crider and Williams saw a flock of 12 on Payne's Prairie December 28, 1965.

26. FULVOUS TREE DUCK. *Dendrocygna bicolor.* Rare and irregular winter visitor, apparently becoming more numerous. Three appeared on Lake Alice December 19, 1961, and remained until February 1962. Two specimens in the UF were shot at Levy Lake December 30, 1964. A flock of 125 was seen on Payne's Prairie December 28, 1965.

*27. MALLARD. *Anas platyrhynchos.* "Not uncommon." Today a winter visitor from mid-November to mid-April, never overly plentiful.

*28. BLACK DUCK. *Anas rubripes.* "Not uncommon." Now a regular but not too common winter visitor.

*29. MOTTLED DUCK. *Anas fulvigula.* "The Florida Black Duck was not found, and was unknown to local sportsmen, even as a summer resident." Baynard (1913a) confirms this: "Unknown in this county to all the old duck hunters until 1906 when it appeared on Payne's Prairie and other similar places and began to nest." Today it is recorded irregularly throughout the year. The UF has a set of eggs taken in nearby Marion County March 23, 1936. James E. Brogdon found a nest with 5 eggs on Payne's Prairie in mid-May 1966.

*30. GADWALL. *Anas strepera.* "A female was taken February 8, the first one, I think, reported from the State. Six were seen and one killed January 11, 1888." The Gadwall is now a fairly common winter visitor, arriving in late October and usually leaving by early April. Karraker (1953) saw a late straggler at Lake Alice May 21, 1952.

*31. PINTAIL. *Anas acuta.* "Not uncommon." Still so, recorded from November to early April.

*32. GREEN-WINGED TEAL. *Anas carolinensis.* "Common." Today a not uncommon winter visitor from November to March.

*33. BLUE-WINGED TEAL. *Anas discors.* "Rather more common than the last. Last records were April 27, two, and April 29, one." Now a common winter visitor from mid-September to late April. Karraker (1953) records a late departure from Lake Alice May 19, 1952.

34. CINNAMON TEAL. *Anas cyanoptera.* Straggler, the only record an adult male seen on Lake Alice March 8, 1953 (Rice and Mockford, 1953).

35. EUROPEAN WIDGEON. *Mareca penelope.* Straggler, the only record an adult male in the UF taken at Orange Lake December 26, 1931 (McClanahan, 1937).

*36. BALDPATE. *Mareca americana.* "Not uncommon." Still so, from late October to late March.

*37. SHOVELER. *Spatula clypeata.* "A single specimen in Mr. Reynold's possession." Today a fairly common winter visitor, October to April. Burns (1952) lists a late record from Newnan's Lake April 14, 1952.

*38. WOOD DUCK. *Aix sponsa.* "Common resident." It still is, perhaps not so plentiful as in 1888, but downy young have been reported on the University campus April 12, 1947, April 11, 1949, July 4, 1950, and the most recent on April 15, 1963. The UF has a set of 14 eggs collected at High Springs April 18, 1930 by C. E. Aschmeier.

39. REDHEAD. *Aythya americana.* Uncommon and irregular winter visitor. Karraker (1953) reports the species on Lake Alice December 12, 1951 to February 10, 1952. Two were seen on Bivins Arm November 4, 1956, and a fine drake on Lake Alice December 29, 1962. A specimen in the UF was taken on Kanapaha Prairie December 30, 1964.

*40. RING-NECKED DUCK. *Aythya collaris.* "The most abundant Duck. At the time of my departure, May 27, a flock of cripples, four males and three females, was in an arm of the lake, and I was told that crippled Ducks (the result of flock shooting during the winter) of different species frequently remain through the summer, but although, as in the present instance, both sexes may be represented, they have never been known to breed." Still true today. Inclusive dates are late October to late April.

41. CANVASBACK. *Aythya valisineria.* Rare winter visitor. A specimen in the UF was taken in Gainesville December 13, 1927; there are several sight records for December and January.

42. GREATER SCAUP. *Aythya marila.* Rare winter visitor. A male in the PBC was taken at Orange Lake November 26, 1951, and a female at Proctor's Pond December 23, 1951.

*43. LESSER SCAUP. *Aythya affinis.* "Common." It still is, from October to April. Karraker (1953) records one lingering on Lake Alice to May 11, 1952.

44. COMMON GOLDENEYE. *Bucephala clangula.* Rare winter visitor. A female in the PBC was taken at Kanapaha Sink December 15, 1954. Two were seen on Lake Alice December 27, 1958.

45. BUFFLEHEAD. *Bucephala albeola.* Uncommon winter visitor. Specimens in UF from Orange Lake February 3, 1958 and Gainesville January 23, 1964, sight records December to March.

46. WHITE-WINGED SCOTER. *Melanitta deglandi.* Straggler, known from a single specimen in the UF taken on Payne's Prairie October 25, 1958.

*47. RUDDY DUCK. *Oxyura jamaicensis.* "Not uncommon." Common today on Orange Lake, November to April.

*48. HOODED MERGANSER. *Lophodytes cucullatus.* "A rare winter resident." Now a fairly common winter visitor recorded from October to April.

49. RED-BREASTED MERGANSER. *Mergus serrator.* Rare winter visitor, a specimen in the UF from Alachua November 30, 1931.

*50. TURKEY VULTURE. *Cathartes aura.* "Abundant." The species is common today rather than abundant, its food being less plentiful than in FMC's day. Pearson (1891b) records fresh eggs at Archer March 28, 1888, March 15 and March 20, 1889, March 15, 1890, March 16, 1891.

*51. BLACK VULTURE. *Coragyps atratus.* "Abundant. There was apparently little difference in the numbers of this and the preceding species but the first named was much more common in the town." Both vultures occur in about equal numbers today, but though they occasionally soar over the town, I have never seen either species on the ground within the city or in the adjoining suburbs. C. E. Doe (notes) found day-old young at High Springs March 21, 1935, and collected at least six clutches of eggs there, the earliest February 16, 1938, the latest April 25, 1936.

*52. SWALLOW-TAILED KITE. *Elanoides forficatus.* "April 29, three, May 9 and 10, one each day. All escaped capture." The few sporadic sight records of the past decade have all been in spring or early summer, except one by Hicks (1955) on Payne's Prairie February 6, 1954.

*53. MISSISSIPPI KITE. *Ictinia mississippiensis.* "Two were noted April 29." Only sporadic sight records since, one by McClanahan (1937a) May 18, 1934, one by Lovett E. Williams, Jr. in early May 1966.

*54. SHARP-SHINNED HAWK. *Accipiter striatus.* "Not uncommon." The species is still a not uncommon winter visitor. Karraker (1953) gives inclusive dates of October 14 to April 20. Baynard's (1913a) claim that it formerly bred here "in great numbers from April 15 to May 1" is questionable.

*55. COOPER'S HAWK. *Accipiter cooperi.* "Not common." Cooper's Hawk is still far less common than the Sharp-shinned in winter, but it breeds here occasionally. A set of eggs in the UF was taken six miles southeast of Gainesville by P. H. White August 21, 1932.

*56. RED-TAILED HAWK. *Buteo jamaicensis.* "Common." The species is still fairly common, and more plentiful in winter than in the breeding season.

*57. RED-SHOULDERED HAWK. *Buteo lineatus.* "Abundant: The nine specimens obtained were all true *lineatus.*" This species is still much more plentiful than the Red-tail the year round. All Florida specimens are now referred to *B. l. alleni,* which Ridgway described from a Tampa specimen and named in 1883 for FMC's friend and mentor J. A. Allen. The UF has a set of three eggs taken in Gainesville April 3, 1894.

58. BROAD-WINGED HAWK. *Buteo platypterus.* Baynard (1913a) says "A very rare bird for this section and found only one nest with two young on May 28, 1909." Burns (1952) gives sight records for June 23, 1950 and October 21-30, 1950. Karraker (1953) reports the species present at Lake Alice from April 21 to July 26, 1952.

59. SHORT-TAILED HAWK. *Buteo brachyurus.* A specimen in the UF taken in Gainesville February 27, 1926 is the only record for the county.

60. ROUGH-LEGGED HAWK. *Buteo lagopus.* A lone adult wintering on Payne's Prairie was seen well by Dale Crider and Lovett Williams several times between December 28, 1965 and March 15, 1966.

*61. BALD EAGLE. *Haliaeetus leucocephalus.* "Common." McClanahan (1936) records "a noticeable decline in the numbers of this bird in the past six years." The decline has apparently continued with even greater speed since the advent of mass insecticide sprayings in the late 1940's. The UF has a set of two eggs taken in Gainesville January 1, 1931. No successful nestings have been reported from this area in recent years.

*62. MARSH HAWK. *Circus eyaneus.* "Common." It is still fairly so, and it has bred here according to Baynard (1913a), but there are no recent nesting records. Karraker (1953) lists it from September 30 to March 31.

*63. OSPREY. *Pandion haliaetus.* "Common." Karraker (1953) noted nest building started at Lake Alice March 24, 1953. The species still breeds regularly at Lake Alice, and is generally absent from November to early February.

64. PEREGRINE FALCON. *Falco peregrinus.* Rare transient and winter visitor; the several scattered sight records are all for December and January.

*65. PIGEON HAWK. *Falco columbarius.* "A single specimen was taken January 4." The species is still a rare to uncommon winter visitor today.

*66. SPARROW HAWK. *Falco sparverius.* "Abundant resident." This species has declined in numbers during the past few years, and particularly the small resident subspecies, *F. s. paulus,* which was not described until 1902. Most wintering birds today are the larger nominate northern race. The UF has a large series of eggs Charles E. Doe collected in the county; their dates range from March 31 (3 sets) to June 30. Doe's field notes show he collected 394 sets of Sparrow Hawk eggs in Florida.

*67. BOBWHITE. *Colinus virginianus.* "Abundant. The call of two, and rarely three, notes was first heard March 17, and although they were now beginning to pair, flocks were seen as late as April 16." Common resident fits the Bobwhite here better than abundant today. The UF has eight sets of eggs C. E. Doe collected in Gainesville; their dates range from May 16 to June 30.

*68. TURKEY. *Meleagris gallopavo.* "Rare." Though the UF has a nest and eggs taken in neighboring Levy County March 26, 1935, the only recent records for the Turkey's occurrence in Alachua County are of wild-caught birds from Glades County the Florida Game and Fresh Water Fish Commission released in the Lochloosa Wildlife Management Area in 1965-66. The wardens report seeing at least one hen with poults in 1966.

69. SANDHILL CRANE. *Grus canadensis.* With Payne's Prairie a lake in 1887, little suitable habitat for cranes existed in the county. Twenty-five years later Baynard (1913a) considered the species "resident but rare" and claimed it nested "in late April on the flooded prairies of two lakes." McClanahan apparently never saw any in the 1930's, and Dickinson (1944) thought seeing three at Micanopy worth recording in print. Since 1958 the Sandhill Crane has become of regular occurrence in winter on Payne's Prairie and on other nearby open cattle ranges. The largest recent count was 350 birds Lovett E. Williams, Jr. found feeding in a cornfield southwest of Payne's Prairie in November

1965. On April 29, 1965 I saw a pair shepherding two downy young on the prairie east of route U.S. 441. On March 5, 1966 Peter W. Post and I saw a pair with two newly-hatched chicks on another part of Payne's Prairie east of route I-75.

70. LIMPKIN. *Aramus guarauna.* Rare to uncommon resident. Kyle (1933) reported finding nests at Orange Lake. Single birds were seen during the summer of 1960 at Lake Alice and December 29, 1963 at Lake Wauburg.

*71. KING RAIL. *Rallus elegans.* "Two specimens taken by Mr. Reynolds at the lake." A not uncommon resident today, but seldom observed in the wet marshes it inhabits and from which it is difficult to flush. In the UF are four specimens from Payne's Prairie taken March 23 to April 3, 1959.

72. VIRGINIA RAIL. *Rallus limicola.* Rare winter visitor. Karraker (1953) saw one at Lake Alice February 17 and 20, 1952. A specimen in the UF was found dead on the road at Micanopy October 18, 1958.

*73. SORA. *Porzana carolina.* "A single specimen in Mr. Reynold's possession was taken at the lake." The species is an uncommon to rare winter visitor today. The UF has a Gainesville specimen taken October 1, 1922. A few scattered sight records have been reported since then.

74. BLACK RAIL. *Laterallus jamaicensis.* Baynard's (1913a) sight record of "an adult with three young on one occasion in June" is the only record for the county. The species, which Sprunt (1954) aptly terms "a feathered mouse," nests fairly commonly in nearby Brevard County.

*75. PURPLE GALLINULE. *Porphyrio martinica.* "None were seen until May 25, when in a part of the lake before unvisited,—a mass of floating islands and 'bonnets',—I found them not uncommon. Four were taken; in the oviduct of one a partially formed egg was found, and several eggs had evidently been deposited." The Purple Gallinule still nests commonly at Lake Alice, where Doe (notes) records collecting 11 sets of eggs between May 12 and 22. The UF also has a set from Archer dated June 12, 1895.

*76. COMMON GALLINULE. *Gallinula chloropus.* "Common resident." It is still so. Karraker (1953) noted courtship at Lake Alice April 20, 1952 and downy young June 14, 1952. The UF has eggs collected at Lake Alice May 1, 1935 and April 7 and 16, 1936.

*77. AMERICAN COOT. *Fulica americana.* "Extremely abundant, every 'bonnet' patch contained its flock, all equally noisy until as spring advanced they became almost silent. A number remained until April 29, all those seen after that date being wing-broken birds, which, unlike the crippled Ring-necked Ducks before mentioned, did not gather in flocks, but were met with singly, lurking in the 'bonnets' at the borders of the lake." The species is still plentiful in winter, and a few remain through the summer. Baynard (1913a) considered it "a very rare breeder," and Howell (1932) cites Gist's report of a few pairs nesting at Orange Lake in 1915. No more recent or authoritative reports of its breeding here exist.

*78. KILLDEER. *Charadrius vociferus.* "An abundant winter visitant. My last records were April 27 and 29, one each day." The Killdeer also breeds here regularly. The UF has four sets of eggs collected near Gainesville between March 30 and June 8. McClanahan (1935) saw downy young May 12, 1934.

79. GOLDEN PLOVER. *Pluvialis dominica.* Rare transient. The UF has a specimen collected on Payne's Prairie March 7, 1961. Leslie M. Tuck and I saw one on Kanapaha Prairie March 7, 1962, and Peter W. Post found another on Payne's Prairie September 26, 1965 that remained there until October 8, 1965.

*80. WOODCOCK. *Philohela minor.* "December 3 and 24, one was seen each day." The Woodcock today is a not uncommon but extremely localized resident, recorded most often in winter. Baynard (1913a) records two nests, one with three eggs, found at Micanopy February 4, 1912. Eight Gainesville specimens in the UF are dated between November 3 and February 2, one in the PBC August 3, 1964. Most are road-kills.

*81. WILSON'S SNIPE. *Capella gallinago.* "Locally abundant, sometimes flocks of fifty or more flushed from favorable feeding grounds. Two seen together April 15, were the last noted." Still a fairly common winter visitor, arriving in November and leaving by mid-April.

*82. UPLAND PLOVER. *Bartramia longicauda.* "April 8, two were seen, April 10, three." A rare transient in Florida, the Upland Plover has not been reported in this region since.

*83. SPOTTED SANDPIPER. *Actitis macularia.* "From April 27 to May 10, seven were noted." The species is a fairly common transient today, recorded from April 20 to May 27 and from late July through September.

*84. SOLITARY SANDPIPER. *Tringa solitaria.* "From April 2 to May 6, twelve were seen or taken." Still a fairly common spring transient, four UF specimens from Gainesville are dated from March 14 to June 1. The southward flight is early; the latest fall record is a bird David W. Johnston saw at Lake Alice September 8, 1965.

85. WILLET. *Catoptrophorus semipalmatus.* The Willet straggles here occasionally from the coast. Karraker (1953) saw one fly over Newnan's Lake May 19, 1952; Charles H. Trost saw one on Payne's Prairie March 4, 1961.

86. GREATER YELLOWLEGS. *Totanus melanoleucus.* This not un-

common winter visitor has been reported on five of the last eight Christmas censuses. Four Gainesville specimens in the UF are dated January 15 to April 16.

*87. LESSER YELLOWLEGS. *Totanus flavipes.* "A flock of five was seen March 5, and a single bird April 5." Still a not uncommon winter visitor, the Lesser Yellowlegs was reported on five of the last eight Christmas counts. It has been seen as early as September 10, 1965 by Peter W. Post and myself, and as late as May 14, 1951 by Burns (1952).

88. PECTORAL SANDPIPER. *Erolia melanotus.* Dickinson (1945) records a specimen of this straggler from the coast taken September 26, 1940, but not preserved. Peter W. Post and I saw five on Payne's Prairie September 10, 1965, a flock of 40 birds there from October 1 to 6, 1965, and three on March 5, 1966.

89. WHITE-RUMPED SANDPIPER. *Erolia fuscicollis.* One well seen on Payne's Prairie by Peter W. Post October 6, 1965; I saw what was probably the same bird the next day.

90. LEAST SANDPIPER. *Erolia minutilla.* This species is a not uncommon transient and winter visitor from August to May.

91. DOWITCHER. *Limnodromus sp.* Dale Birkenholtz reported one on Payne's Prairie December 20, 1961 as *L. scolopaeus;* Lovett Williams identified a flock of 20 there December 28, 1965 as *L. griseus.* Without the bird in hand these two species are difficult to differentiate.

92. BLACK-NECKED STILT. *Himantopus mexicanus.* Minter Westfall and his bird class saw one clearly over Payne's Prairie July 18, 1957, a straggler from the coast.

[WILSON'S PHALAROPE. *Steganopus tricolor.* Burns (1952) reports "A pair of these birds was observed by Mr. E. C. May on May 1, 1951, at close range by circling around them by boat as they swam in the middle of (Newnan's) Lake."]

93. HERRING GULL. *Larus argentatus.* This species, now a not uncommon winter visitor, has apparently pushed in from the coast in increasing numbers during the last several decades, probably attracted by the food to be scavenged at city dumps. McClanahan (1937a) regarded it as "rare," having seen it only once at Newnan's Lake, where Burns (1953) reports they "occurred irregularly in various-sized flocks flying over the lake from November 9, 1950 to March 3, 1951." The UF has two Gainesville specimens, January 16, 1959 and February 23, 1962, and one from Orange Lake March 27, 1958.

94. RING-BILLED GULL. *Larus delawarensis.* This common winter visitor today has become so only in the last three decades. Its absence from Chapman's list reflects the rarity and shyness of all colonial birds that were then egged and slaughtered for their feathers. The Ring-bill does not seem to have ventured inland in Florida much before the

1930's. However, McClanahan (1937a) calls it "not uncommon," and both Burns (1952) and Karraker (1953) report seeing it regularly from November 30 to April 28.

95. LAUGHING GULL. *Larus atricilla.* Straggler from the coast. Mary Heimerdinger and I saw one at Lake Alice on the Christmas count December 29, 1962.

96. BONAPARTE'S GULL. *Larus philadelphia.* Uncommon winter visitor, specimens in the UF from Newnan's Lake December 31, 1958 and January 13, 1959.

97. FORSTER'S TERN. *Sterna forsteri.* Uncommon transient and winter visitor, most likely to appear during or after bad blows on the coast. Howell (1932) lists a specimen from Orange Lake May 25, 1929. I collected one for the UF in the same place February 3, 1959.

98. COMMON TERN. *Sterna hirundo.* Dickinson (1945) saw three on Bivins Arm December 18, 1941. He also identified several there September 21-23, 1948 and September 5, 1950, each time after a hurricane had passed.

99. SOOTY TERN. *Sterna fuscata.* Howell (1932) writes: "On September 19 and 20, 1928, following the violent hurricane of September 16, thousands were seen in the city limits of Gainesville and several were picked up dead or exhausted. On this occasion, many of the birds tried to alight in trees." McClanahan (1937a) notes that three of these birds were brought to the Florida State Museum, but they were evidently not preserved, for no trace of them remains today.

100. ROYAL TERN. *Thalasseus maximus.* Karraker (1953) saw a flock of 12 on Lake Alice November 4, 1950 and two on January 17, 1951.

101. BLACK TERN. *Chlidonias niger.* Irregular transient, usually appearing in the fall when the equinoctial blows drive it inland. Dickinson (1945) reports about 50 on Bivins Arm September 14, 1941, some of which lingered a week. He saw two in spring plumage there July 24, 1946 and three on August 4, 1950.

102. BLACK SKIMMER. *Rynchops nigra.* Vagrant, usually driven in from the coast by storms. An immature banded the previous July at Tampa Bay was picked up at Newnan's Lake after a hurricane October 8, 1941; J. C. Dickinson, Jr. saw three on Bivins Arm September 5, 1950 after a hurricane hit Cedar Key; one appeared on Lake Alice September 27, 1963 after a blow on the east coast.

103. ROCK DOVE. *Columba livia.* Feral flocks of mongrel stock are common in many parts of the city, and scattered pairs nest on the campus buildings where Fish Crows prey on their eggs. I can find no record of the species' first appearance here, but they were probably brought by some of the first white settlers.

*104. PASSENGER PIGEON. *Ectopistes migratorius.* "Said by sportsmen to be a rare winter visitant; Mr. Reynolds had two in his possession." Pearson (1893) reports a flock of 50 or more seen at Archer. Now extinct.

*105. MOURNING DOVE. *Zenaidura macroura.* "Common resident." It is still so today. I banded two juveniles just out of the nest February 17, 1963.

106. RINGED TURTLE DOVE. *Streptopelia risoria.* A pair nested unsuccessfully on the University campus March 27, 1963. The nearest known colony of this exotic is in St. Petersburg from where these birds may have strayed.

*107. GROUND DOVE. *Columbigallina passerina.* "Common. A nest found May 12, on the ground beneath a small scrub palmetto, contained two eggs." The species is still a common year-round resident. Sets of eggs from Gainesville in the UF are dated March 4, 1939, April 27, 1933, and May 16, 1937.

108. CAROLINA PARAKEET. *Conuropsis carolinensis.* Hahn (1963) reports the only record for the county, a skeleton in the New York State Museum (*ex* Shuffeldt collection) taken in Gainesville in March 1885.

*109. YELLOW-BILLED CUCKOO. *Coccyzus americanus.* "A not common summer resident. Arrived April 27." Fairly common today, arriving in early April (4th) and leaving in late October (23rd). Doe (notes) collected eggs in Gainesville May 20 and June 12, 1937.

110. BLACK-BILLED CUCKOO. *Coccyzus erythropthalmus.* A rare transient. McClanahan (1937a) reports three at Gainesville May 11, 1935 and two at High Springs May 12, 1935. L. O. Rowland netted and banded one in Gainesville October 12, 1962.

*111. BARN OWL. *Tyto alba.* "I saw but two; one, an almost fully grown male, was brought me alive May 30. During his short life (his death, June 19, was due to an accident) he proved an interesting but perfectly untamable pet; fresh meat was refused, but Sparrows (*Passer domesticus*) he devoured with great relish, pulling out most of the wing and tail-feathers and swallowing the body without further dissection." (FMC had taken the owl back to Englewood, New Jersey, where House Sparrows were then common.) The Barn Owl is resident here today, but not plentiful.

*112. SCREECH OWL. *Otus asio.* "Said to be common. A single specimen was secured March 12." A fairly common resident today. Pearson (1888b) reports collecting a set of three fresh eggs in Archer March 30, 1888, and the UF has a set he collected there April 15, 1889. Doe (notes) collected six sets of eggs in Gainesville between March 31 and May 24, 1939.

*113. GREAT HORNED OWL. *Bubo virginianus.* "A specimen in the possession of Mr. Reynolds was taken at Gainesville." Today the species is a not uncommon resident.

114. BURROWING OWL. *Speotyto cunicularia.* Uncommon resident locally, evidently a recent intrusion, probably within the last decade. Ligon (1963) reports a nesting pair seven miles west of Gainesville with three young in the burrow June 7, 1962.

*115. BARRED OWL. *Strix varia.* "Common. Two nearly grown young attended by the parent bird were seen May 9." Now by far the commonest of the resident owls, this species is a frequent road-kill.

*116. CHUCK-WILL'S-WIDOW. *Caprimulgus carolinensis.* "Common summer resident." It still is, usually arriving in late March (22nd). Doe (notes) collected a large series of eggs, mostly in Levy and Pinellas counties, ranging in dates from April 25, 1937 to May 28, 1938.

*117. WHIP-POOR-WILL. *Caprimulgus vociferus.* "None were heard, and a female taken March 3, was the only one observed." An uncommon transient. McClanahan (1937a) cites specimen records November 23 to March 13.

*118. NIGHTHAWK. *Chordeiles minor.* "Arrived April 17, and became common on the 21st, after which date no change was noted in numbers. 'Bullbat,' or as it is more frequently termed 'Bat,' shooting here is a popular pastime, great numbers being killed for food, and in August, when the birds have gathered in flocks, favorite fields may be occupied at nightfall by as many as a dozen shooters." Fortunately bullbat shooting is a thing of the past, and the nighthawk is now a common summer resident. Recent arrival dates are April 4, 1952 and April 7, 1948. In the UF are eggs collected May 18, 1932, May 31, 1937, and June 4, 1938.

*119. CHIMNEY SWIFT. *Chaetura pelagica.* "Arrived April 5, and was common after the 16th." The earliest recent arrival date is March 18, 1950. The species nests commonly from May to July—I noted the first young on the wing July 14, 1961—and departs in late October, early November.

*120. RUBY-THROATED HUMMINGBIRD. *Archilochus colubris.* "Five were observed from March 8 to April 27." This is still the earliest arrival date on record. The species usually appears in late March—two recent records for the 22nd—and leaves in October. Two UF nests were collected in Gainesville July 1, 1930 and September 27, 1933.

*121. BELTED KINGFISHER. *Megaceryle alcyon.* "Common during the winter, but after April 2 their numbers had greatly diminished." The same is true today, though the species is by no means as plentiful as it was formerly. Baynard (1913a) reports it nesting at Micanopy.

Burns (1952) observed it regularly at Lake Alice from August 19, 1950 to April 16, 1951.

*122. FLICKER. *Colaptes auratus.* "Abundant up to the last of March, after which date they were less numerous." A common resident today. Six sets of eggs in the UF from Gainesville range from April 6, 1939 to June 2, 1930.

*123. PILEATED WOODPECKER. *Dryocopus pileatus.* "Rather rare. The individuals met with were extremely unsuspicious; I have even placed my ear at the base of the tree on which they were pounding." A not uncommon resident in suburban Gainesville today.

*124. RED-BELLIED WOODPECKER. *Centurus carolinus.* "Abundant." This is still the commonest of the resident woodpeckers. In the UF is a set of five eggs collected in Micanopy June 12, 1910.

*125. RED-HEADED WOODPECKER. *Melanerpes erythrocephalus.* "But thirteen birds of this species were seen until April 16, when new arrivals were noted, and after the 26th of that month they were very numerous. This species was common throughout the winter of 1887-88." It is still a common resident, less plentiful in winter than in spring and summer, despite a rather high mortality in road-kills by cars. A set of eggs in the UF was collected in Gainesville June 11, 1938. P. W. Post saw adults still feeding young in a nest at Gainesville September 9, 1965.

*126. YELLOW-BELLIED SAPSUCKER. *Sphyrapicus varius.* "Common, and very generally distributed. Last noted April 21." A fairly common winter visitor today, the UF has specimens taken here October 12 to March 16.

*127. HAIRY WOODPECKER. *Dendrocopos villosus.* "Common." Rather uncommon resident better describes its status today. Doe (notes) collected eggs June 4, 1938 and April 8, 1940.

*128. DOWNY WOODPECKER. *Dendrocopos pubescens.* "Slightly more numerous than the last." Still true today. McClanahan (1937a) states it "nests in May."

*129. RED-COCKADED WOODPECKER. *Dendrocopos borealis.* "Common, but confined exclusively to the pineries." Not uncommon is a better status estimate now. The UF has eggs from Archer May 8, 1889 and from Gainesville June 4, 1938.

130. IVORY-BILLED WOODPECKER. *Campephilus principalis.* Baynard (1913a) "Found one nest in the County that contained young," probably about the turn of the century. It has not been recorded in the county since, and it was doubtless rare in the Gainesville region in FMC's time. He was constantly on the lookout for it, and collected his first (and only) specimen on the Suwannee in 1890.

*131. EASTERN KINGBIRD. *Tyrannus tyrannus.* "A common summer resident. Arrived April 2 and became common on the 5th." No change today. The species usually departs by mid-October. In the UF are eggs taken near Gainesville May 9, 1931 and June 3, 1939.

132. GRAY KINGBIRD. *Tyrannus dominicensis.* Rare visitor, usually wandering in from the coast in the fall after breeding. The PBC has a specimen taken in Evinston October 24, 1953.

133. WESTERN KINGBIRD. *Tyrannus verticalis.* Rare fall transient. A specimen in the PBC was taken at Wacahoota October 14, 1949. L. O. Rowland took one west of Gainesville October 6, 1963. Peter W. Post saw one south of Gainesville October 22, 1965.

*134. CRESTED FLYCATCHER. *Myiarchus crinitus.* "An abundant summer resident. Arrived March 31 and became common April 5." The species is common rather than abundant today. Earliest spring record is a UF specimen taken March 25, 1930. Four sets of eggs are dated May 8, 1900 to May 26, 1937. The species usually disappears before September, but I collected a winter straggler at Newnan's Lake December 28, 1965.

*135. PHOEBE. *Sayornis phoebe.* "An abundant winter visitant, and very generally distributed. Last records were March 21 and April 4, one each day." Still a common winter visitor, the earliest record is a UF specimen taken in Gainesville September 28, 1950.

*136. ACADIAN FLYCATCHER. *Empidonax virescens.* "Not uncommon in the denser woods; arrived April 20. A completed nest, found May 9, was constructed almost entirely of 'Spanish moss,' and contained on the 27th two eggs with half-formed embryos." No change today. Usually leaves in September.

*137. WOOD PEWEE. *Contopus virens.* "A rather common summer resident, arriving April 7. A nest found May 9 was placed on the horizontal limb of a pine, about forty feet from the ground." Still a fairly common transient and summer resident, this is about the species' southern breeding limit. Latest fall record a bird Peter W. Post saw October 8, 1965.

138. VERMILION FLYCATCHER. *Pyrocephalus rubinus.* A single specimen of this straggler in the UF was taken on Payne's Prairie, February 12, 1951.

*139. TREE SWALLOW. *Iridoprocne bicolor.* "Abundant up to the date of its departure, May 6." Tree Swallows usually appear in mid-October; a few remain through the winter, and their numbers build up again in April before the flocks leave in early May.

140. ROUGH-WINGED SWALLOW. *Stelgidopteryx ruficollis.* Uncommon transient. McClanahan (1937a) lists sight records without data by Doe and by Baynard. Karraker (1953) saw eight at Newnan's Lake September 22, 1952.

141. BARN SWALLOW. *Hirundo rustica.* A common migrant in April and May and from late July to October. UF specimens August 18, 1958 and September 4, 1950, both from Gainesville.

142. CLIFF SWALLOW. *Petrochelidon pyrrhonota.* McClanahan (1935) saw the species over Payne's Prairie October 27, 1933, as did Charles E. Doe.

*143. PURPLE MARTIN. *Progne subis.* "A common summer resident, breeding where boxes and gourds are erected for its occupation. Arrived March 3." Earliest recent arrival February 8, 1965, departure September 26-30. Eggs in the UF were collected near Gainesville May 1, 1894 and May 5, 1906.

*144. BLUE JAY. *Cyanocitta cristata.* "Extremely tame and everywhere abundant, frequenting the live and water oaks of the city streets, where it appears half domesticated. It possesses greater vocal powers than the northern bird; twenty or more distinct calls were counted." The race *C. c. florincola* to which Chapman assigned the Gainesville birds has been synonymized with the northern *cristata.* The species is still plentiful and common in the city. UF eggs from the county are dated from March 9, 1888 to April 23, 1940. The first young are usually out of the nest by May 20-25. My banding records show some seasonal movement occurs; most of the local breeding birds leave the city in October and return late in March.

145. SCRUB JAY. *Aphelocoma coerulescens.* A not uncommon resident in the scrub habitat east of Orange Lake, two miles south of Cross Creek.

*146. COMMON CROW. *Corvus brachyrhynchos.* "I saw less than ten, all some distance from town in the large pineries." Still resident in small numbers in the surrounding countryside; seldom are more than a dozen birds encountered together. Doe (notes) collected a set of three eggs April 24, 1939.

*147. FISH CROW. *Corvus ossifragus.* "Common only in the vicinity of small ponds and the lake." The species today is common in town and on the University campus, where it preys on the eggs of the feral Rock Doves that nest on the University buildings. A winter roost on the northwest edge of town on the Millhopper Road contained several hundred birds in 1963-64. A set of eggs in the UF was collected in Gainesville May 22, 1942.

*148. CAROLINA CHICKADEE. *Parus carolinensis.* "On two occasions single birds of this species were seen with flocks of *Sitta pusilla* in the pines, but with these exceptions it was a bird of low swamps and scrubs, frequently associating with the [Tufted Titmouse]. A partly formed egg was found in the oviduct of a female taken March 15." Today the species is a common resident locally. In the UF are eggs from Micanopy March 20, 1909 and from Gainesville April 2, 1933 and April 27, 1940.

*149. TUFTED TITMOUSE. *Parus bicolor.* "Abundant. Young attended by the parents were taken May 27." The species is still a common resident.

*150. WHITE-BREASTED NUTHATCH. *Sitta carolinensis.* "A not uncommon resident of the pineries." Today the species is a rare resident locally in the pinelands. Baynard (1913a) calls it "Rare; breeds here in March in small numbers." Burns (1952) reports three individuals in the pine flatwoods near Newnan's Lake from February to May, 1951. The PBC has a laying female collected in Waldo March 14, 1951.

*151. BROWN-HEADED NUTHATCH. *Sitta pusilla.* "Common in small troops in the pines. One of three fully grown young, taken May 5, exhibits rather peculiar albinistic markings, the bill, head, and tertiaries being whitish, the toe nails flesh color." Today a locally common resident in the pinelands. In the UF are eggs from Archer March 23, 1889 and Micanopy April 7, 1935.

152. BROWN CREEPER. *Certhia familiaris.* A rare winter visitor. The UF has Gainesville specimens taken March 18, 1930 and January 22, 1964. The PBC has one from Newnan's Lake February 26, 1951 and one from Gainesville January 2, 1964.

*153. HOUSE WREN. *Troglodytes aedon.* "Abundant, both in town and surrounding country, wherever there is sufficient growth to afford it concealment. Singing was commenced March 20, and none were observed after April 15." Today a fairly common winter visitor, October 4 to April 30.

[WINTER WREN. *Troglodytes troglodytes.* McClanahan (1935) states, "Seen only once, November 10, 1933; however, a specimen was taken March 6, 1927, by H. B. Sherman." The specimen, now in the UF, is a House Wren.]

[BEWICK'S WREN. *Thryomanes bewickii.* McClanahan (1937a) states, "Winter resident, rare. Earliest fall record, September 20, 1919, collected by F. W. Walker (specimen #67, Department of Biology, University of Florida); latest spring record, February 4." According to its label the specimen now in the UF, was collected not in Alachua, but in Macon, Georgia.]

*154. CAROLINA WREN. *Thryothorus ludovicianus.* "Abundant. A single specimen (No. 1111, ♀, Dec. 13, 1887) in my series of eleven birds has faint wavy marks upon the flanks, thus approaching the *berklandieri* form." FMC referred his specimens to the race of northeastern Mexico, apparently unaware that Ridgway had described the race *miamensis,* to which Gainesville birds are referable, in 1875. The species is still a common resident. Six sets of eggs in the UF are dated from April 10, 1937 to July 16, 1931.

155. LONG-BILLED MARSH WREN. *Telmatodytes palustris.* Uncommon and irregular winter visitor. Dickinson (1939) records seeing one October 3, 1939 in the marshes bordering Lake Alice, where Karraker (1952) saw one December 22, 1951, Peter W. Post saw one November 17, 1965, and I saw one December 29, 1962. In the absence of specimens these records cannot be assigned to subspecies, five of which occur in Florida's coastal marshes.

156. SHORT-BILLED MARSH WREN. *Cistothorus platensis.* Not uncommon winter visitor in old weedy fields. Gainesville specimens in the PBC were taken January 27, 1952 and February 3, 1953, and in the UF December 27, 1939 and March 13, 1964. FMC thought he saw one December 27, 1886, but in the absence of a specimen he omitted it from his formal list.

*157. MOCKINGBIRD. *Mimus polyglottos.* "Abundant everywhere. The birds of the town commenced to sing January 26, and were in full song February 3, while those of the surrounding country were not in full song until March 7. The same difference was noticed in times of breeding, my first notes on the subject being April 20, when almost fully grown young were seen in the city and a nest containing one egg was found a few miles out in the country." Nesting dates vary considerably from year to year, but eggs are seldom laid before mid-March. Second broods are usually started by late May or early June. Local eggs in the UF are dated from April 14, 1934 to July 17, 1940.

*158. CATBIRD. *Dumetella carolinensis.* "Common, but silent and retiring. None were observed after May 10." Baynard (1913a) claims it has bred here in April. Burns (1952) and Karraker (1953) record it present from September 27 to May 9. No definite summer or nesting records exist.

*159. BROWN THRASHER. *Toxostoma rufum.* "A common resident. The first song was heard February 8." Still a common resident. The UF has Gainesville eggs dated April 17, 1935 and April 25, 1941.

*160. ROBIN. *Turdus migratorius.* "Abundant in large flocks, and in full song until December 31, no songs being heard later. The greater portion of their number had departed March 15, but several birds were seen in April, on the 11th, 21st, and 27th, one observed each day." Robins are rarely heard in "full song" in Florida today. They arrive in November and usually remain to mid-April, a few stragglers to mid-May. Most of the UF series of wintering specimens are assignable to the nominate race, but *T. m. achrusterus* and *T. m. nigrideus* are also represented.

161. WOOD THRUSH. *Hylocichla mustelina.* Rare transient and re-

cently a local summer resident. Albert M. Laessle found two singing males apparently on territory in deciduous woods on the northeast edge of Gainesville from late May to mid-July. David W. Johnston and I both saw and heard the birds, but we were unable to locate a nest.

*162. HERMIT THRUSH. *Hylocichla guttata.* "Abundant in the hummocks and common in the pineries. Several were heard singing January 8, and from March 10 to 26 they sang occasionally. Few were noted after the last named date until the time of their final departure, April 15." Now a common winter resident, Burns (1952) gives inclusive dates of October 25 to April 19. Broun (1935) heard one in full song near Gainesville April 1. The series of wintering birds in the UF are assignable to the eastern race, *faxoni,* except two dark birds taken March 12, 1930 and February 27, 1961 that represent the Newfoundland form, *H. g. crymophila.*

163. SWAINSON'S THRUSH. *Hylocichla ustulata.* A rare transient. I netted and banded two in Gainesville October 17, 1964 and October 30, 1965 and a third October 30, 1966.

*164. GRAY-CHEEKED THRUSH. *Hylocichla minima.* "A male was taken April 26." An uncommon and irregular transient, the PBC has a male taken in Gainesville October 9, 1951. I netted and banded four on October 17 and 18, 1964.

165. VEERY. *Hylocichla fuscescens.* Uncommon transient. The PBC has Alachua County specimens of the race *salicicola* taken September 23, 1953; September 10, 1954; September 27, 1955; and September 30, 1960, also one *H. f. fuscescens* taken October 2, 1960. In the UF is a *fuscescens* found dead in Gainesville September 11, 1966. I banded one October 30, 1966, that remained in my shrubbery through the next day.

*166. BLUEBIRD. *Sialia sialis.* "Resident birds inhabit the pineries, while the large flocks of wanderers were probably winter visitants. Young just from the nest were taken April 20." The same is true today. Doe (notes) collected eggs in Gainesville April 23, 1933 and April 27, 1940. The winter influx of migrants is often marked, but varies considerably from year to year.

*167. BLUE-GRAY GNATCATCHER. *Polioptila caerulea.* "A rare winter resident, becoming common March 8. The first song was heard February 28." Now a common resident, less plentiful in winter. McClanahan (1935a) states it "nests in April."

168. GOLDEN-CROWNED KINGLET. *Regulus satrapa.* Uncommon winter visitor. The UF has Gainesville specimens taken November 20, 1929 and January 3, 1962.

*169. RUBY-CROWNED KINGLET. *Regulus calendula.* "Abundant. In full song from March 15 to the date of its departure, April 16." A common winter visitor today, inclusive dates are October 17 to April 24.

*170. WATER PIPIT. *Anthus spinoletta.* "Abundant in flocks of twenty to fifty, frequenting the shores of the lake, hummock clearings, and freshly plowed ground." Still a common winter visitor, November 10 to April 12.

*171. CEDAR WAXWING. *Bombycilla cedrorum.* "Common but irregular winter visitant in flocks of ten to twenty. None were observed after April 28." Wintering flocks of several hundred are not unusual in the Gainesville suburbs today. The first appear in late October and remain to late April. A late departure May 6, 1964.

*172. LOGGERHEAD SHRIKE. *Lanius ludovicianus.* "Common, particularly in the town. Young were seen from April 7 to May 12." This common resident seldom occurs within the city today, but is plentiful in the suburbs and along the country roadsides. Eggs from the county in the UF are dated March 12, 1887, to May 12, 1895; most are late March and early April.

173. STARLING. *Sturnus vulgaris.* The Starling first appeared here in the mid-1930's. It now nests regularly and winters commonly in the city. I saw four young of the year on the wing June 20, 1965.

*174. WHITE-EYED VIREO. *Vireo griseus.* "Probably a common winter resident, although few were seen until January 31, when they announced their presence from the depths of dense thickets where, silent, they would have passed unnoticed." Actually uncommon in midwinter, the species is plentiful the rest of the year. A set of eggs from Gainesville in the UF was taken May 21, 1933.

*175. YELLOW-THROATED VIREO. *Vireo flavifrons.* "Not uncommon summer resident. Arrived April 6." The species apparently nests here in small numbers, but it is more common during migration from mid-March to mid-April and October to mid-November.

*176. SOLITARY VIREO. *Vireo solitarius.* "Not uncommon." Still a not uncommon winter visitor, November to April 30.

*177. RED-EYED VIREO. *Vireo olivaceus.* "A common summer resident, arrived April 4." Recent dates are March 14 to October 22.

*178. BLACK AND WHITE WARBLER. *Mniotilta varia.* "A rare winter resident, becoming common March 15, and was last noted April 20." The species arrives in late July and leaves in late April. While most plentiful during migration, it is uncommon rather than rare in winter.

*179. PROTHONOTARY WARBLER. *Protonotaria citrea.* "Two males taken April 5, were the only ones observed." Today an uncommon transient and summer resident. Burns (1952) found a nest with five young at Newnan's Lake May 21, 1950, and again in the same stub May 21, 1952. I banded a late migrant in Gainesville September 23, 1958.

180. SWAINSON'S WARBLER. *Lymnothlypis swainsonii.* Rare transient. One in the PBC was collected at Newnan's Lake April 18, 1951.

*181. WORM-EATING WARBLER. *Helmitheros vermivorus.* "A single male was taken April 11, and a female December 26, 1887." Rare transient. Two males in the PBC were collected at Newnan's Lake April 20 and 27, 1951.

182. TENNESSEE WARBLER. *Vermivora peregrina.* Uncommon transient. A female in the UF was collected at Lake Alice September 21, 1964; one in the PBC was found dead under the WUFT-TV tower October 8, 1964. David W. Johnston netted and banded single birds at Lake Alice October 11, 20, and 28, 1965.

*183. ORANGE-CROWNED WARBLER. *Vermivora celata.* "A not uncommon winter resident. None were observed after April 11." About right for today. Earliest record is one Peter W. Post observed December 9, 1952.

*184. PARULA WARBLER. *Parula americana.* "Commenced to arrive February 22, was abundant on the 25th, and common at the date of my departure." A common transient and summer resident, Burns (1952) noted fledglings on the wing June 15 and July 31, and last saw it in the fall October 20, 1951.

185. YELLOW WARBLER. *Dendroica petechia.* Uncommon migrant in April and May and from late July to October. Gainesville specimen in UF August 25, 1959.

186. MAGNOLIA WARBLER. *Dendroica magnolia.* Uncommon, irregular transient. Peter W. Post saw single birds clearly near Bivins Arms October 10, 12, and 18, 1965.

*187. CAPE MAY WARBLER. *Dendroica tigrina.* "A male was taken April 14." Uncommon spring transient. UF specimens April 26, 1950, May 6, 1964, and October 29, 1966.

*188. BLACK-THROATED BLUE WARBLER. *Dendroica caerulescens.* "April 5, two males, April 20 and 26, a male each day, May 6, two females, were the entire number observed." A not uncommon transient in April and May and from late August to mid-October. The UF has Alachua County specimens of both races, *caerulescens* and *cairnsi.*

*189. MYRTLE WARBLER. *Dendroica coronata.* "The most abundant bird of any species, and very generally distributed. Fully ninetenths of their numbers departed after a severe northeast storm on April 8 and 9." Today a common winter visitor from mid-October to mid-April. The Myrtle Warbler is still the commonest of its family.

[BLACK-THROATED GREEN WARBLER. *Dendroica virens.* Dickinson (1939) records a sight record of an adult male in the fall of 1937.]

[BLACKBURNIAN WARBLER. *Dendroica fusca.* Mary Heimerdinger

reported one near the airport on the Christmas census, December 28, 1962.]

*190. YELLOW-THROATED WARBLER. *Dendroica dominica.* "Rather rare winter resident. March 2, migrants in full song began to arrive, and on the 4th of that month they were abundant in the cypresses and common in the pines near water. After this there was little or no change in their numbers or distribution. A partly formed egg was found in the oviduct of a female taken April 14. Several birds in my series of thirty-two are *albilora* so far as measurements are concerned, but none are without at least a trace of yellow over the eye." The breeding form in this area is *D. d. dominica.* The UF series of winter specimens contains individuals taken locally of both *albilora and stoddardi.*

*191. BLACKPOLL WARBLER. *Dendroica striata.* "April 23 and 26, a male each day, May 9, two males and a female, constitute the entire record." An uncommon transient in spring, April 23 to May 8, we have no fall records.

*192. PINE WARBLER. *Dendroica pinus.* "An abundant resident of the pineries, in full song February 1, and frequently heard before that date. Young, about two days from the nest, were taken April 18." Today a common resident, more plentiful in winter. The Alachua County specimens in the UF series are indistinguishable from northern *D. p. pinus.*

[KIRTLAND'S WARBLER. *Dendroica kirtlandi.* McClanahan (1936) gives a sight record for Bivins Arm April 26, 1934 with no further details.]

*193. PRAIRIE WARBLER. *Dendroica discolor.* "Arrived March 31, became common April 5, and remained common until May 5, after which date none were observed." Baynard (1913a) claims it nests here in April, but we have no summer records, and all the UF Alachua County specimens (August 23 to May 2) are referable to northern *discolor,* not to the resident Florida subspecies *paludicola.*

*194. PALM WARBLER. *Dendroica palmarum.* "Abundant and very generally distributed; numbers appearing in the streets and gardens of the town, reminding one of Chipping Sparrows as they hopped around our doors and piazzas. They commenced to moult about March 15, and had not acquired their new plumage at the time of their departure, April 29, up to which date they were common." For the Yellow Palm Warbler, *D. p. hypochrysae,* FMC adds "Occasionally found associated with the last, in all about fifteen individuals being noticed." Next to the Myrtle, this is the most plentiful of the wintering warblers, arriving in late September (27th, Burns, 1951) and leaving in late April. Most specimens taken in this area are intermediate between the two races.

*195. OVENBIRD. *Seiurus aurocapillus.* "A not uncommon inhabitant of the hummocks." Still a not uncommon transient and winter visitor today. Burns (1952) collected a male July 26, 1950 and recorded the species irregularly from October 6 to December 20, 1950 and from February 11 to May 14, 1951.

196. NORTHERN WATERTHRUSH. *Seiurus noveboracensis.* Uncommon transient. Gainesville specimens in the UF: May 13, 1928; April 11 and September 25, 1940; November 16, 1958; March 27 and September 27, 1964. David W. Johnston banded one at Lake Alice September 7, 1965.

*197. LOUISIANA WATERTHRUSH. *Seiurus motacilla.* "Arrived March 8. Very few were seen." Uncommon transient and recently a summer resident. Burns (1952) collected one at Newnan's Lake July 26, 1950 and found it common from then until September 29. McClanahan (1937a) gives sight records for March and April and October 27. I reported (1965) one nesting on the outskirts of Gainesville May 15, 1965.

[KENTUCKY WARBLER. *Oporornis formosus.* Dickinson (1944) reports an unelaborated sight record by Jack C. Russell for September 19, 1940.]

[MOURNING WARBLER. *Oporornis philadelphia.* Dickinson (1939) states: "one reasonably good sight record was made at Hatchet Creek by Mr. George Bentley and Mr. Charles E. Mounts, November 11, 1939."]

*198. YELLOWTHROAT. *Geothlypis trichas.* "Common." It still is. The resident population is the race *ignota* that Chapman described from Tarpon Springs in 1890. The UF also has transient and wintering specimens assignable to the races *brachidactylus, trichas,* and *typhicola.*

199. YELLOW-BREASTED CHAT. *Icteria virens.* Rare transient, known from a single specimen in the UF taken on Payne's Prairie February 6, 1961.

*200. HOODED WARBLER. *Wilsonia citrina.* "April 2 and 11, a male observed each day." Not uncommon transient, breeding nearby in northern and western Florida, commonest in late summer. Specimen and sight records are: March 27, 1940; April 3, 1930; July 28, 1941; August 6, 1950; August 11, 1954; September 10, 1923; and October 20, 1950.

*201. REDSTART. *Setophaga ruticilla.* "April 7 to May 9, six males, and on the last date three females, were the entire number seen." Fairly common migrant from March 28 to May 16 and from July 26 to October 22.

202. HOUSE SPARROW. *Passer domesticus.* Barrows (1889: 203) lists this species present in Florida at Lake City in 1882, and by the

fall of 1886, at Cerro Gordo (?), Crescent City, and Tampa. He notes it as not present in Archer or Micanopy on the report of their post-masters, and also absent from Waldo, Jacksonville, Bronson, and Gainesville, the last on the authority of FMC. Mortimer (1890) mentions a female present at Sanford (Seminole County) the autumn of 1887. The first mention of the species for Alachua County is Pearson's (1897) report "I killed a male *P. domesticus* at Archer on July 1 [1896]. I can find no record of it having been recorded from the section before, and a number of persons to whom I showed the specimen said they had never seen one there before." The next mention of the species is Baynard's (1913a) statement "This pernicious nuisance is abundant over the entire county."

*203. BOBOLINK. *Dolichonyx orzivorus*. "January 5, a female having the secondaries missing from one wing was caught by our dogs while Quail shooting. April 26, small flocks were heard passing over, and on the 29th flocks of several hundred in full song were seen.

"The oats were now nearly ready to harvest and considerable damage was done to them by these birds. On my last visit to the oat-fields, May 25, both sexes were as abundant as at any previous time." Today the Bobolink is a common spring transient from April 17 to May 19, less plentiful during the autumn flights in September and October.

*204. MEADOWLARK. *Sturnella magna*. "Abundant." FMC noticed his Florida specimens were smaller and darker than northern *S. m. magna*, but he referred them to the Mexican race, *mexicana*, which "while they are not fully typical . . . they approach it so closely as to apparently render subsequent separation impossible." It remained for Bangs to describe the Florida subspecies, *argutula*, in 1899. A UF specimen taken in Gainesville January 17, 1958 shows nominate northern *magna* winters here occasionally. Doe (notes) collected eggs here April 28, 1938 and June 11, 1938.

205. YELLOW-HEADED BLACKBIRD. *Xanthocephalus xanthocephalus*. Rare winter visitor from the westward. An adult male remained at Lake Alice from December 9, 1957 to January 21, 1958; another was seen there January 5-6, 1963. The UF has a female taken on the campus September 17, 1965.

*206. RED-WINGED BLACKBIRD. *Agelaius phoenecius*. "Abundant, the sexes being generally in separate flocks; the males frequenting the pines, the females open fields; but in the vicinity of water both sexes were associated. A nest containing four eggs was found May 6." Still one of our commonest birds, the resident population is intermediate between nominate *phoenecius* and *A. p. mearnsi*. Five sets of eggs in the UF from Gainesville range in dates from May 7 to June 3.

*207. ORCHARD ORIOLE. *Icterus spurius*. "A rare summer resident."

Baynard (1913) claims the species nests here in early June, and Mc-
Clanahan (1936) gives an arrival date of April 13. Doe (notes) saw
a male May 13, 1932. Though the species migrates plentifully along
both coasts and nests just north and east of here—the UF has a nest
and eggs collected in Jacksonville May 9, 1931—it is still an uncommon
bird in Alachua County.

*208. BALTIMORE ORIOLE. *Icterus galbula.* "A male was taken December 15, and on February 4 a second was seen and heard calling
among the blossoms of the cypress." Today the species is a not uncommon winter visitor from early December through March.

209. BULLOCK'S ORIOLE. *Icterus bullockii.* Rare winter visitor from
the westward, increasing in Florida in recent years. A male Robert
Ackerman banded on the University campus February 22, 1963 returned to his feeder December 5, 1963.

*210. RUSTY BLACKBIRD. *Euphagus carolinus.* "A common winter
resident. Last seen April 14." The species today occurs irregularly,
usually in flocks, from December to early April.

211. BREWER'S BLACKBIRD. *Euphagus cyanocephalus.* Uncommon
and irregular winter visitor from the westward. The UF has three
specimens taken on Payne's Prairie March 4-10, 1961.

*212. BOAT-TAILED GRACKLE. *Cassidix mexicanus.* "Abundant. On
one occasion a number were noticed jumping from the ground at passing insects. A singular note of this species greatly resembles the flapping of wings, as of a Coot tripping over the waters; this sound was
very familiar to me, but so excellent is the imitation that for a long
time I attributed it to one of the numerous Coots which abound in
most places favored by [the Boat-tails]." A common resident today in
and around most marshes and bodies of water. The UF has 11 clutches
of eggs from Lake Alice dated from April 18 to May 12. The resident
population is assignable to *C. m. major.*

*213. COMMON GRACKLE. *Quiscalus quiscula.* "Common only in
the city where there were a number of flocks, all very tame." Still fairly
common in the suburbs. The A.O.U. Check-list (1957) lists the race
stonei as occurring in Gainesville in winter, but all the UF specimens
from this area are referable to nominate *quiscula.*

*214. BROWN-HEADED COWBIRD. *Molothrus ater.* "Not uncommon."
Now a common winter visitor, generally appearing in late August and
remaining until early April. A female young of the year in the UF was
collected near Lake Alice July 28, 1958.

215. SCARLET TANAGER. *Piranga olivacea.* Though this species is a
regular transient along both coasts, it is only of casual occurrence inland. In the PBC is a specimen taken at Newnan's Lake April 20,
1951.

*216. Summer Tanager. *Piranga rubra.* "Males in full song arrived April 14, females two days later, and after this date they were common in pairs, not inhabiting pine lands exclusively, but being equally common in dense scrubs." Today a common summer resident from March 22 to October 31. McClanahan (1937a) states "nests in early May."

*217. Cardinal. *Richmondena cardinalis.* "Abundant. The first song was heard January 17, and on February 1, they were in full song. April 17, a completed nest was found, and May 27, young just from the nest were taken." I would call the species common rather than abundant today. The resident population is *R. c. floridana.* Eggs in the UF taken locally are dated from April 19 to May 24.

218. Rose-breasted Grosbeak. *Pheucticus ludovicianus.* Rare transient, known from a single specimen in the UF taken in Gainesville September 29, 1964 until I netted and banded one at my home, October 23, 1966.

219. Black-headed Grosbeak. *Pheucticus melanocephalus.* Straggler from the westward. Mounts (1955) reports one at a Gainesville feeding station from late March to April 10, 1955, that he trapped, banded, and photographed in color. Mounts said (in Sprunt, 1963) he saw another bird in town March 16-30, 1956.

220. Blue Grosbeak. *Guiraca caerulea.* This species has become a not uncommon summer resident within the last few years. David W. Johnston has found a number of pairs apparently on territory and, on July 11, 1966, collected an adult female with a pronounced brood patch. I saw three winter stragglers December 30, 1965, one of which I netted and banded. Though Howell (1932) gives a breeding record for Tarpon Springs in 1891, the species was probably at best an uncommon transient here in the 1880's.

*221. Indigo Bunting. *Passerina cyanea.* "A female, captured January 27, was the only one observed." Today the species is rare in winter, common during migration, and breeds in small numbers regularly (Johnston, 1965a,b). The birds usually appear in mid-April. Bailey (1925) found "young in the nest on July 17th and 18th near Gainesville." A late fall record is November 7, 1963.

222. Painted Bunting. *Passerina ciris.* Though the Painted Bunting nests and is a common transient on both coasts, it occurs here rather uncommonly during migration in the fall. David W. Johnston banded four at Lake Alice October 18-22, 1963; a specimen in the UF was taken on the campus September 14, 1964.

223. Dickcissel. *Spiza americana.* Uncommon and irregular transient and winter visitor. David W. Johnston banded a pair at Lake Alice October 28-29, 1963. A Gainesville specimen in the UF was collected

November 19, 1963. A male hobnobbed with the House Sparrows and sang on the campus March 7-13, 1964.

*224. PURPLE FINCH. *Carpodacus purpureus.* "Rather rare during the winter of 1886-87, but not uncommon the following year." Now an uncommon winter visitor, appearing erratically, usually during cold years. An adult male, one of eight Purple Finches I banded here February 18, 1958, was killed in Andalusia, Alabama, February 21, 1959. A small influx appeared at local feeding stations in January and February, 1966.

225. PINE SISKIN. *Spinus pinus.* Brewster and Chapman (1891) state: "Mr. Chapman has heard the species on several occasions at Gainesville, and these records are supported by his capture there of a male specimen on February 15, 1890." The species has not been recorded here since.

*226. GOLDFINCH. *Spinus tristis.* "Common in small flocks up to April 15." A common winter visitor from mid-November to April 27.

*227. RUFOUS-SIDED TOWHEE. *Pipilo erythrophthalmus.* Of the nominate northern race FMC says "Abundant up to the date of its departure, April 27." Of the resident *alleni* he notes. "Common. Not found associating with [*erythrophthalmus*] which inhabits thickets in or near hummocks, while *alleni* prefers the dense growths of scrub palmetto in the pineries. The difference in their calls is marked, and the familiar *chewink* of *erythrophthalmus* is easily distinguished from the clear, whistled, *cherwee* of *alleni*, which gives it its local name of '*Joree.*'" The resident *alleni* is present the year round, common in summer, less so in winter. We have specimen and banding records for the northern *erythrophthalmus* from October 30 to April 23. Doe collected eggs of the species in Gainesville June 20, 1937 and May 30, 1939.

*228. SAVANNAH SPARROW. *Passerculus sandwichensis.* "Even more abundant than the [Vesper Sparrow]. My last record was May 6." A common winter visitor today in open fields and along the roadsides from mid-October to mid-April (latest May 8). Most are *P. s. savanna,* but the UF has Alachua County specimens of the races *oblitus* and *labradorius.*

*229. GRASSHOPPER SPARROW. *Ammodramus savannarum.* "Common." Though Baynard (1913) claims he "found one pair with young that could barely fly late in June on Paine's Prairie," the northern race, *pratensis,* is not known to breed today south of central Georgia, nor the Florida subspecies, *floridanus,* north of Kissimmee Prairie. Mc-Clanahan (1937a) called the species rare, but he probably did not know where to find it in winter. Today *pratensis* winters regularly and not uncommonly in the county's broomsedge fields from late October to late March.

230. LECONTE'S SPARROW. *Passerherbulus caudacutus.* From the record a rare winter visitor, but perhaps not uncommon, for it is very shy and hard to flush from the dense grass it inhabits. A Gainesville specimen in the UF was taken December 16, 1963.

231. HENSLOW'S SPARROW. *Passerherbulus henslowi.* Locally common winter visitor in open, grassy fields. The UF has specimens from Gainesville taken December 16, 1963 to March 13, 1964, all assignable to the eastern race *sussurans.* FMC thought he saw one December 27, 1886, but with no specimen he omitted it from his formal list.

[SHARP-TAILED SPARROW. *Ammospiza caudacuta.* McClanahan's (1937a) reference to "six specimens in the Florida State Museum; taken by C. F. Aschemeier from December 2, 1930, through January 6, 1931" is puzzling. No record remains of any such specimens, and the species in Florida is strictly a salt-marsh inhabitant found only in the coastal marshes.]

*232. VESPER SPARROW. *Pooecetes gramineus.* "Very abundant. Last noted April 9." Still a common winter visitor, recorded from November 17 to early April.

*233. BACHMAN'S SPARROW. *Aimophila aestivalis.* Of the resident nominate race FMC states "Arrived March 31. Common in only one locality, a high, open palmetto pinery, where, May 21, a nest with four fresh eggs was found." Of the northern and western *bachmanii* he adds "Three were taken during the winter in a 'black-jack' pinery: March 25, one was captured at the edge of a palmetto pinery, and on the 26th one in an open field a mile or more from the nearest pines. These last were probably migrants, as both were found in localities which had before been thoroughly searched." Today *aestivalis* is a fairly common resident, more plentiful in spring and summer, but present throughout the year. Typical *bachmanii* is an uncommon winter visitor; two in the PBC were taken on Sugarfoot Prairie March 13, 1948, and April 1, 1950. A number of winter specimens in the UF are intermediate between the two races.

234. SLATE-COLORED JUNCO. *Junco hyemalis.* An uncommon and irregular winter visitor. UF Gainesville specimens taken February 19, 1958 and January 4, 1959 are both of the nominate northern race. David W. Johnston and I saw one November 19, 1964.

*235. CHIPPING SPARROW. *Spizella passerina.* "Abundant in large flocks at the borders of fields." A common winter visitor from mid-October to mid-April, latest April 23, 1964.

236. CLAY-COLORED SPARROW. *Spizella pallida.* A rare and irregular winter visitor, perhaps more plentiful than the record indicates because

of the difficulty of distinguishing it from the Chipping Sparrow in the field. A Gainesville specimen in the UF was taken April 14, 1963.

*237. FIELD SPARROW. *Spizella pusilla.* "A common winter resident, found in the same situations as the [Chipping Sparrow]. I saw none after April 16." Today the Field Sparrow is far less common than the Chipping Sparrow with which it so often associates. Usually one or two can be found with the large flocks of Chippies from late November (30th) to mid-April (17th).

238. WHITE-CROWNED SPARROW. *Zonotrichia leucophrys.* A rare and irregular winter visitor. Gainesville specimens in the UF taken October 11 and November 16, 1958 are both young of the year. Dennis (1950) reports a sight record at a Gainesville feeder March 14, 1950.

*239. WHITE-THROATED SPARROW. *Zonotrichia albicollis.* "Common, as late as April 27." The White-throats arrive in early November (6th) and remain common until early April, latest record April 30.

240. FOX SPARROW. *Passerella iliaca.* Two were reported at a backyard feeder in East Gainesville November 30, 1964. I netted and banded one of these December 2, 1964, and photographed it in color before releasing it.

*241. SWAMP SPARROW. *Melospiza georgiana.* "Few were found in low or swampy ground, but in certain old fields they were very abundant. Two seen April 27 were the last noted." A common winter visitor from early October (7th) to late April (27th). The extensive UF series is about equally divided between the races *georgiana* and *ericrypta*.

*242. SONG SPARROW. *Melospiza melodia.* "Common in thickets everywhere. Last noted March 31." While of regular occurrence between November 21 and April 21, the Song Sparrow is not nearly so plentiful as the Chipping, White-throated, Vesper, or Swamp Sparrows today. All the UF specimens are referable to nominate *melodia.*

BIBLIOGRAPHY

AMERICAN ORNITHOLOGISTS' UNION COMMITTEE.
    1957. "Check-list of North American Birds." 5th edition, American Ornithologists' Union, Baltimore, Maryland. 691 pp.
ANONYMOUS
    1941. "Report of Warden at Bivin's Arm Rookery." Florida Nat., 14: 73-74.
AUSTIN, OLIVER L., JR.
    1963. "Gainesville Christmas Bird Count (1962)." Audubon Field Notes, 17: 161.
    1964. "Gainesville Christmas Bird Count (1963)." Audubon Field Notes, 18: 176.

1965a. "Gainesville Christmas Bird Count (1964)." Audubon Field Notes, 19: 185.
1965b. "Louisiana Waterthrush nesting in Gainesville." Florida Nat., 38: 144.
1966. "Gainesville Christmas Bird Count (1965)." Audubon Field Notes, 20: 208.

BAILEY, HAROLD H.
1925. "The birds of Florida." Williams & Wilkins Co., Baltimore, 146 pp., ill.

BARROWS, WALTER BRADFORD
1889. "The English Sparrow (*Passer domesticus*) in North America. U.S. Dept. of Agr., Bull. No. 1.

BAYNARD, OSCAR EDWARD
1909a. "Echoes from Florida." Oologist, 26: 5-7.
1909b. "Notes from Florida on *Catharista urubu*." Oologist, 26: 191-193.
1909c. "Nesting of Florida Wren." Oologist, 26: 213-215.
1911a. "A List of Birds found on Bird Island in Orange Lake." Oologist, 28: 14.
1911b. "Louisiana Heron on nest on Bird Island, Florida." Oologist, 28: 105.
1911c. "American Egret feeding young." Bird-Lore, 13: 332.
1912a. "Food of herons and ibises." Wilson Bull., 24: 167-169.
1912b. "Young American Egret, Orange Lake, Florida rookery." Bird-Lore, 14: 382.
1913a. "Breeding Birds of Alachua County, Florida." Auk, 30: 240-247.
1913b. "Home Life of the Glossy Ibis." Wilson Bull., 25: 103-117.
1914a. "Orange Lake Bird Reservation." Blue-Bird, 7: 275-281.
1914b. "The rare Glossy Ibis in the Audubon Sanctuary at Orange Lake, Florida." Bird-Lore, 16: 484.
1916. "The Bald Eagle in Florida." Oologist, 33: 18-20.

BENTLEY, GEORGE, AND CHARLES E. MOUNTS
1940. "Mourning Warbler." Florida Nat., 13: 43.

BREWSTER, WILLIAM, AND FRANK M. CHAPMAN
1891. "Notes on the birds of the lower Suwannee River." Auk, 8: 125-138.

BROUN, MAURICE
1935. "Eastern Hermit Thrush in song in Florida." Auk, 52: 311.

BURNS, BARTLEY J.
1952. "A survey of the birds of Newnan's Lake, Florida." Master's thesis, Univ. of Florida, unpublished, pp. 112, 11 pl., 1 fig., 1 table.

CHAPMAN, FRANK M.
1888. "A list of birds observed at Gainesville, Florida." Auk, 5: 267-277.

CISNE, L. E.
1961. "Gainesville Christmas Bird Count (1960)." Audubon Field Notes, 15: 174.

DENNIS, JOHN V.
1950. "White-crowned Sparrow at Gainesville feeding station." Florida Nat., 23: 102.

DICKINSON, JOSHUA CLIFTON, JR.
1939. "Addenda to the list of birds of Alachua County, Florida." Proc. Florida Acad. Sci., 2: 106-107.
1945. "Addenda to the list of birds of Alachua County, Florida." Proc. Florida Acad. Sci., 7: 191-192.
1946. "A census of the nesting birds in the Bivin's Arm rookery." Florida Nat., 20: 9-10.
1962. "Gainesville Christmas Bird Count (1961)." Audubon Field Notes, 16: 168.

DOE, CHARLES E.
1931-1942. Annual field notebooks, unpublished, in Florida State Museum files.

HAHN, PAUL
1963. "Where is that vanished bird?" Royal Ontario Mus., Univ. of Toronto, photo-offset, 347 pp.

HICKS, THOMAS W.
1955. "An early seasonal record of the Swallow-tailed Kite in Florida." Wilson Bull., 67: 63.

HOWELL, ARTHUR H.
1932. "Florida Bird Life." Coward-McCann, Inc., New York. 579 pp., ill.

JENNI, DONALD A.
1961. "The breeding ecology of four species of herons at Lake Alice, Alachua County, Florida." Ph.D. Thesis, Univ. of Florida, unpublished, 115 pp.

JOHNSTON, DAVID W.
1965a. "An effective method for trapping territorial male Indigo Buntings." Bird-Banding, 36: 80-83.
1965b. "Ecology of the Indigo Bunting in Florida." Quart. Jour. Fla. Acad. Sci., 28: 199-211.

KARRAKER, DAVID C.
1953. "The birds of Lake Alice." Master's Thesis, Univ. of Florida, unpublished, 99 pp., 12 pl., 5 figs.

KYLE, JENNIE LYNNE
1933. "White Ibises at Orange Lake, Florida." Florida Nat., 6: 45-47.

LIGON, J. DAVID
1963. "Breeding range expansion of the Burrowing Owl in Florida." Auk, 80: 367-368.

MCCLANAHAN, ROBERT C.
1935. "Fifty years after." Florida Nat., 8: 53-59; 9: 1-6.
1937a. "An annotated list of the birds of Alachua County, Florida." Proc. Florida Acad. Sci., 1: 91-102.
1937b. "European Widgeon in Florida." Auk, 54: 533.

MILLS, L. P.
1946. "Report of Bivin's Arm Sanctuary." Florida Nat., 20: 44.
1948. "Report of Bivin's Arm Sanctuary." Florida Nat., 21: 75.

MORTIMER, D.
1890. "Notes on the habits of a few birds of Orange County, Florida." Auk, 7: 337-343.

MOUNTS, C. E.
1955. "Black-headed Grosbeak at Gainesville." Florida Nat., 28: 91.

PEARSON, PAUL
1950. "A report from the Bivin's Arm Sanctuary." Florida Nat., 23: 39.

PEARSON, T. GILBERT
1888a. "A day with the herons in Florida." Oologist, 5: 8-9.
1888b. "Notes from Alachua County, Florida." Oologist, 5: 150.
1890. "Nesting of the Pied-billed Grebe." Orn. & Ool., 15: 152-153.
1891a. "The Wood Duck." Orn. & Ool., 16: 134-135.
1891b. "Turkey Vulture." Oologist, 8: 164.
1891c. "The American Anhinga." Orn. & Ool., 16: 49-50.
1892a. "The ibises of Ledworth Lake, Florida." Oologist, 9: 99-100.
1892b. "The herons of Alachua County, Florida." Orn. & Ool., 17, 36-37, 71-72.
1893. [Florida notes.] Proc. Linnaean Soc., New York, 5: 5.
1897. "*Passer domesticus* at Archer, Fla., and other Florida notes." Auk, 14: 99.

RICE, DALE W.
1956. "Dynamics of range expansion of Cattle Egrets in Florida." Auk, 73: 259-266.
RICE, DALE W., AND EDWARD L. MOCKFORD
1953. "Cinnamon Teal and Avocets in Florida." Wilson Bull., 65: 211-212.
RUSSELL, MR. & MRS. J. C.
1937. "Bivins Arm bird rookery." Florida Nat., 10: 80-82.
RUSSELL, JACK
1938. "Bivins Arm Sanctuary report." Florida Nat., 11: 45-46.
SHERWOOD, MARY
1958. "Gainesville Christmas Bird Count (1957)." Audubon Field Notes, 12: 140.
1960. "Gainesville Christmas Bird Count (1959)." Audubon Field Notes, 14: 165.
SPRUNT, ALEXANDER JR.
1954. "Florida Bird Life." Coward-McCann, Inc., New York, 527 pp., ill.
1963. "Addendum to 'Florida Bird Life,'" Coward-McCann, Inc., New York, 24 pp.
SPRUNT, ALEXANDER 4TH ("SANDY")
1949. "Wilson's Petrel in interior Florida." Auk, 66: 76.

Index

227